remote sensing

Techniques for Environmental Analysis

Edited

by

John E. Estes
University of California, Santa Barbara

and

Leslie W. Senger
Dames & Moore, Santa Barbara

HAMILTON PUBLISHING COMPANY
Santa Barbara, California

The false infrared ektachrome Central California scene (E-1002-18134, 25 July 1972) depicted on the cover was produced using color separation positives produced by Earth Satellite Corporation. The scene, which shows an area approximately 100 nm by 100 nm, extends from Monterey Bay on the South and West, across the California Coast Ranges, to the northeastern San Joaquin Valley, and includes the foothills of the Sierra Nevada Mountains on the North and East. San Jose, California (at the southern end of San Francisco Bay) is seen at center left, while the Isleton flood area in the delta of the Sacramento River is visible at the upper left. The image was acquired by the NASA Earth Resources Technology Satellite, and processed by a digital computer. An IBM 360/65 corrected the geometry and radiometry of the sensor data using advanced digital image processing techniques. The corrected digital data was then recorded on black-and-white film using an IBM Drum Plotter. Three of the four bands (0.5-0.6, 0.6-0.7, 0.8-1.1 mm) were then used to generate an IR color composite of the scene. The original processing work was performed under a NASA ERTS contract (NAS5-21716) by the IBM Corporation.

Published by Hamilton Publishing Company,
a Division of John Wiley & Sons, Inc.

Library of Congress Cataloging in Publication Data

Estes, John E.
Remote sensing: techniques for environmental analysis.

Bibliography: p.
1. Geography--Methodology. 2. Astronautics in geographical research. 3. Remote sensing systems. I. Senger, Leslie W., joint author. II. Title.
G70.E84 910'.02'028 73-8601
ISBN 0-471-24595-X

Printed in the United States of America

10 9 8 7 6 5 4 3 2

REMOTE SENSING

Techniques for Environmental Analysis

Table of Contents

1.	K. Stone Developing Geographical Remote Sensing	1
2.	J. Estes Imaging with Photographic and Nonphotographic Sensor Systems	15
3.	D. Simonett Quantitative Data Extraction and Analysis of Remote Sensor Images	51
4.	R. Rudd Remote Sensing of Natural Resources	83
5.	A. Lewis Geomorphic-Geologic Mapping from Remote Sensors	105
6.	S. Morain Interpretation and Mapping of Natural Vegetation	127
7.	N. Nunnally Interpreting Land Use from Remote Sensor Imagery	167
8.	R. Thaman Remote Sensing of Agricultural Resources	189
9.	D. Lindgren Urban Applications of Remote Sensing	225
10.	F. Horton Remote Sensing Techniques and Urban Data Acquisition	243
11.	R. Peplies Regional Analysis and Remote Sensing	277
12.	H. Aschmann and L. Bowden Remote Sensing of Environmental Quality: Problems and Potential	293
	Appendix 1: Glossary	303
	Appendix 2: Selected Bibliography of Remote Sensing Research	311
	Appendix 3: Institutions and Organizations Engaged in Remote Sensing Research in the United States	329
	Index	339

ABOUT THE EDITORS

John E. Estes

Dr. Estes received his Ph.D. in geography from the University of California, Los Angeles. He has been involved in the field of remote sensing since 1963, contributing through federal government, private industry, and university employment. He has published over 35 articles in the field with an emphasis on sensor systems, land use, evaluation of regional resource bases, and the assessment and monitoring of environmental pollution. He has been a Principal or Co-Principal Investigator for contracts and grants with the National Aeronautics and Space Administration, U.S. Coast Guard, U.S. Forest Service, and Department of the Navy. Dr. Estes has served as Director of remote sensing workshops for the Association of American Geographers (AAG) and the International Geographical Union. He is a member of the Remote Sensing Advisory Committee to the President of the University of California and the AAG Commission on Geographic Applications of Remote Sensing. Dr. Estes is presently an assistant Professor of Geography at the University of California, Santa Barbara and Acting Vice-Chairman of the Geography Program.

Leslie W. Senger

Dr. Senger received his Ph.D. in geography from the University of California, Los Angeles. He has been actively publishing in the field of remote sensing for over six years. His contributions have been primarily in the areas of land use, agriculture, urban systems, and environmental quality. He was a co-author of two major works in the field, "Land Use in the Southwestern United States From Gemini and Apollo Imagery" and "The Multispectral Concept as Applied to Marine Oil Spills," and is a contributing author to a chapter on water quality in the forthcoming *Manual of Remote Sensing*. Dr. Senger was a Research Geographer with the Geography Remote Sensing Unit at the University of California, Santa Barbara until mid-1973. Since that time, he has accepted a position as a geographic specialist with the international firm of Dames & Moore, consultants in the environmental and applied earth sciences. Dr. Senger is responsible for managing environmental impact projects out of the Santa Barbara office, particularly in regard to the social environment.

ABOUT THE CONTRIBUTORS

H. Homer Aschmann (Ph.D., University of California, Berkeley). Dr. Aschmann served as Chairman on a panel for the NAS-NRC Conference on the Use of Orbiting Spacecraft in Geographic Research (1965), and is currently a Member of the Panel on Geography, Committee on Remote Sensing of Earth Resources (NAS-NRC). In 1971, he published a philosophical paper entitled "Prolegomena to the Remote Sensing of Environmental Quality." Dr. Aschmann is presently a Professor of Geography at the University of California, Riverside.

Leonard W. Bowden (Ph.D., Clark University). Dr. Bowden has been active in the field of remote sensing since 1967. He has been a Principal Investigator for several federal contracts and grants, including the U.S. Department of Interior (Geological Survey), NASA, and Office of Naval Research. He is the author of numerous publications in the field, and is editor of Volume II of the forthcoming *Manual of Remote Sensing* (American Society of Photogrammetry). Dr. Bowden is an Associate Professor of Geography at the University of California, Riverside.

Frank E. Horton (Ph.D., Northwestern University). Dr. Horton has published numerous articles relating to the utilization of remote sensing in urban areas. He has also written articles dealing with information systems and remote sensing inputs to such systems. His primary interest has been in urban and transportation planning and analysis. Dr. Horton is a contributing author to the chapter on urban analysis in the forthcoming *Manual of Remote Sensing*. Dr. Horton is currently Dean for Advanced Studies at the University of Iowa, Iowa City, Iowa.

Anthony J. Lewis (Ph.D., University of Kansas). Dr. Lewis has been evaluating the potential of side-looking airborne radar (SLAR) imagery for geoscience investigations over the past eight years. Most of his published work has focused on the geomorphic analysis of radar, both qualitative and quantitative. He has also worked on the detection of cultural features, sea ice, and land use on radar imagery, and the mapping of wet-land soils from color infrared photography. He is a contributing author to several remote sensing texts, including *The Surveillant Science* and the *Manual of Remote Sensing*. Dr. Lewis is presently with the Department of Geography and Anthropology at Louisiana State University, Baton Rouge.

David T. Lindgren (Ph.D., Boston University). Dr. Lindgren has been active in the field of remote sensing for the past ten years in a variety of capacities (private industry, federal government, and university teaching). He has authored or co-authored a number of articles and monographs on remote sensing. He is also a contributing author to the chapter on urban applications in the forthcoming *Manual of Remote Sensing*. Dr. Lindgren is presently an Assistant Professor Geography at Dartmouth College.

Stanley A. Morain (Ph.D., University of Kansas). Dr. Morain has been active in the field of remote sensing since 1964. His contributions have focused primarily on the use of imaging radar in studies of agriculture, natural vegetation, and soils. More recently, he has been investigating the use of satellite imagery for obtaining agricultural statistics. His most recent contributions include chapters in *The Handbook of Vegetation Science* and the symposium volume entitled *Phenology and Seasonality Modelling*. Dr. Morain is presently an Assistant Professor of Geography at the University of Kansas, and a research scientist at the Space Technology Laboratories, Center for Research, Inc., Lawrence.

Nelson R. Nunnally (Ph.D., University of Illinois, Urbana). Dr. Nunnally is a member of the staff of the Geography Department, University of Oklahoma, Norman, Oklahoma. He has been actively involved in remote sensing research for approximately eight years and has published articles treating land use, regional analysis, and the physics of electromagnetic radiation. He is a member of the Association of American Geographers Commission on Geographic Application of Remote Sensing and the Remote Sensing Division of the American Society of Photogrammetry.

Robert W. Peplies (Ph.D., University of Georgia). Dr. Peplies has published and directed research in the field of remote sensing for a number of years. He has served as Project Director and Chairman of the Association of American Geographers Commission on Geographic Applications of Remote Sensing. His publications primarily concern regional analysis and land use. Dr. Peplies is a Professor of Geography at East Tennessee State University.

Robert D. Rudd (Ph.D., Northwestern University). Dr. Rudd has been active in the field of remote sensing for over ten years. He was appointed to the AAG Commission on Geographic Applications of Remote Sensing in 1968 and served five years on it (chairing the Commission during 1971-72). He was Director of the NSF-funded Short Course in Remote Sensing held at the University of Denver in the summer of 1971. Dr. Rudd is the author of numerous articles, technical papers, and bulletins in physical geography and in remote sensing. He is presently the chairman of the Department of Geography at the University of Denver.

David S. Simonett (Ph.D., University of Sydney, Australia). Dr. Simonett is Director of Land Use and Urban Applications in Earth Satellite Corporation, Washington, D.C. During the past three years, Dr. Simonett has been an invited contributor to more than thirty national and international symposia, panels, working groups, or university lecture series dealing with remote sensing applications. He has conducted research in aircraft and spacecraft remote sensing, particularly for resource evaluation in underdeveloped regions. He is the author of more than fifty major publications in the fields of remote sensing, land evaluation, and land use, soil geography, and geomorphology.

Kirk H. Stone (Ph.D., University of Michigan). Dr. Stone is a Professor in the Department of Geography, as well as in the Institute for Behavioral Research, at the University of Georgia. He first began working in airphoto interpretation in 1935, continued as an interpreter in the Office of Strategic Services during World War II, and afterwards developed the instructional program in the subject at the University of Wisconsin. He has given particular attention to the use of small scale imagery from the Apollo and ERTS programs for geographical analyses of population distribution and rural settlement morphology.

Randolph R. Thaman (Ph.D. Candidate, University of California, Los Angeles). Mr. Thaman has been actively involved in remote sensing research since 1966. He is the author or co-author of over twenty publications relating to the use of remote sensing techniques for agricultural surveys, land use classification, vegetation mapping and pollution monitoring. He has also presented papers at, or has been a contributor to, over fifteen international symposia, remote sensing workshops, university lecture series, and professional meetings. Mr. Thaman is presently a lecturer in the Geography Program and a Research Geographer with the Geography Remote Sensing Unit at the University of California, Santa Barbara and is serving as consultant to the Indonesian government as part of a multispectral remote sensing project.

DEDICATION

This book is respectfully dedicated to
Gentles, Eidemiller, Finch, Yahr, Thrower,
and especially Logan and Spencer,
who teach much more than geography.

Preface

The field of remote sensing is an outgrowth of aerial photographic interpretation,and has been rapidly expanding and evolving since the term was first coined by Evelyn Pruitt in 1960. Remote sensing involves the collection of data by systems which are not in direct contact with the objects or phenomena under investigation. In many instances, technological development of remote sensing systems (sensors and platforms) has outstripped corresponding development of interpretation methodologies and techniques, which are needed to convert remotely sensed data into usable information. However, increasing attention is being directed towards the interpretative and analytical phases of remote sensing. Now emphasis is being placed on problem-oriented research and the development of operational interpretation methodologies and techniques.

Since remote sensing imagery is non-selective with respect to information content (i.e., data may be interpreted from an individual image that is applicable to a diversity of interests), research in the field is being conducted by individuals and groups with many different disciplinary backgrounds. Geographers, with their interdisciplinary training and interests, have made valuable contributions to many aspects of remote sensing research--urban, land use, agriculture, and others. Remote sensing courses, as a consequence of the need for geographers trained in the field, are being offered at an increasing rate in geography departments throughout the United States. In 1950, only 11 geography departments in the United States offered a course in aerial photographic interpretation. By 1973, 97 institutions offered courses in aerial photographic interpretation/remote sensing in geography.

A major problem facing remote sensing courses in geography, as well as in other earth science disciplines, is the lack of a textbook which adequately defines the limits of the field. There is a great deal of literature available in the form of articles and reports from sources such as the University of Michigan's *Symposia on Remote Sensing of Environment*, various journals, and government publications. The volume and specialized nature of this literature, however, makes it difficult to use for introductory classroom instruction. There are some books, the *Manual of Photographic Interpretation* and the forthcoming *Manual of Remote Sensing*, that provide in-depth perspectives on photo interpretation and remote sensing. These are limited in utility for instructional purposes and, because of their scope and design, serve a better function as references and/or supplemental reading.

Remote Sensing is an outgrowth and expansion of a series of reference readings written specifically for participants at two, one-day remote sensing workshops offered at the 24th International Geographical Union meetings in Montreal, Canada (August 1972). The purpose of these workshops was to provide geographers and other scientists from developing nations with a basic introduction to the field of remote sensing. Invited speakers were asked to submit written materials for their discussion topics, which could be assembled and integrated into a useful reference text for participants at the workshops. Consequently, it was possible to prepare a text of original papers that would document the state of development in various areas of remote sensing at an introductory level of understanding, and provide references to direct readers to more advanced works on given topics. Participant and review response to this Montreal reference book was so encouraging that a decision was made to attempt to publish the material, with revisions and additions for a more complete product.

As conceived by the editors, *Remote Sensing* is not designed purely as a textbook or as a reference work. The book is more than a collection of readings for reference, but less than the fully integrated concept normally associated with a textbook. However, it may be effectively utilized within either context, depending upon the needs and background of the reader. *Remote Sensing* is intended primarily to fill an instructional void and perform several functions: (1) it serves as a basic introduction to remote sensing technology, (2) it discusses research in subjects of interest to geography and other disciplines, (3) it provides substantial bibliographies to lead the student into the abundant remote sensing literature, and (4) it indicates institutions and organizations where particular types of studies are being conducted. Contributions to this book have been solicited from among some of the leading people in the field. Chapters have been written at a level comprehensible to upper division undergraduates and to graduate students. Editorial comments are provided at the beginning of each chapter to provide cohesiveness to the book and to add a degree of continuity between chapters.

The editors wish to acknowledge the contributions of many individuals to this work: Mrs. Jeradean Graumann for her excellent typing and shepherding of the final book copy; Edwin A. Gustafson who did the illustrations for the book; Robert H. Alexander who perceptively reviewed the original manuscript; Drs. R. N. Colwell, D. M. Carneggie, R. Welch and G. A. Thorley, as well as J.D. Lent and W. G. Brooner, who critically reviewed particular chapters; the members of the Geography Remote Sensing Unit at the University of California, Santa Barbara (D. Brunelle, F. Evanisko, D. Hoffman, S. P. Kraus, B. Palmer, and T. Soper) for their help and cooperation when needed; Dorine Schichner, Cynthia Knight, and others who participated in the preparation of the Montreal reference text from which this book is derived; and, most importantly, Mrs. Konai Thaman who compiled Appendices 2 and 3 and proofed much of the final book copy. The editors would also like to thank each of the authors for their contributions and excellent cooperation. The authors are likewise to be complimented for their unanimous agreement, along with the editors, to donate the proceeds from this work to the Association of American Geographers, which will be used by the Commission on Remote Sensing for the advancement of remote sensing in geographic education and research. Finally, as with any work of this nature and scope, certain errors and shortcomings are inevitable. The editors assume responsibility for these deficiencies and welcome constructive suggestions for improving this book.

John E. Estes
University of California, Santa Barbara

Leslie W. Senger
Dames & Moore, Santa Barbara

I

Developing Geographical Remote Sensing

Kirk H. Stone
University of Georgia

The development of remote sensing technology has afforded an opportunity for many and diverse research efforts to be conducted in a variety of disciplines and along interdisciplinary lines. The major themes in this chapter concern the historical development of this technology and, in particular, the ways in which remote sensing data have been incorporated into geographic methodology. Stone examines the relationship between geographic research and remote sensing as it has progressed from an initial concern with conventional aerial photographs to more recent developments in the nonphotographic portion of the electromagnetic spectrum. The possible future directions which geographical remote sensing may take are presented at the end of the chapter. This treatment provides an overview and perspective which the reader will find useful for understanding and relating the contents of subsequent chapters.

Every discipline enjoys the sense of accomplishment attending treatises on its development. So it is with geography. As the "Mother of the Sciences," this method of locational analysis has origins deep in antiquity and a continuity ever since that led to its present respected professional stature. Such progress should be recorded, since it has been marked by persistent improvement in methods of making and analyzing maps, the primary tools of geographic description and analysis.

Clearly geographical efforts have been, are, and will be closely connected with any means of locating an object and determining its characteristics. Whether the methods are by direct contact and close vision during field work or by sensing these qualities from remote positions makes no difference as long as accuracy, completeness, and comparability are attained. For much of history, the basis for mapping was largely the former; but in modern times the remote sensing of objects, first with cameras and more recently with recordings of energy beyond visible light, has been a real boon. In those parts of the world with high degrees of different kinds of isolation, remote sensing has made possible geographic inventories and analyses that would have been too expensive by direct observation.

Further, remote sensing has made possible multiple-scaled geographic analyses.

Initially, it presented large-scale data in the visible part of the electromagnetic (EM) spectrum. Presently this has been enlarged to several scales in the visible range and to large and medium scales immediately beyond visible. As future improvements in both techniques and analyses are made, geographical work at all scales of consideration may be expected to be among the leaders.1*

INITIAL SUMMARY

Since 1860, geographical uses of remote sensing have gone through at least five phases. These have mirrored not only the changes in materials and methods, but also differences in the objectives of practitioners of the discipline. Each of the phases overlapped adjoining ones, all were progressively shorter, and the first four were concerned with aerial photos.

The first phase was one of slow recognition that the first photographs taken from the air had utility for mapping. This was followed by a period of short-lived experiments on the uses of air photos for the mapping of various physical and cultural elements of a landscape as well as a time of rapid wartime development of air-photo interpretation as a sophisticated intelligence-gathering technique. It was followed by some years of extending wartime procedures to peacetime uses by way of considerable formalized instruction, during which, however, undue emphasis was given to techniques rather than analytical uses of results. A fourth phase corrected this by centering on the applied uses of air-photo interpretation in geographic work. Most recently came the adjustment of these applications to the expansion of data gathering and analysis into portions of the EM specturm beyond the small visible sector. It is in both these visible and non-visible divisions of the total spectrum that the future of remote sensing lies, with the greater promise to geography lying, however, in analytical applications rather than in the easing of observations in the field.

1860-1930: THE FIRST AIR PHOTOS

As soon as the practice of photography started in 1839, improvements were made rapidly. By 1851, both daguerreotype (metal plate) and calotype (paper negatives and prints) processes were available. The next 28 years were characterized by the wet-collodion plate process resulting in printings on albumenized paper. Then, by 1900, came the major developments of dry plates with silver bromide coatings in gelatin, paper prints with coverings of silver chloride or silver bromide in gelatin, and flexible roll film. Thus was created the mechanical perception of objects from a distance, now called remote sensing.

Aerial photography began during the first period. In 1857, air photos were made from a free balloon, and in 1860 the first air photos were made in the United States--of a part of Boston, Massachussets, from a captive balloon at 1,200 feet. Kites, pigeons, and rockets were tried later, but the instability of these carriers and the quality of the results left much to be desired. By the time airplanes were operational, the photographic processes were improved; the

* Notes will be found in separate section at end of chapter.

first photo to be taken from a plane was a motion picture photographed from a plane piloted by Wilbur Wright over Centocelli, Italy, on April 24, 1909.

Long before that time, some significance of air photos was recognized. "Spying" during the American Civil War and general mapping were two uses. However, aerial photography of a practical nature dates from the early days of World War I; it was introduced by Lieutenant Lawes of the British flying forces when he took the first pictures of enemy territory. Vigorous efforts were then launched by the Allied forces to develop proper equipment and methods of operation.

Some geographers associated with World War I military units envisaged peacetime use of this early military coverage. A few spoke of archeological uses and more detailed mapping of roads, buildings, and fields. Others commented about physical features, such as swamps and bedrock outcrops. Although the coverage was poor and the area photographed was limited, the potentials for inventory and cartography were recognized readily.

Improvements in planes, cameras, and films resulted in more peacetime photography. In geographic study there were two types. First was the single-shot coverage, usually from hand-held instruments. These ranged from verticals through low obliques to high obliques. Generally they were illustrative, but in 1922, Lee pointed out some potentials of data gathering from air photos with respect to both physical and cultural features.[2] Other examples of recognition of utility were Joerg's urban research[3] and attention to archeological features by Johnson and Platt at the end of the period.[4] This first type was of random areas, various subjects, and photos taken at different times and with different scales.

The second type of coverage differed in that it was taken for topographic mapping purposes, which quickly became the dominant use of air photos. By the mid-1920s, parts of the United States were recorded with triple-mounted cameras providing a vertical synchronized with two low-oblique air photos; the vertical had a scale of about 1:35,000, and there were small amounts of side-lap and flightline overlap. The coverage was mostly flown by the U.S. Army Air Corps, but by then coverage of other parts of the United States was being taken by new mapping firms. All persons working with these photos stressed the photogrammetric (mapping with high degrees of accuracy from photographs) aspects, for the effort was leading into a major long-time program of photographing the whole United States; it began about 1930.

1920-1950: INCREASED AIR-PHOTO COVERAGE

The photographic plan had two primary objectives initially. One was for medium-scale topographic mapping of the whole nation. The other was for large-scale localized mapping but was designed for official payments, based on the acreages of individual fields, to farmers participating in crop-payment programs for various kinds of conservation. For these two uses, plans called for vertical air photos at contact-print scales of 1:20,000 with 60 percent overlap along east-west or north-south flightlines and 30 to 40 percent side-lap. It became clear immediately that this scale was unsuitable for both uses, so reductions were made for the mapping work and enlargements for the crop-payment program.

A few geographers were working with these photos. Some were in the mapping firms and some in the subsidy work. American geographers primarily experimented, and rather randomly, with regard to both topic and area during the period. Much was done by taking photos to the field and trying to determine causes of observable differences in texture and tone. The results, of course, ran the gamut of physical and cultural features in an area. Of the little that was published, the article by Russell, Foster and McMurry was a classic of overall inventory uses; unfortunately the paper came out during wartime and in a periodical with somewhat limited circulation.[5] Meanwhile, the illustrative uses continued in small-scale geographic studies like those on South America and Africa.[6] Near the end of the period, an article on Alaskan vegetative keys illustrated the use of air-photo interpretation of small-scale coverage (1:35,000 to 1:50,000) for land classification as well as for field crews traversing unsettled areas.[7]

As the Department of Agriculture, the principal contractor in the American plan, obtained more and more coverage during the period, geographers tried them out only here and there. Roscoe attributed this to lack of information on the extent and access of coverage, the multiplicity of geographic objectives, and the intensity of theoretical interest or lack of commercial demand for their interpreted products.[8] Yet some of the experimentation and lack of use probably reflected changes in objectives of American geography at the time; strong physical interests were weakening in favor of more culturally oriented man-land focuses.

Meanwhile, European geographers retained the physical specialization and put air photos to use in it. During the period, Troll and Bobek were early leaders in this respect.[9] A number of scientists in other disciplines, like geology and forestry, began interpreting many types of data. Some of this was geographic in viewpoint and found its way into geographical outlets but most went into publications of other disciplines.[10] The primary outlet for all types of articles on air-photo interpretation became *Photogrammetric Engineering* after 1945.

Special attention is focused on the period of World War II. This was the time when air-photo interpretation became a full-fledged intelligence-gathering technique which often was granted credit for dramatic achievements.[11] Several geographers, both foreign and domestic, were assigned to "PI" work and were specially trained. The location of military targets and the assessment of damages were the primary tasks. The work was done at two levels, tactical and strategic. Emphasis was given to the preparation and use of interpretational "keys" by which identifications of items with immediate military significance could be made rapidly regardless of an interpreter's previous experience. English interpreters set enviable records for this work at the strategic levels.

Wartime interpretation was done mostly with large-scale photos, with scales ranging from about 1:5,000 to 1:10,000. For mapping and strategic study, efforts were made to obtain overlapping verticals, while for assessing tactical intelligence, varying types and qualities of photos were obtained; interpreters learned to use whatever came in, including wet negatives. This was good experience for postwar interpretation, leading many qualified geographers to peacetime uses and instruction with both wartime and contemporary photography. At the end of the period, the principal geographical articles published in the United States were still largely general and descriptive.[12] Meanwhile, there were also some unfortunate consequences of the wartime development.

1945-1960: EXAGGERATION OF INTERPRETATION TECHNIQUES

Unnecessary assumptions from previous experience led to too much emphasis on the techniques of interpretation after World War II. In part, this was because so much progress was made in photogrammetry before and during hostilities. Making maps from even good verticals required engineering tools and training. Inasmuch as most interpretational articles were published in *Photogrammetric Engineering*, the association with such specialized articles was misleading. Further, wartime training and experience led to preoccupation with "how to" rather than "what for."

In addition, to do interpretation required a process that was strange to many people. Even though grandparents had used stereopticans for the parlor viewing of pictures in third dimension, this newer procedure had more movable parts and involved eye-muscle movement that was different. Necessary equipment included a stereoscope (of which there were several types), a ruler (usually graduated to thousandths of a foot), a grease pencil, some erasing fluid, and (usually) lots of photos (which one might have to take himself).[13] Attention to technique, particularly in a new method of gathering data from all over the world, was quite normal. This was a "gee whiz" stage during which many geographers, and others as well, became acquainted enthusiastically with a new tool that had great potentials.

Formalized instruction developed rapidly and emphasized technique. In 1946 there were 13 courses in the subject in the United States; overseas it was combined with other techniques at a few institutions. By 1954, there were 173 courses in the United States, while at foreign locations both universities and governmental agencies were introducing such training.[14] In most situations, the principal references available were military manuals, the instructors had had military experience, and the foreign coverage obtainable for exercises was of military origin; emphasis on technique was to be expected. All kinds of interpretational keys were developed for physical and cultural elements of the landscape, and the underlying tone of most was overly optimistic in spite of occasional warnings.[15] However, too much geographical work involving air-photo interpretation at this time ended with description and without analysis.[16]

Some overemphasis on technique resulted from special attention to the existence of coverage. When the International Geographical Union set up its Commission on the Utilization of Aerial Photographs in 1949, its members[17] emphasized the need for knowledge of what parts of the world were photographed. The point was pressed during this period.[18] Again, with so much attention given to the physical essentials for interpretation and because it was a new tool, it is natural that some 15 years of American geographic interests were centered on the methods rather than considering it only one more way of acquiring data for spatial analysis and getting on with the reasoning. But this changed.

1955-1962: GEOGRAPHIC APPLICATIONS

In a fourth phase, American geographical photo interpretation became much more an applied technique than a theoretical one. General geographical efforts were more sharply focused on man-land relations; geography's fundamental interdisciplinary qualities showed more clearly. Analyses of data derived from photo interpretation now became the end result. In fact, it was the beginning of a time of geographic applications which really extended to the present day but had a name change part way along.

Uses of interpreted data were on all sorts of topics and problems. Several bibliographies demonstrate this.[19] Early applications were related to specific urban problems, such as analyses of distributions of neighborhoods with different levels of economic status.[20] Traffic direction and volume, industrial-plant classification, mapping of various land-use zones, and developmental planning have been favorite topics.

Equal progress was made in the interpretation of rural features. On the cultural side were the uses of crop identification through various stages of growth for land-use analyses.[21] Of the physical-element topics, the interpretation of vegetation for a variety of objectives was exemplary.[22]

Of course, many uses of air photos were buried in the content of geographical work at this time. Occasional footnotes disclosed the dependence of research on commercial or private coverage,[23] but in many instances the data were unspecified as to source. Foreign geographical research followed the same pattern.

Also, considerable advances in interpretation were made in other disciplines. Geology, forestry, agriculture, and archeology represent areas in which applications increased in academic and nonacademic pursuits. As a result, recorded uses no longer appeared primarily in engineering outlets, but occurred in books and periodicals dealing with both areal and disciplinary specialties.

Some academic geographic interests still centered on the aspects of technique during the period. Regionalizing and keying continued.[24] Procedures for specific interpretation of major physical and cultural elements of the landscape were summarized.[25] Instrumented interpretation was investigated.[26] Formalized instruction emphasized technique as well as uses of air photos for analyses in regional and topical courses. This was all to the good, for it made the transition to the space age one during which the focus on technique was not exaggerated as it had been previously.

1960 - PRESENT: EXPANSION TO OTHER REMOTELY SENSED DATA

On April 1, 1960, a new system of sensing the earth from remote heights was introduced. This was TIROS-1, providing television and infrared observations, which was launched as a research and development project following the Explorer program (1958) and the Discoverer program (1959); very quickly TIROS evolved into an operational system for weather observation. The results attracted much attention, and recognition came quickly of other possible uses. Then in 1964, the NIMBUS satellite was sent aloft with advanced television cameras and a high-resolution infrared observational system, providing the first day-and-night pictures of the earth.

Meanwhile U.S. manned space-flight programs began with Mercury's first manned flights in 1961, and continued through Gemini and Apollo. During the Gemini-3 flight in March 1965, some 25 color pictures were obtained with a hand-held camera.[27] Three months later, the next flight included photographic experiments with similar equipment and produced many pictures. In August 1965, 250 pictures were taken with similar equipment. The areas of coverage were limited to low latitudes, with the best photos being imaged over dry lands; the views of gross weather, geologic, and agiruc1tural-use patterns in color attracted widespread interest in many disciplines. However, specific applications were a bit slow in evolving owing to the very small scales and the different positions of camera axes.[28] Still, within just five more years, landings on the moon were made and U.S. flights of up to 244 hours were completed; hand-held cameras were still in use, but mounted instruments for sensing in several parts of the EM spectrum supplied new data. Topical and areal interests in the NASA programs expanded greatly.[29]

The supply of remotely sensed data about the earth greatly increased with the launching of ERTS-1 (Earth Resources Technology Satellite) on July 23, 1972. A concomitant development was the U.S. Geological Survey's program called EROS (Earth Resources Observation Systems). ERTS-1 was placed in a sun-synchronous, polar orbit about 600 miles out from the earth, and it completes a full observational sequence of the earth every 18 days. Its RBV (return beam vidicon) imagery was to be recorded on three bands (0.475 to 0.575 um [green], 0.580 to 0.680 um [red], and 0.690 to 0.830 um [solar infrared]), but the system had to be shut down a month after launching; its MSS (multispectral scanner) imagery is recorded on four bands; 0.5 to 0.6 um, 0.6 to 0.7 um, 0.7 to 0.8 um, and 0.8 to 1.1 um. Contact prints are on 70-mm film with scales of 1:3,369,000. These are available for purchase in various formats at cost of reproduction from the EROS Data Center at Sioux Falls, South Dakota. So-called "browse files" for public inspection of imagery are maintained in updated form at 19 offices in the United States by the U.S. Geological Survey and at 22 more offices by the National Oceanic and Atmospheric Administration of the Department of Commerce. Computerized cataloging of the coverage and automated printing make possible the filling of purchase orders in reasonable times. Thus, data for the United States and the many countries participating in the program are available in amounts and qualities never before equaled.

This availability will continue. Future programs include the expected one-year life of ERTS-1 to be overlapped by Skylab and supplemented by ERTS-B. The former is a 10,000-cubic-foot manned workshop which will orbit 235 miles above the earth and carry out astronomic, biologic, and earth-oriented research; this last will be in agriculture and forestry, oceanography, hydrology, geology, and geography by remote sensing equipment mounted in the multiple docking adapter. ERTS-B will be a modified ERTS-1 with imagery from at least one additional band.

In retrospect, it was 1962 when "remote sensing" became a common term. It is rather unfortunate that "remotely sensed data interpretation" was not introduced in order to be more accurate; yet, "remote sensing" has come to mean both taking the imagery as well as analyzing it. At any rate, it was in 1962 that two geographers, Evelyn L. Pruitt and Walter H. Bailey, initiated efforts leading to the First Symposium on Remote Sensing of the Environment, held at the University of Michigan. This was the beginning of a phase when the "black-box" technicians and scientists needing remotely sensed data were brought together; its early evangelistic overtones were soon drowned out by many articles demonstrating uses in various disciplines.[30]

However, geographers were rather slow about getting deeply into remote sensing. Modest participation by colleagues in the four national symposia held in 1962, 1964, and 1966[31] was noted, and it was stated as recently as 1967 that "the response of the profession was cautious or indifferent."[32] But some colleagues were busy. General uses and overall regional interpretation were two topics covered.[33] A major initiating step was taken in 1966 when *Spacecraft in Geographic Research* was published with recommendations for use of remotely sensed data in eight subdivisions of geography.[34] Specific potentials of aerial infrared imagery were outlined.[35] Meanwhile the applicability of air photos in land use and historical geography gained more attention.[36] Also in 1966, there was recognition of geography's interdisciplinary characteristic and, therefore, its potential for physical and cultural analyses of data from spacecraft.[37] In 1967, the general potentials were outlined again in a forceful manner.[38]

Of course, mapping was a major concern in many disciplines. Some geographers engaged in this; but, even as early as 1965, the overall problem of multiple scales and multiple resolutions in different parts of the EM spectrum was causing a division of efforts in many fields. As one reference noted: "A necessary task of the photo interpreter will be to gain experience in the recognition of common features at widely different scales and resolutions in order to make optimum use of space photography."[39]

In short, by 1966 American geography was "tooling up" to meet the responsibilities of remote sensing. In addition to the individual efforts noted above, there were disciplinary ones as well. For example, in 1966 the Association of American Geographers set up its Commission on the Geographic Applications of Remote Sensing. Under its first project director, R. W. Peplies, the commission was quite active for about five years in research and educational tasks. Among several projects initiated, there was a summer short course for staff and graduate students that ran for four years starting in 1968. The commission worked closely with the Geographic Applications Program, initiated by Chief Geographer Arch C. Gerlach in the U.S. Geological Survey, which is still a major program of execution, evaluation, and research.

By 1971, several geographers were deeply engrossed in content analyses employing space-imagery data. No longer was there caution or indifference. Applications to urban land uses were pressed.[40] Camera systems were investigated.[41] Rural land-utilization classifications and recognition techniques were developed.[42] Settlement analyses were improved greatly.[43] Automation of and the systems approach to the interpretation of imagery were examined.[44] Formal courses were increasing, some allied with photogrammetry and some not.[45] Certainly the chapters in this book affirm the great breadth and depth of geographical uses of space imagery. The discipline, with its related fields, is beyond the uses of visible light and well into the understanding and employment of remotely sensed data in the sectors of reflected or near-infrared, thermal or emitted infrared, radar, and passive microwave. Perhaps best of all, some geographers are acting as interdisciplinarians to tie together the numerous remote sensing efforts in several fields.[46]

THE FUTURE

The years immediately ahead will be exciting. Geographical remote sensing cannot help but develop at an accelerating rate in both theoretical and applied aspects. All science is in the midst of an explosion of data gathering, analysis, and publication. The quality, rather than the quantity, of geographical remote sensing will be dependent upon a few sober thoughts and deliberate actions among which are the following:

(1) Agreement on a major focus of general geographical effort. Several times in the history of the field, and during at least one of the periods outlined above, progress has been delayed by the poor definition of a disciplinary core. "Man-land relationships" is not acceptable to some. "Description and interpretation of the earth" is too general for others. "Anthropocentricity" is rejected by still others. These differences are mirrored in the employment of techniques. Remotely sensed data interpretation is a technique; its values depend on the field's basic philosophy first.

One possible central theme could be established by accepting locational analysis, the geographical method, as a technique. If adaptable, the interdisciplinary function is then a dominant one. Of course, any science is interdisciplinary in some way, but some are more so than others. Thus, efforts to develop geographical remote sensing in the future may be made efficiently by concentrating on the acquisition of any data necessary for theoretical or applied locational analysis.

(2) Resistance to dedication to detailed techniques and evangelism. This mistake was made with respect to air-photo interpretation. In our zeal to produce increased efficiency, we do not need to be "black box" specialists nor is another "gee whiz" phase necessary. Of course, one should be aware of the electronic pitfalls characteristic of that part of the spectrum in which work is being carried out. However, the details of technique are no more necessary than specific knowledge of the internal combustion engine is to driving an automobile properly. With respect to evangelism, good work has always been its own best salesman.

(3) Methodical procedures. These are more essential than ever. In the future, one major problem will doubtless be data selection from a great mass of imagery covering differences in place, time, position in the EM spectrum, scale, and resolution. It is, of course, recommended that multiple imagery be used. Further, results are obtained more efficiently by working from the smaller-scaled coverage to the larger. It is not clear whether a similar procedure may be used to go through the spectrum, but it should be sought. The launching of Skylab in 1973 and ERTS-B later will result in masses of data that will force well-controlled procedures.

(4) Field work. Remote sensing is not likely to reduce geographical study to armchair research. It will make field work more productive, but there can be no true substitute for direct observation--nor should there be!

(5) Analysis as the goal of geographic research. Description is basic, but it is doubtful that it has much lasting appeal. Fundamentally, our task remains to explain why selected physical or cultural elements of the landscape are where they are and are not where they are not. Therein lies our contribution and the necessity (and pleasure) of interdisciplinary work.

Beyond these first general steps are those at the topical level. These are covered well in the following chapters, both as to what is now known and what may be learned in the future. It will be clear that for the future development of geographical remote sensing, it is literally true that the sky is the limit!

NOTES

1. K. H. Stone, 1972, "A Geographer's Stength: The Multiple-Scale Approach," *Journal of Geography,* 81:354-362.

2. W. T. Lee, *The Face of the Earth as Seen from the Air,* 1922, Special Publication 4, American Geographical Society, New York.

3. W. L. G. Joerg, 1923, "The Use of Airplane Photography in City Geography," *Annals of the Association of American Geographers,* 13:211.

4. G. R. Johnson and R. R. Platt, 1930, *Peru from the Air,* Special Publication 7, American Geographical Society, New York.

5. J. A. Russell, F. W. Foster, and K. C. McMurry, 1943, "Some Applications of Aerial Photographs to Geographic Inventory," *Papers of the Michigan Academy of Science, Arts, and Letters,* 29:315-341.

6. J. L. Rich, 1942, *The Face of South America,* Special Publication No. 26, American Geographical Society, New York: R. U. Light, 1944, *Focus on Africa,* Special Publication 25, American Geographical Society, New York.

7. K. H. Stone, 1948, "Aerial Photographic Interpretation of Natural Vegetation in the Anchorage Area, Alaska," *Annals of the Association of American Geographers,* 38:465-474.

8. J. H. Roscoe, "Photo Interpretation in Geography," Chapter 14 in *Manual of Photographic Interpretation,* 1960, American Society of Photogrammetry, Washington, D.C.

9. C. Troll, 1939, "Luftbildplan and okologische Bodenforschung," *Zeitschrift des Gesellschaft fur Erdkunde zu Berlin,* 7/8:241-298; C. Troll, 1943, "Fortschritte der Wissenschaftlichen Luftbildforschung," *Zeitschrift des Gesellschaft fur Erdkunde zu Berlin,* 7/10:277-311; H. Bobek, 1941, "Luftbild and Geomorphologie," *Luftbild und Luftbildmessung,* 20:8-161.

10. American Society of Photogrammetry, *Manual of Photographic Interpretation, op. cit.,* Chapters 4-13 and 15.

11. C. Babbington-Smith, 1957, *Air Spy: The Story of Photo Intelligence in World War II,* Harper and Row, New York.

12. N. Carls, 1947, *How to Read Aerial Photos for Census Work,* U.S. Department of Commerce, Washington, D.C., H. R. Long, 1947, "A Geographer's Role in Aerial Photointerpretation," *Professional Geographer,* 6:23-26; G. A. Stokes, 1950, "The Aerial Photograph: A Key to the Cultural Landscape," *Journal of Geography,* 49:32-40; F. W. Foster, 1951, "Some Aspects of the Field Use of Aerial Photographs by Geographers," *Photogrammetric Engineering,* 17:771-776; J. E. Kesseli, 1952, "Use of Air Photographs by Geographers," *Photogrammetric Engineering,* 18:737-741; C. H. MacFadden, 1952, "The Uses of Aerial Photographs in Geographic Research," *Photogrammetric Engineering,* 18:732-737. Overseas, several books of air photos of various elements of the landscape captured attention. However, in the United States, encouraging signs of analytical uses of air photos were beginning to appear in such

publications as M. C. Branch, Jr., 1948, *Aerial Photography in Urban Planning and Research,* Harvard City Planning Studies 14, Harvard University, Cambridge, Mass.; and C. F. Kohn, 1951, "The Use of Aerial Photographs in the Geographical Analysis of Rural Settlements," *Photogrammetric Engineering,* 17:759-771.

13. C. H. MacFadden, 1949, "Some Preliminary Notes on the Use of the Light Airplane and 35 mm. Camera in Geographic Field Research," *Annals of the Association of American Geographers,* 39:188-200.

14. American Society of Photogrammetry, *Manual of Photographic Interpretation, op. cit.,* Chapter 16.

15. K. H. Stone, 1951, "Geographical Air-Photo Interpretation," *Photogrammetric Engineering,* 17:754-759.

16. Note the items referred to in K. H. Stone, 1954, "A Selected Bibliography for Geographic Instruction and Research by Air Photo Interpretation," *Photogrammetric Engineering,* 20:561-565; K. H. Stone, 1956, "Air Photo Interpretation Procedures," *Photogrammetric Engineering,* 22:123-132. H. V. B. Kline, Jr., 1954, "The Interpretation of Air Photographs" in C.F. Jones and P. E. James, Eds., *American Geography, Inventory and Prospect,* Syracuse University Press, N. Y., pp. 530-552.

17. There were six commission members: Le Mehaute and Barrerre of France, Von Frijtag Drabbe of the Netherlands, Linton of the United Kingdom, and Roscoe and Stone of the United States: these represented the major areas where geographical air photointerpretation was being done.

18. K. H. Stone, 1953, "World Air Photo Coverage for Geographic Research," *Annals of the Association of American Geographers,* 43:193; K. H. Stone, 1959, "World Air Photo Coverage," *Professional Geographer,* N.S. 11:2-6; H. V. B. Kline, *op. cit.,* pp. 539-541.

19. R. B. Honea and V. C. Prentice, 1968, *Selected Bibliography of Remote Sensing,* Interagency Report NASA-129, U.S. Geological Survey, Washington, D.C., R. B. Honea and V. C. Prentice, 1970, *Selected Bibliography of Remote Sensing,* Supplement to Interagency Report NASA-129, U.S. Geological Survey, Washington, D.C.; *Bibliography of Remote Sensing,* 1966, East Tennessee State University, Department of Geography, Johnson City; R. B. Honea, 1967 (?), *Tentative Remote Sensing Bibliographies,* East Tennessee State University, Department of Geography, Johnson City, Tenn.

20. N. E. Green, 1956, "Aerial Photographic Analysis of Residential Neighborhoods: An Evaluation of Data Accuracy," *Social Forces,* 35:142-147; N. E. Green, "Aerial Photographic Interpretation and the Social Structure of the City," *Photogrammetric Engineering,* 23:89-99.

21. D. H. Brunnschweiler, 1957, "Seasonal Changes of the Agricultural Pattern --A Study in Comparative Airphoto Interpretation," *Photogrammetric Engineering,* 23:131-139; M. S. Goodman, 1959, "A Technique for the Identification of Farm Crops in Aerial Photographs," *Photogrammetric Engineering,* 25:131-137; P. P. Karan, 1960, "A Land Use Reconnaissance in Nepal by Aero-Field-Techniques and Photography," *Proceedings of the American Philosophical Society,* pp. 172-187.

22. V. P. Finley, 1960, *Photo Interpretation of Vegetation--Literature and Analysis*, Technical Report 69, U.S. Army S.I.P.R.E., Wilmette, Ill.

23. K. H. Stone, 1963, "The Annual Emptying of Lake George, Alaska," *Arctic*, 16:26-39.

24. L. D. Black, 1955, "Regional Keys Are Valid Geographical Generalizations," *Photogrammetric Engineering*, 21:706-708; G. K. Lewis, 1957, "The Concept of Analogous Area Photo Interpretation Keys," *Photogrammetric Engineering*, 23:874-878; Y. Kedar, 1958, "Geographic Approach to the Study of Photo Interpretation," *Photogrammetric Engineering*, 24:821-824.

25. K. H. Stone, 1964, "A Guide to the Interpretation and Analysis of Aerial Photos," *Annals of the Association of American Geographers*, 54:318-328.

26. J. P. Latham, 1959, *Possible Applications of Electronic Scanning and Computer Devices to the Analysis of Geographic Phenomena*, University of Pennsylvania, Geography and Industry Department, Philadelphia; J. P. Latham, *Methodology for Instrumented Geographic Analysis*, Department of Geography, Bowling Green State University, Bowling Green, Ohio.

27. It was a Hasselblad, modified model 500 C with f/2.8 Zeiss Planar lens with a focal length of 80 mm. The film was 70 mm Ektachrome MS. Flight heights of Gemini-3 ranged from 100 to 140 miles.

28. National Aeronautics and Space Administration, 1967, *Earth Photographs from Gemini III, IV, and V*, Washington, D.C.

29. O. W. Nicks, Ed., 1970, *This Island Earth*, NASA Special Publication 250, Washington, D.C.

30. Note the numerous articles on potential uses of remote sensing during the mid-1960s that are listed in the bibliographies referred to in note 19 above.

31. J. P. Latham, 1966, "Remote Sensing of the Environment," *Geographical Review*, 56:288-291.

32. J. P. Latham, 1967, *Remote Sensing Papers at the AAAS--Impact and Implications*, Technical Report 2, Florida Atlantic University, Boca Raton, Fla.

33. R. H. Alexander, 1964, "Geographic Data from Space," *Professional Geographer*, 16:4-5; D. S. Simonett and S. A. Morain, 1965, *Remote Sensing from Spacecraft as a Tool for Investigating Arctic Environments*, CRES Report 61-5, University of Kansas, Lawrence; R. B. Simpson, 1966, "Radar: Geographic Tool," *Annals of the Association of American Geographers*, 56:80-90.

34. N.A.S.-N.R.C., 1966, *Spacecraft in Geographic Research*, Publication 1353, National Academy of Sciences, Washington, D.C.

35. J. E. Estes, 1966, "Some Applications of Aerial Infrared Imagery," *Annals of the Association of American Geographers*, 56:673-682.

36. D. Steiner, 1965, "Use of Air Photographs for Interpreting and Mapping Rural Land Use in the United States," *Photogrammetria,* 20:65-80; R. M. Newcomb, 1966, "Two Keys for the Historical Interpretation of Aerial Photographs," *The California Geographer,* 7:37-46.

37. NASA, 1966, *Peaceful Uses of Earth-Observation Spacecraft,* CR-256, Washington, D.C., pp. 15-19.

38. R. H. Alexander, "Man's New Views of the Earth: The Potential of Remote Sensing," in S. B. Cohen, Ed., 1965, *Problems and Trends in American Geography,* Basic Books, New York, pp. 239-250.

39. J. Van Lopik et al., 1965, "Photo Interpretation in the Space Sciences," *Photogrammetric Engineering,* 31:1060-1075.

40. J. P. Latham, 1971, "Urban Applications of Remote Sensing," *Geographical Review,* 61:139-142.

41. R. Welch, 1971, "Earth Satellite Camera Systems: Resolution Estimates and Mapping Applications," *The Photogrammetric Record,* 7:237-246; R. Welch, 1972, "Quality and Applications of Aerospace Imagery," *Photogrammetric Engineering,* 38:379-398.

42. R. D. Rudd, 1971, "Macro Land-Use Mapping with Simulated Space Photos," *Photogrammetric Engineering,* 37:365-372; J. R. Anderson et al., 1972, *A Land-Use Classification System for Use with Remote Sensor Data,* U.S. Geological Survey Circular 671, Washington, D.C.; N.A.S.-N.R.C., 1970, *Remote Sensing, with Special Reference to Agriculture and Forestry,* Washington, D.C.; N. J. W. Thrower, 1970, "Land Use in the Southwestern United States from Gemini and Apollo Imagery," *Annals of the Association of American Geographers,* vol. 60, Map Supplement 12, Scale 1:1,000,000.

43. W. R. Tobler, 1969, "Satellite Confirmation of Settlement Size Coefficients," *Area,* 1:30-34.

44. C. P. Low, 1971, "Modern Use of Aerial Photographs in Geographical Research," *Area,* 3:164-169.

45. B. T. Stanton, 1971, "Education in Photogrammetry," *Photogrammetric Engineering,* 37:293-303.

46. R. K. Holz, Ed., 1973, *The Surveillant Science: Remote Sensing of the Environment,* Houghton Mifflin Company, Boston.

2

Imaging with Photographic and Nonphotographic Sensor Systems

John E. Estes
University of California, Santa Barbara

A fundamental prerequisite to interpreting information from remote sensing data is an understanding of the processes affecting the recording and display (imagery) of electromagnetic energy. It is difficult to condense and simplify the necessary explanations, but an attempt has been made in this chapter for the sake of beginning students. The organization of the chapter encompasses a discussion of (1) the factors involved in image formation, (2) sensor systems, and (3) collection, processing, and presentation of remote sensing data. A glossary of important remote sensing terminology appears as Appendix I.

This chapter is designed to acquaint the beginning student with the basic systems and concepts involved in acquisition and interpretation of remotely sensed data. This material is presented in the form of an energy-flow system which includes the following features: (1) the source of illumination of a given scene; (2) the type of energy emanating from this source; (3) what happens to this energy as it passes through the atmosphere, interacts with surface objects, and is again transmitted to a sensing device; and (4) how this energy return is imaged, processed, and utimately interpreted.

The major objective of remote sensing is to detect and record energy in a selected portion of the electromagnetic (EM) spectrum (Figure 2-1), the detection made possible because of tone or color enhancing the contrast between an object or phenomenon of interest and its background. Researchers seeking to derive useful information from multispectral imagery should acquire a basic understanding of energy-matter-environment-sensor interactions involved in image formation. Remote sensors acquire imagery by detecting or sensing levels of emitted and/or reflected radiation in various portions of the electromagnetic spectrum. The term "electromagnetic spectrum" is applied to all radiant energy that moves with the constant velocity of light in a harmonic wave pattern. There are three basic measurements which define the character of waves of the electromagnetic spectrum: wave length (distance from one wave crest to the next), wave velocity (speed at which the wave crests advance), and wave frequency (number of wave crests which pass a given point in a specified period of time). Because wave velocity is constant (the speed of light) throughout the entire electromagnetic spectrum, a reciprocal relationship exists between wave frequency and wave

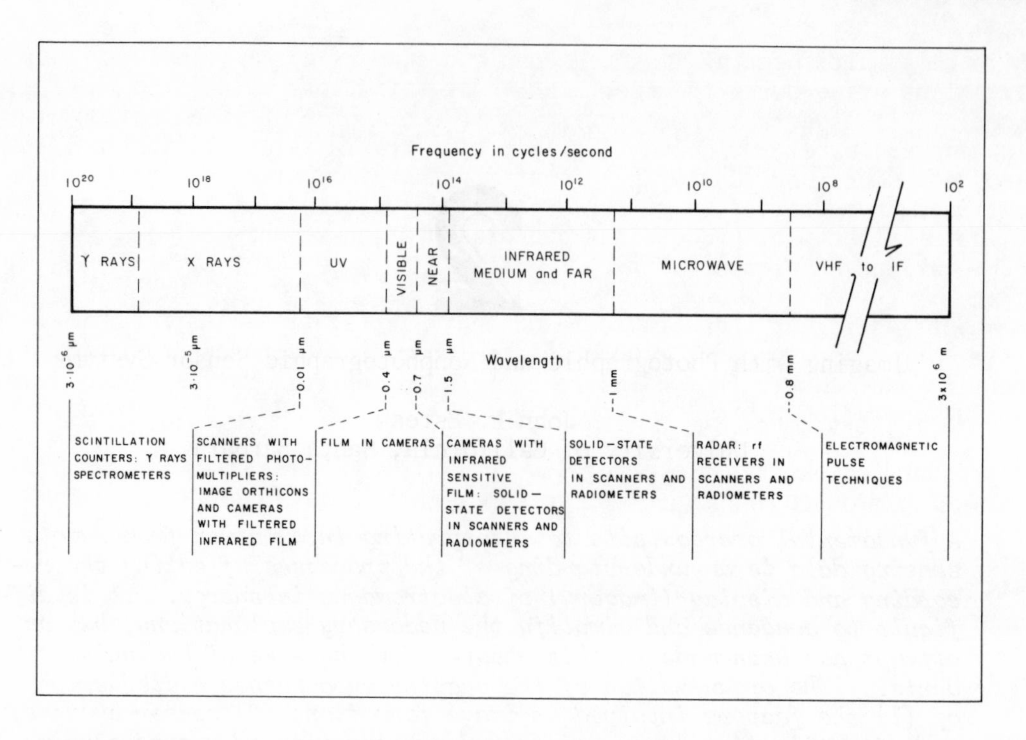

Figure 2-1. The electromagnetic spectrum and some sensors that image in it (adapted from Parker and Wolf, 1965).

length. In the field of remote sensing, the latter term (written as one word, "wavelength") is far more commonly employed than is the term "frequency" (American Society of Photogrammetry, 1963).

Electromagnetic radiation, then, presents a continuum of frequencies, wavelengths, and quanta (the minimum energy units of electromagnetic radiation, more commonly known as photons by those working in remote sensing) from long, very low frequency radio waves to the very short, high-frequency gamma and cosmic waves. In common practice, this continuum of electromagnetic energy, as seen in Figure 2-1 is broken down into various wavelength bands or spectral regions, such as x-ray, ultraviolet, visible, infrared, etc. In reality, none of these regions has distinct boundaries, and there is a great deal of overlap in the regions and in the terminology applied to them (Nunnally, 1969).

The level of energy reflected or emitted from objects normally varies with wavelength throughout the electromagnetic spectrum. The signature of an object on an image is governed by the amount of energy transmitted to the sensor within the wavelength range in which that sensor images. Therefore, a unique tonal signature of an object can often be identified if the energy that is being reflected and/or emitted from it is broken down into carefully chosen wavelength bands. While many conventional systems with wide range or broad-band sensitivity may tend to inhibit object-to-background differentiation, by selectively recording energy from or within particular wavelength bands, discrimination capability can generally be improved.

While this multispectral imaging technique appears to be relatively simple, complications arise owing to uncertainties or variations related to the following factors: (1) spectral characteristics of the source of illumination; (2) illumination angles of incidence; (3) selective transmission, reflection, absorption, emission, and scattering effects of the atmosphere; (4) reflectance and emittance characteristics of the objects; (5) altitude of the sensor system; (6) data collection, processing, and presentation techniques; and (7) data interpretation techniques.

An understanding of these factors and the uncertainties associated with their distribution, measurement, and relative importance is necessary in order to identify and measure the object-to-background contrast ratios in any remote sensing operation.

At present, scientists are generally concentrating their studies on those systems which produce imagery or photography in the wavelength bands between approximately 0.3 micrometers (um) in the near ultraviolet to about 1 to 3 centimeters in the microwave portion of the electromagnetic spectrum (see Figure 2-1). In this relatively broad band, sensing systems may include the use of cameras, vidicons, optical-mechanical scanners, or radiometers.

Most systems operating in the bands mentioned above are, in general, passive as opposed to active; passive systems they record the natural level of radiation emanating from a given scene. Active systems utilize artificial energy sources such as radar pulses, photo flash bombs, and laser beams. There are, at present, means of producing electromagnetic radiation of almost any desired wavelength for use in active remote reconnaissance systems. For example, x-radiation can be obtained from high-voltage cathodes, radar and microwave radiation from specialized tubes and resonating cavity sources, radio-frequency radiation from oscillating dipole sources, and radiation for most other parts of the spectrum from masers, filaments, and gas lamps. Unfortunately, with the major exception of radar (which will be discussed later), few of these systems are in common use. Other operational active systems include laser line scanners, which record a scene on a point-by-point basis, or active optical systems, which employ flash units for scene illumination. In the case of the flash-type units, the overall quality of the photography is poor compared with daytime photography owing to the relatively low level of illumination and associated rapid fall-off with increased range (Jensen, 1968). Laser line scanners provide more detail than can be achieved with a flash, but width of coverage is limited by irradiation fall-off with range.

SPECTRAL CHARACTERISTICS OF THE SOURCE OF ILLUMINATION

Passive systems record energy which nature provides directly, the two most common examples being reflected light energy and emitted thermal energy from the earth's surface. Although this type of energy comes from the earth's surface, solar radiation is indirectly responsible for almost all of it, with the exception of geothermal energy. An energy-flow diagram depicting the changes that both solar and geothermal energy undergo between the time they leave the source to the time they reach the sensing device can be seen in Figure 2-2.

The radiant power peak of the sun (its irradiance, or the radiant flux striking a surface of unit area varies as a function of wavelength) is about 0.5 um (the

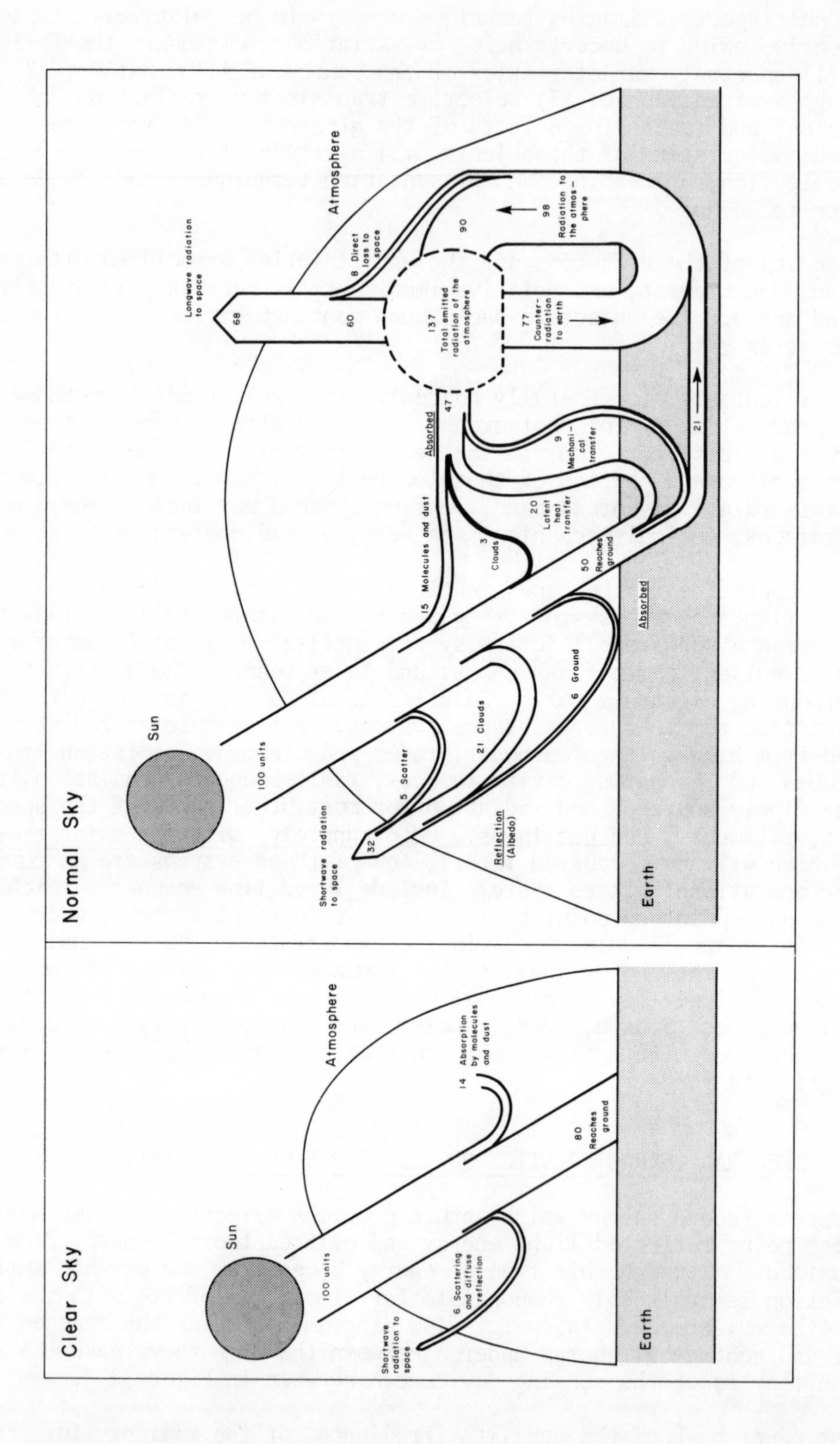

Figure 2-2. Energy flow diagram

green band of the visible portion of the electromagnetic spectrum) (see Figure 2-3). The sun, then, is an excellent energy source when we wish to measure reflectance phenomena in the visible (0.4 to 0.7 um), the photographic infrared (0.7 to 1.0 um), or, to a lesser extent, in the near-ultraviolet (0.3 to 0.4 um) portions of the electromagnetic spectrum. When emission phenomena are being measured for objects that are near the average ambient temperature of the earth (300°K), the earth's radiant power peak (as opposed to the sun's radiant power peak) is at a wavelength of about 9.6 um (see Figure 2-4). As a result, the earth itself is an excellent energy source for passive remote reconnaissance of the earth's surface utilizing emitted energy in the thermal infrared region (Colwell, 1968).

In order to fully understand passive remote sensing techniques and the inherent problems involved in the optimization of such techniques, a better understanding of the concept of illumination is necessary. Illumination can be defined as light (luminous flux) falling on a given area (National Academy of Sciences, 1970). For the purpose of remote sensing, illumination (light) is generally made up of a combination of direct sunlight penetrating the atmosphere and diffuse sunlight, or skylight, resulting from atmospheric scattering and reflection. Luminous reflectance and emittance from ground targets varies considerably, both between different types of materials and as a function of time. Because of these differences in reflectance and emittance between different objects, it is possible to identify and differentiate terrestrial objects or features on the basis of differential reflected or emitted energy responses on a given type of remote sensing imagery. These differences generally appear on the imagery in the form of tonal differences between an object and its background, and are usually referred to as contrast. The amount or relative

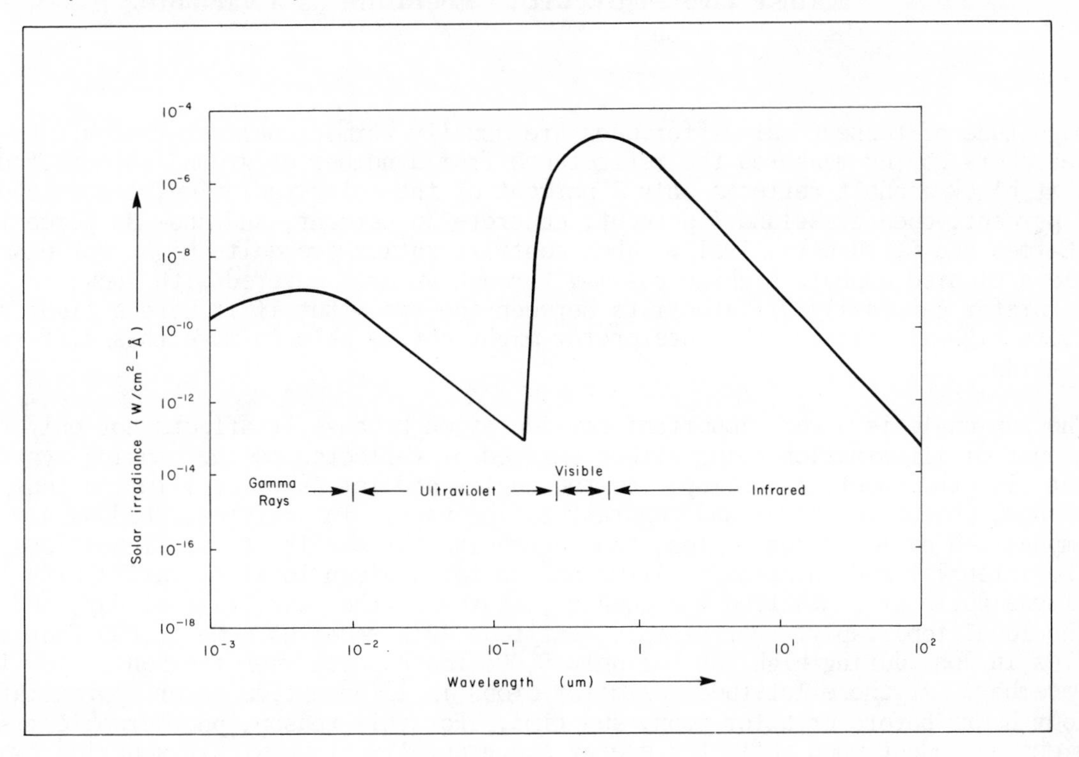

Figure 2-3. Spectral irradiance of the sun.

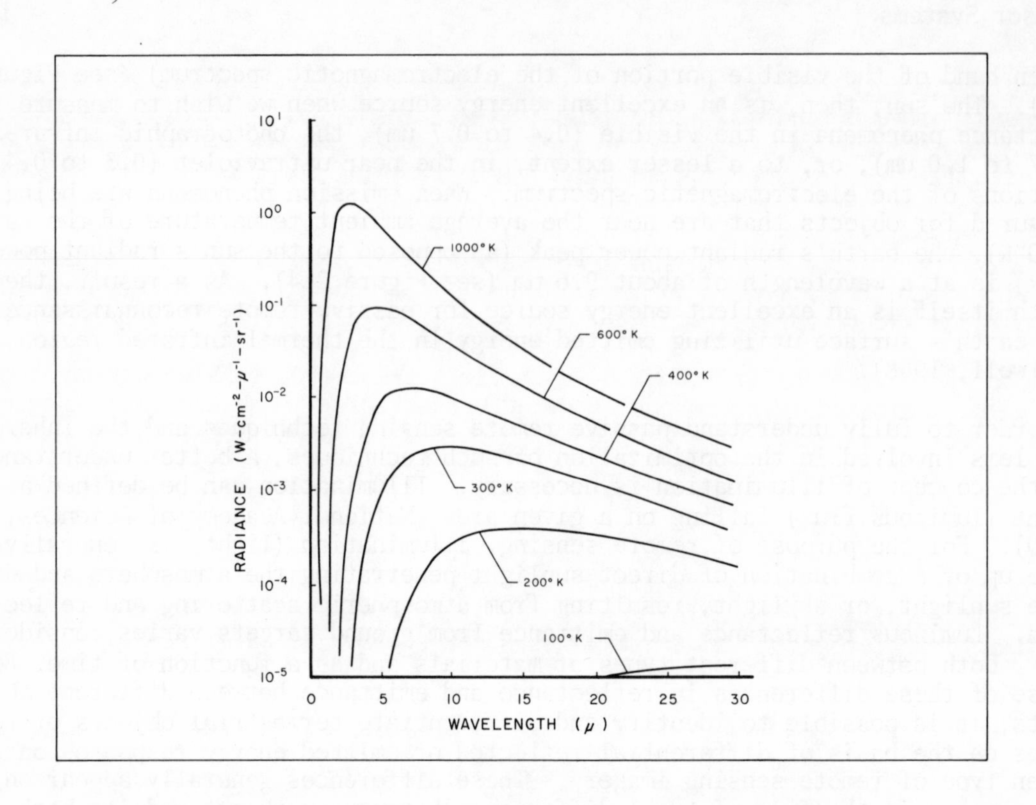

Figure 2-4. Plot of radiance from a blackbody against wavelength, with temperature as a variable.

magnitude of these tonal differences are usually termed contrast ratios. Researchers having measured the reflectance from a number of ground objects,found that black asphalt reflects only 2 percent of the solar radiation, timberland 3 percent, open grassland 6 percent, concrete 36 percent, and snow 80 percent (Carmen and Carruthers, 1951). When contrast ratios are quite high, for example a cleared asphalt highway passing through an area covered with snow, an interpreter can easily differentiate between the two. But if it were a light concrete highway instead, the interpreter might not be able to make this differentiation.

The sun angle is a very important consideration because it affects not only the amount of illumination being either emitted or reflected to the sensing system but also the spectral quality. As the angles and intensity of illumination change, object-to-background contrast ratios vary. In addition, shadows are emphasized at lower sun angles, thus enhancing the ability to see lineations. The intensity and duration of illumination for a given locality varies with latitude north or south from the equator, season of the year, time of day, and the local topography. For example, latitude 40°N receives some 11,000 footcandles in June during high sun but only 5,000 footcandles when the sun is low in December. At these latitudes, similar drops in illumination occur approximately four hours before or after noon, sun time. For this reason, photographic missions dependent upon reflected energy are generally flown within a period two hours before or after local apparent noon.

Thermal contrasts (as opposed to tonal contrasts based on reflective energy differences) between land and water may be masked diurnally by differential heating caused by a change in illumination. Just as changing angles of illumination may decrease object-to-background contrast ratios, making interpretation more difficult when passive sensing systems are used, it can also affect "signatures" of active sensing systems. It also has been shown that variations in slope angle of basically similar terrain can produce significant variations in the amount of illumination received by an area. These variations cause a definite spectral response on radar imagery.

Because of the variability cause by changes in the angle of illumination, care should be exercised in the planning of any research or image acquisition program. Some researchers have even gone so far as to suggest that, since levels of solar illumination are subject to variation, not only as a function of time but from area to area, the best method of obtaining precise and consistent information from photographic density measurements is to use sensors which create their own energy, or to use a calibrated light source as artificial illumination. While artificial illumination might alleviate part of the problem of variation in the level of solar illumination, there is still a need for further study leading to better understanding of such sophisticated sensors.

ATMOSPHERIC EFFECTS

One major consideration in the interpretation of data acquired by means of remote sensing is the effect of the earth's atmosphere on electromagnetic radiation. The atmosphere is an extremely complex medium through which electromagnetic energy must pass in order to be remotely sensed. The change in character which solar radiation undergoes as it passes through the atmosphere affects the energy levels which can be recorded on the surface. A summary of factors affecting the utility of remote sensing in various parts of the spectrum is presented in Table 2-1. A complex process of scattering, reflection, and absorption by the atmosphere alters the amount of solar energy striking the earth. Further alteration occurs as energy reflected from or emitted by a feature on the earth's surface travels back through the atmosphere and is recorded by a sensing device (e.g., camera, radiometer). In the visible and near-visible portions of the spectrum, scattering is the chief cause of the reduction of energy; in the infrared, absorption is the chief cause; at wavelengths longer than 18 mm (in the microwave portion of the electromagnetic spectrum), there is no appreciable atmospheric attenuation (see Figure 2-5) (American Society of Photogrammetry, 1963).

With respect to the process of scattering, Rayleigh scattering and Mie scattering are important in the visible spectrum. Confining remote sensing interest to the earth, a clear atmosphere is composed mainly of nitrogen and oxygen gas molecules along with traces of various other gases. The molecules of these gases are of smaller diameter than the mean wavelength of the visible light. Scattering is troublesome when r (the radius of the gas molecules) is, roughly speaking, equal to or greater than 0.1λ (0.1 times the wavelength of electromagnetic energy). When this type of clear atmospheric condition occurs it is sometimes called a Rayleigh atmosphere (Hall and Howell, 1966). Rayleigh scattering is inversely proportional to the fourth-power of wavelength. Thus the blue portion of the spectrum, being shorter in wavelength than the red, is scattered more and gives the sky its blue appearance. A white-to-red-appearing sky may

Table 2-1. General Characteristics of Remote Sensor Systems

Spectral Region and Sensor Systems	Approximate wavelength interval (micrometers)	Approximate spatial resolution attainable (milliradians)	Atmospheric penetration capability*	Day-night capability	Real-time capability+	Geometric rectification++
Ultraviolet (Optical-mechanical scanners, image orthicons, and cameras w/IR film)	0.01 - 0.4	.01 - 0.1		Day only	Yes	Good
Visible (Optical-mechanical scanners, conventional cameras with film, and vidicons)	0.4 - 0.7	0.01 - 0.001	H	Day only**	Generally no^x	Potential metric quality
Reflectance IR (Conventional cameras w/IR sensitive film, solid-state detectors in scanners and radiometers)	0.7 - 3.5	.01 - 0.1	H, Sg	Day only	Generally no^x	Potential metric quality
Thermal IR (Solid-state detectors in scanners and radiometers, quantum detectors)	3.5 - 30.0	1.0	H, S	Day or night	Yes	Good
Microwave (Scanners and radiometers, antennas and circuits)	10^3 - 10^6	10	H, S, F	Day or night	Yes	Poor/fair
Radar# (Scanners and scatterometers, antennas and circuits)	8.3 X 10^3 1.3 X 10^6	10	H, S, F, Rϕ	Day or night	Potential exists	Fair

* Denotes the atmospheric conditions which can be penetrated by energy in this portion of the electromagnetic spectrum where
H = haze, S = smoke, Sg = smog, F = fog or clouds, R = rain.

+ This refers to the ability to evaluate a sensor system's output as the original information is acquired.

While radar operates within the microwave region, its utility is significantly different than that of radiometers.

ϕ Penetration capability increases with increasing wavelength.

x The potential for real-time viewing exists in scanner systems, and panchromatic film could be viewed in near-real-time utilizing a Bimat type of process.

++ Denotes the potential for plannimetric mapping.

** Discounting the use of active optical systems such as the Edgerton flash units or laser line tracers or light amplification systems.

Resolution in the short wavelengths is limited primarily by atmospheric scattering

$$S = k_1 \cdot \frac{1}{\lambda^4}$$

where S = scattering
K = constant

Resolution in the long wavelengths is limited primarily by aperture of the sensors

$$R = k_2 \cdot \frac{\lambda}{D}$$

where R = Resolution
D = Diameter of the "collection optics"

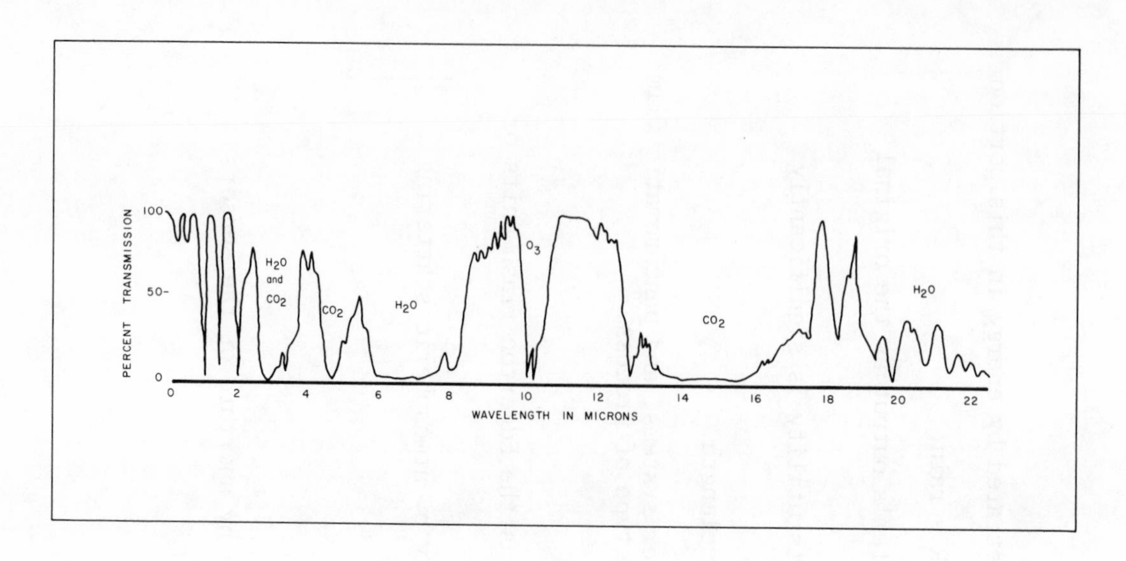

Figure 2-5. Atmospheric absorption schematic (adapted from Parker and Wolf, 1965).

be produced by scattering from particles of larger radius, approximately $0.1\ \lambda < r < 25\ \lambda$. This type of scattering is called Mie scattering. Atmospheric aerosols, dust, haze, smoke, etc., whose particle size may equal or exceed the wavelength of light, are called Mie particles. Whereas Mie scattering is restricted generally to the lower atmosphere (below 15,000 feet [4,560 meters]), Rayleigh scattering occurs to an altitude of some 30,000 feet (9,120 meters). Above that altitude, there is little atmospheric scattering.

Absorption dominates the reflectance infrared (1.0 to 20 microns [u]) portion of the electromagnetic spectrum. Various absorption bands (bands of electromagnetic energy which are absorbed to a very high degree) are caused by the presence of gases such as H_2O, CO_3, O_2, and O_3, which are present in the atmosphere (see Figure 2-4). The principal atmospheric window (portion of the electromagnetic spectrum where little or no absorption takes place) for imaging in this portion of the spectrum is the 8-to-14-u band, where atmospheric absorption is at a minimum and provides the highest level of transmission of energy that can be detected by thermal infrared detectors. At longer wavelengths, strong absorption bands (owing to the presence of atmospheric moisture) are found; but, as previously stated, at wavelengths longer than 18 mm (18,000 u), atmospheric attenuation decreases (American Society of Photogrammetry, 1963).

As altitude above the earth increases, the amount of atmosphere through which energy emanating from terrestrial materials must pass in order to be remotely sensed increases. As much as 50 percent of the earth's atmosphere lies within

17,500 feet (5,320 meters) of the earth's surface, 75 percent within 35,000 feet (10,640 meters), whereas 99 percent is believed to extend no farther outward than 25 miles (40.2 kilometers) from the earth's surface (Rumney, 1968).

As had been discussed above, the angle of incidence of solar radiation is dependent upon many factors. These include slope of the surface, aspect of surface with reference to the source of illumination, latitude, time of day, and time of year. In addition to these factors, the spectral characteristics of each terrestrial feature also affect the return of energy to a remote sensor. Because of this, reflectance and emittance characteristics of surface features should be studied in order to facilitate the selection of appropriate sensors best suited to detect features of interest.

SPECTRAL CHARACTERISTICS OF OBJECTS

Signal intensity (the magnitude of energy emanating from a source) as a function of wavelength varies with surface roughness and dielectric properties of objects to be sensed. Field and laboratory spectrographic systems have been used to measure the spectral characteristics of terrain features. Figure 2-6 is a schematic of the Purdue Laboratory for Agricultural Remote Sensing field spectrometer. Spectral characteristics are used as a standard upon which decisions as to type of sensor and wavelength can be based. It is reasoned that this type of study is essential for any quantitative analysis of the final output data (Avera et al., 1966). In present practice, techniques of gathering spectral

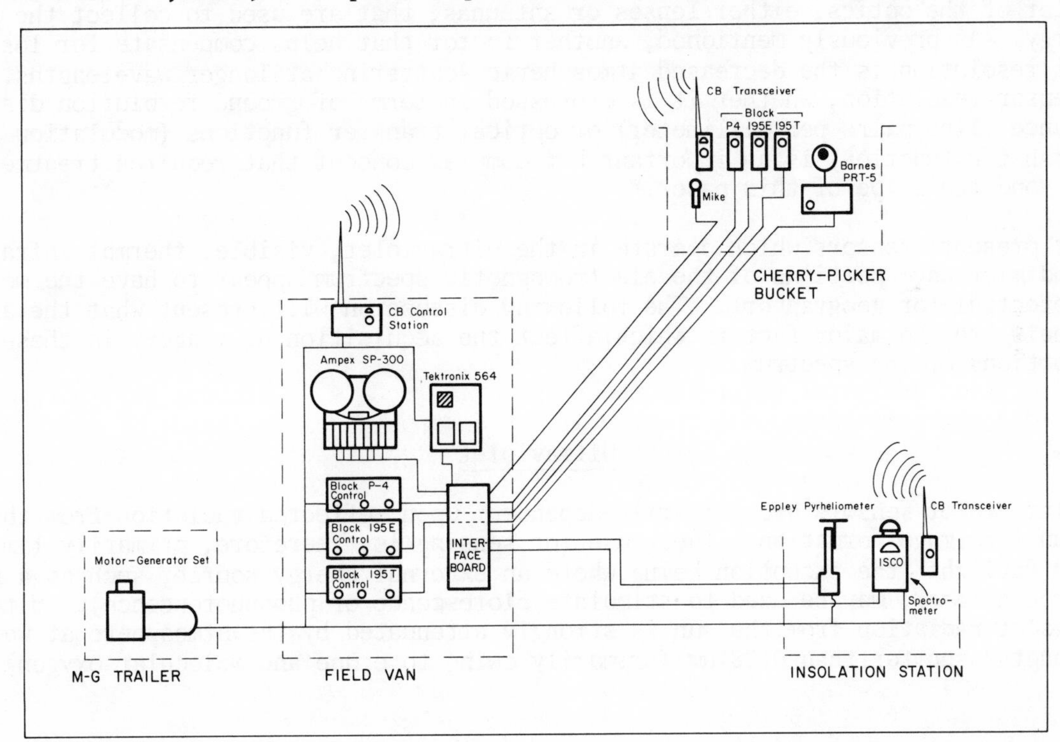

Figure 2-6. Diagram of Purdue Laboratory for Agricultural Remote Sensing field spectrometer (Courtesy Laboratory for Agricultural Remote Sensing, Purdue University).

data on surface features leave much to be desired, and a method which will accurately present the "on site" emittance and reflectance properties of objects at the time of imaging must be found (Myers et al., 1966). Research on this subject is progressing in many countries, and more and more information is being obtained (Avera et al., 1966; Limperis, 1964; Steiner and Guterman, 1966).

DATA COLLECTION SYSTEMS

As can be seen from Figure 2-1, there are sensors that have the ability to detect electromagnetic energy in each portion of the spectrum. For example, Geiger-Muller counter, scintillometers, and other ionization detectors can be used in the gamma-ray and x-ray regions; phosphors can be used in parts of the x-ray and ultraviolet portions of the spectrum; photographic emulsions can be used in the near-ultraviolet, visible, and near-infrared regions (up to 1.2 um); thermal or quantum detectors (e.g., mercury-doped germanium) can be used in the thermal infrared region, particularly the 3.5-to-5.5-um and 8-to-14-um regions where atmospheric windows exist; and antennas and circuits can be used for detecting energy in the microwave and radio wave regions (Colwell, 1968).

The resolving power, i.e., the ability of a particular sensor to render a sharply defined image (see Figure 2-7 for a schematic presentation of factors leading to imperfect image formation), is an important consideration in the choice of a given sensor. Resolving power is inherently poorer as we move to long wavelengths. This difficulty, however, is somewhat overcome by increasing the diameter of the optics, either lenses or antennas, that are used to collect the energy. As previously mentioned, another factor that helps compensate for loss of resolution is the decreased atmospheric scattering at longer wavelengths. Sensor resolution, whether it is expressed in terms of ground resolution distance (line pairs per millimeter) or optical transfer functions (modulation transfer function) is an important but complex concept that requires treatment beyond the scope of this paper.*

At present, sensors which operate in the ultraviolet, visible, thermal infrared, and microwave portions of the electromagnetic spectrum appear to have the most potential for geographers. The following discussion will present what the author feels are the major factors which affect the acquisition of imagery in these portions of the spectrum.

Ultraviolet

Ultraviolet sensors are primarily dependent upon reflected radiation from the sun for image formation. Their use for sensing is, therefore, primarily limited to daylight (the exception being where an external energy source, such as a nitrogen laser, may be used to stimulate florescence or phosphorescence). Ultraviolet radiation from the sun is strongly attenuated by the atmosphere at wavelengths shorter than 0.28 um (primarily owing to ozone and molecular oxygen).

---

* For a more lengthy discussion, the reader is referred to the following works: Jensen, 1968; Hall and Howell, 1966; and American Society of Photogrammetry, 1966.

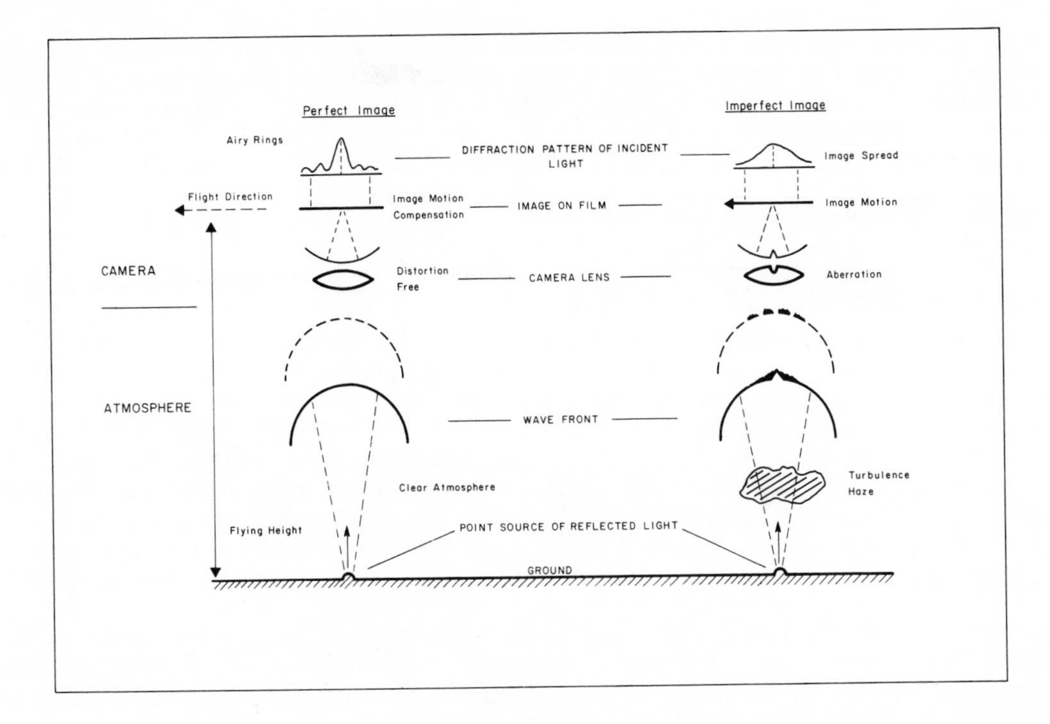

Figure 2-7. Factors leading to imperfect image formation. At (a), a point source of reflected light is shown as emitting a wavefront from the ground into a clear atmosphere. The wavefront is undeformed as it passes through a distortion-free lens and, consequently, a perfect image is formed. At (b), a similar wavefront is affected by the principal factors causing wave spread/image distortion. After passing through the troposphere, the wavefront is reshaped by a convergent lens and may be subjected to further distortions caused by camera motion or vibration.

Conventional cameras provide a high degree of resolution and may be used in the near-ultrabiolet since film emulsions presently are available with sensitivities ranging down to 0.29 um (the near-ultraviolet). A limiting factor in the use of photographic systems (i.e., cameras) in the ultraviolet is that some lens materials are opaque at wavelengths shorter than 0.36 um, and lenses with high quartz content must be used. Scanning systems, including television, can also be utilized for remote sensing in the near-ultraviolet by selectively employing appropriate detectors, filters, and/or optics. A simplified schematic of a scanning system is shown in Figure 2-8. These systems may exhibit poorer resolution characteristics than conventional cameras, but they offer the advantage of a real-time viewing capability. In addition, scanning systems normally have an advantage over photographic and video systems in their ability to "see" through radiation scattered by the atmosphere. Whereas conventional cameras image directly onto photographic emulsions, scanning systems record their signals as electronic impulses on magnetic tape and can therefore electronically subtract (or filter) some of the "noise" in the signal owing to scattering. This type of processing permits observation of greater surface detail in many cases than is possible with video or photographic imagery, although some electronic enhancement can improve photographic image quality.

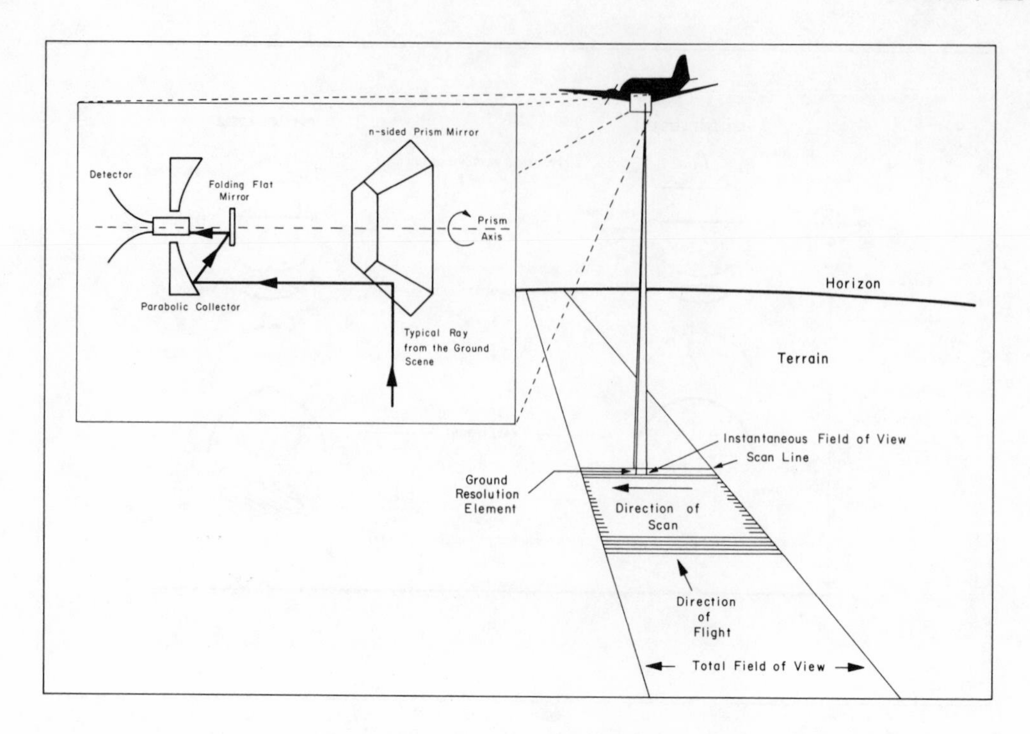

Figure 2-8. Simplified schematic of a scanning system.

Figure 2-9 is an ultraviolet scanner image of soybean oil off Santa Barbara, California, which was taken by North American Rockwell. It illustrates the type of detailed background information which aids in the optimization of information extraction from remote sensing imagery. The image was acquired in the spring of 1972 as part of an experiment to determine the efficiency of a high seas oil containment device. To the right of the image is an interpretation showing ships in the area (B and 5) and the oil itself (0). The times at which the oil had spread to specific points are also indicated. These data were used to calculate the amount of oil leakage from the containment device at particular points in time.

Visible and Reflectance Infrared

In this portion of the electromagnetic spectrum conventional and multilens camera systems, as well as optical-mechanical scanners, are utilized to obtain photographs and other images (a photograph being defined as an image produced when reflected energy impinges directly on a photographic emulsion. An image, on the other hand, is produced by emitted or active-system-reflected energy which has been converted by a detector into a picturelike format).

Although the specific requirements of a given aerial image acquisition mission may vary, the following considerations generally apply to most missions: (1) rapid coverage of large land areas; this is accomplished by using a system that

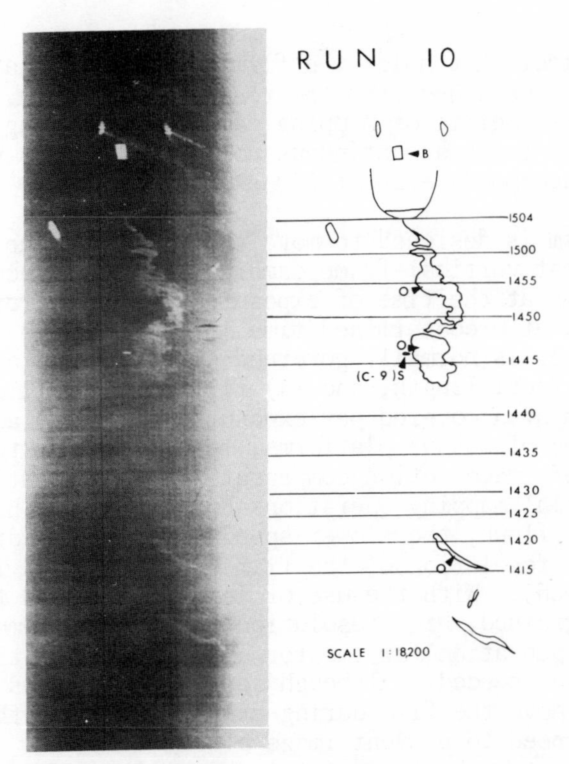

Figure 2-9. Ultraviolet scanner image of soybean oil on the Pacific Ocean off the Santa Barbara coast (Courtesy North American Rockwell).

will photograph or scan a maximum ground area per unit time; (2) production of a maximum amount of extractable information per image; here a system should yield the highest possible ground resolution throughout the entire image format, using either a film-filter combination or spectral band that combines highest possible resolution with spectral sensitivity in an optimum portion of the electromagnetic spectrum; and (3) dependability and economy of operation (Strandberg, 1967).

There are basically six types of aerial camera systems: (1) vertical-frame, (2) panoramic, (3) strip-film, (4) trimetrogon, (5) divergent forward oblique, and (6) forward oblique. Each of these systems possesses advantages for particular types of studies. Of these six types of camera systems, the vertical-frame camera is the most commonly used, while panoramic cameras are somewhat less important. The remaining camera systems are used today mainly for special-purpose missions.*

Conventional aerial cameras in general have four basic components (see Figure 2-10): a magazine, a drive mechanism, a cone, and a lens. The magazine is a

* For more information on these other types of camera systems, the reader is directed to Strandberg, 1967, and American Society of Photogrammetry, 1966.

light-tight container that holds the film. In operational systems, the magazine can usually be detached from the rest of the camera. In conventional aerial camera systems (metric or mapping cameras, producing vertical frames), the film ordinarily forms a continuous roll 9-1/2 inches wide and 200 feet long. Such a roll will accommodate about 250 exposures, each 9 inches square.

The drive mechanism is designed to move the film from the supply spool to the take-up spool. Most vertical-frame cameras utilize a vacuum to hold the film rigidly in position at the time of exposure. As the aircraft moves forward, exposures are made at predetermined time intervals. The length of time between individual exposures is normally governed by (1) flight altitude, (2) aircraft speed, (3) camera focal length, and (4) film format; all of which govern the size of the ground area covered per exposure. Owing to advances in the operational capabilities of sensor platforms, most camera systems used today must employ some form of image motion compensation (IMC). Until recently, IMC was unnecessary in aerial mapping operations because of the high altitudes at which many missions were flown, the slower speed of propeller-driven aircraft, and the relatively low resolution of the film bases utilized (American Society of Photogrammetry, 1966). With the use of jet aircraft and the development of slow-speed, fine-grained, high-resolution photographic emulsions, the need for some method of compensation for the forward movement of the aircraft during the time of exposure was needed. Although several techniques can be employed, the most common is to move the film during exposure so that the film and the image move at the same speed to prevent image blur.

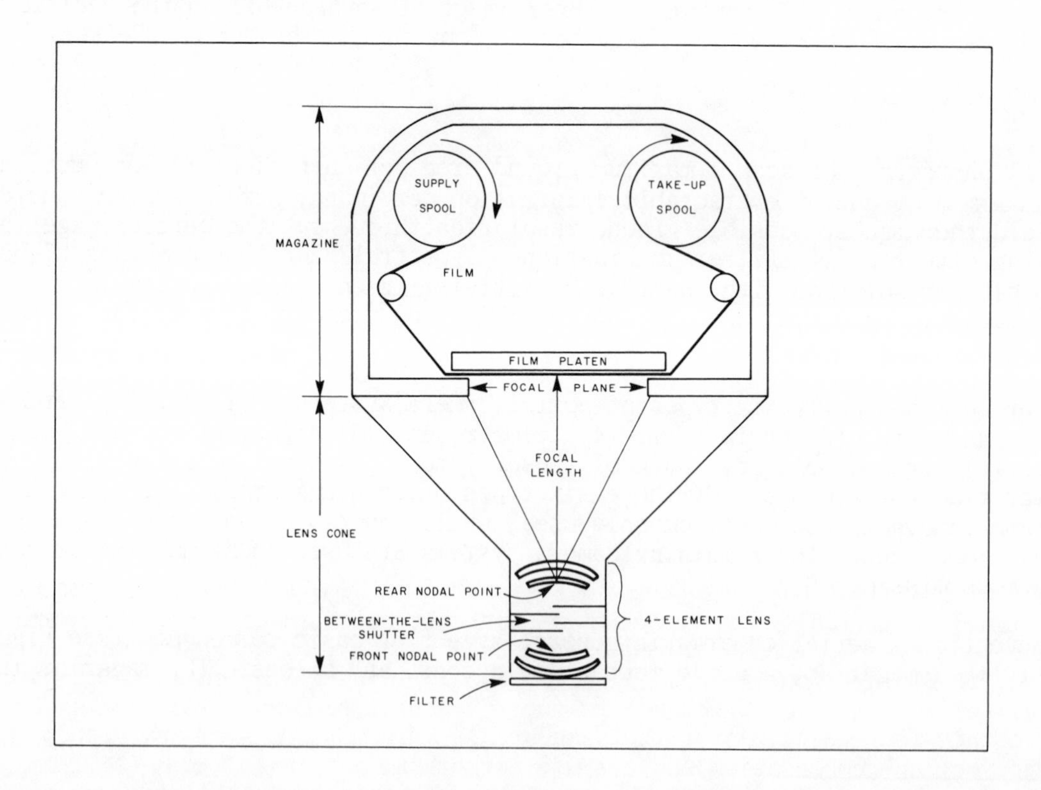

Figure 2-10. Conventional aerial camera system.

The basic functions of the lens cone or camera cone differ with various camera systems, but, in general, they are (1) to support the entire lens assembly including filters and (2) to prevent any light, except that coming through the lens, from striking the film. The length of the cone is determined by the focal length of the lens, which is the perpendicular distance from the rear nodal point of the lens to the film. Most aerial photography for the inventory of natural resources use focal lengths of 6, 8-1/4, or 12 inches. However, on 70-mm (film-width) multiband cameras, a focal length of 80 mm commonly is used.

The lens of an aerial camera is a compound one that is designed to produce an undistorted image. Aerial cameras usually have fixed-focus lenses set at infinity because the camera is generally far enough above the datum base that such a focus will provide a sharp image of ground detail. Most conventional aerial camera systems place the shutter between the front and rear elements of the lens. The drive mechanism of the camera recocks the shutter automatically after each exposure.

Multilens photographic systems are an extension of this type of camera system and are analogous in some ways to the optical-mechanical scanners which will be discussed later in this chapter. Multilens photographic systems have also been developed specifically to obtain simultaneous photography in various parts of the visible and near-visible portions of the electromagnetic spectrum. Multilens photographic systems can be composed of a single camera frame with matched multiple lenses or of multiple cameras adopted to synchronous use. Unlike conventional aerial cameras, which generally provide only a single photograph of a scene, these systems provide the interpreter with a number of photographs taken with different film-filter combinations at a single point in time and space.

One of the first widely used multilens camera systems in remote sensing in the United States was the Itek 9-lens camera system (Figure 2-11). The camera employs nine matched lenses with different filters to take nine simultaneous exposures of the same scene. Nine 6-inch (15.2-cm) f/2.8 Schneider Xenotar matched lenses are used to expose two strips of 70-mm aerographic plus X film and one strip of 70-mm infrared aerographic film. These are the films generally employed, but it should be emphasized that any combination of films and filters could be used. With these particular film types, six bands in the visible and three in the photographic (near) IR are imaged. Three exposures are taken on each roll of film at the same time, producing a total of nine frames of photography, each 2-1/4 inches by 2-1/4 inches (5.7 cm by 6.4 cm). For correct exposure, three focal plane shutters of three slits each are used to expose all nine frames simultaneously. The system also has image motion compensation (Molineaux, 1964).

Another multilens camera in use today is seen in Figure 2-12. This camera was designed specifically for use with an optical, multi-image correlation and enhancement system. Manufactured by the Fairchild Camera and Instrument Corporation, it employs four 7-inch (17.8-cm) focal length f/2.5 lenses which have been precisely matched, with respect to their spectral response, and bore sighted to obtain four negatives of the same area. This multilens camera system employs image motion compensation and can use either standard 9-1/2-inch (24.1-cm) roll film, or, by changing magazines, can take four separate rolls of 70-mm film. In the building of this system, special pains were taken to ensure that all components of the system were precisely matched. Precision extends into the correct

Figure 2-11. Itek 9-lens camera system (Courtest of Itek Corporation).

Figure 2-12. Long Island University 4-lens camera system (Courtesy of the Science and Engineering Research Group, Long Island University).

calibration of exposure settings and control of film processing to correct for variations in gamma which otherwise would result from film-filter-optics exposure sources. Careful control of all of these factors (i.e., matched lenses, exposure, etc.) is essential for repeatable results (Yost and Wenderoth, 1967).

An example of multiband photography taken by this multiband system can be seen in Figure 2-13. These photographs of Century City in West Los Angeles were taken from an altitude of 15,000 feet. From top to bottom, the images are filtered to expose for the blue, green, red, and reflectance infrared portions of the electromagnetic spectrum.

The primary advantages of multilens photographic systems are (1) they can take simultaneous multiband images of the same area at the same time; (2) the geometric fidelity and great resolving power of these systems provides the image interpreter with a more familiar type of information; (3) film-filter combinations are exposed simultaneously, therefore any variations of illumination conditions (which would possibly occur when the individual bands are taken at different times of day or year) are minimized or nonexistent; and, (4) several film-filter combinations can be exploited with these systems.

When selecting the spectral bands or film-filter combinations, care should be taken to avoid redundancy; i.e., to avoid choosing combinations which produce a similar effect. It should also be remembered that multiband photographic systems are limited by the spectral sensitivity of photographic emulsions. At the present time, photographic emulsions have a spectral range from about 0.29 u in the ultraviolet to approximately 1.1 u in the near-infrared (Orr, 1968).

Although there are many advantages to using a multiband camera system, some disadvantages should also be mentioned. (1) Image formats of multilens photographic systems are usually smaller than those of conventional aerial cameras; it is necessary to increase the number of exposures or the flight altitude in order to obtain equal area coverage.(2) The calibration and control needed to ensure accurate results make these systems quite expensive. (3) The amount of data acquired make it difficult for the interpreter to use, let alone comprehend, the data.

The panoramic camera is capable of taking high-resolution photography of a large area in a single exposure. Whereas with conventional camera systems the image sharpness falls off as a function of distance from the photo center, panoramic cameras provide a high degree of image sharpness in every part of the photograph. In order to produce a sharp image when photographing large areas, one paradoxically needs a narrow angular field to minimize any lens aberrations. The panoramic camera produces this field by a narrow slit in an opaque partition near the focal plane of the camera. The slit is parallel to the camera platform's line of flight, and the image is obtained when the panoramic camera pans from side to side as the aircraft advances. Panoramic cameras maintain a uniformly clear focus for the entire area panned because the film is exposed in the form of an arc, instead of being kept flat as in a conventional camera. Consequently, the photographic scale on panoramic imagery becomes progressively smaller in either direction away from the flight path.

Some advantages of panoramic camera systems include (1) the precise flying necessary for vertical photography is not required; (2) a side swath of terrain may be imaged with high resolution on a single photograph; and (3) personnel,

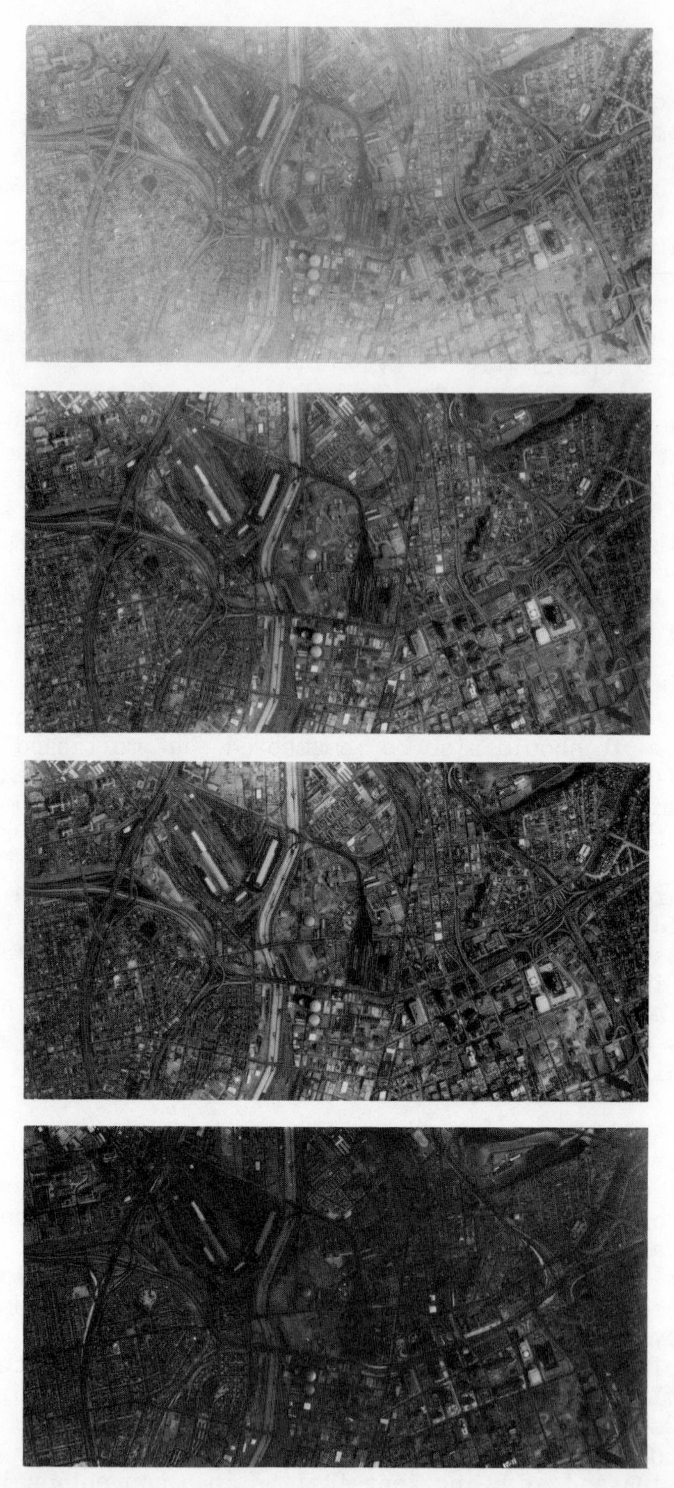

Figure 2-13. Multiband photography of Century City (West Los Angeles, California) imaged by Long Island University 4-lens camera system (Courtesy of the Science and Engineering Research Group, Long Island University).

aircraft, cameras, and film requirements per unit area are much lower, since large areas are scanned on a single image. Among the disadvantages are (1) constantly changing scale necessitates that special rectification procedures be employed; and (2) relatively slow cyclic rate of panoramic cameras restricts their use to higher altitudes.

A scanning system can be used to produce imagery not only in the visible and reflectance infrared, but the near-ultraviolet and thermal infrared portions of the EM spectrum as well. In a scanning system (such as a thermal infrared scanning system), a rotating mirror directs energy emanating from the terrain to a detector. At any given instant in time, the rotating mirror views only a small segment of terrain. The infrared energy strikes the detector, generating an electrical impulse that varies in intensity according to the amount of thermal energy coming from the part of the terrain then being viewed by the mirror. The signal may then be used to modulate a beam of electrons, such as the moving luminous spot on the face of an intensity modulated cathode-ray tube. A spot is thus modulated, growing brighter or dimmer in direct proportion to the intensity of the electron beam. An image of the light is recorded on photographic film, and the system produces what is, in effect, a thermal map of the ground (Colwell, 1968). Another more complex system is the optical-mechanical scanner developed at the University of Michigan. Figure 2-14 shows a schematic of a multispectral scanner system. This system can divide the electromagnetic spectrum, between 0.32 u and 14 u, into 18 separate channels and can provide a great many data for the study of reflectance and emittance phenomena of surface features. This information is collected and stored on magnetic tape, which can

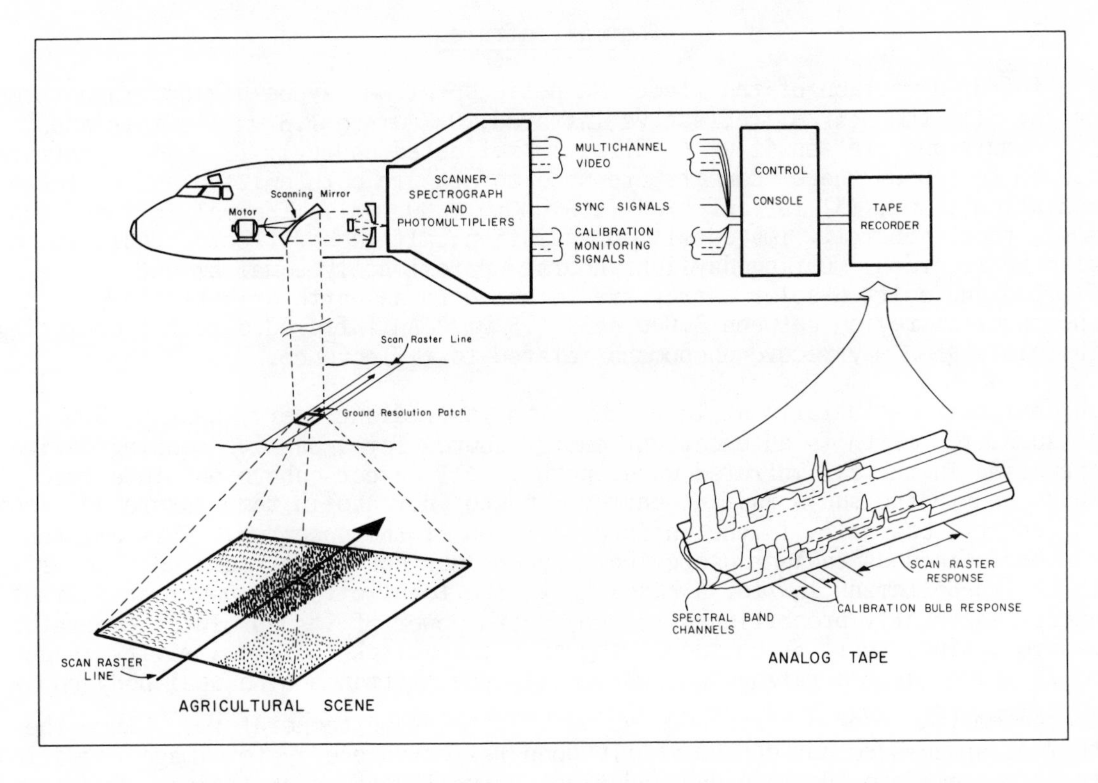

Figure 2-14. Diagram of a multispectral scanner system.

later be recombined into an image format or manipulated by statistical processing techniques in computer interpretation procedures (see Chapter 3). As previously stated, one advantage of recording in this manner (over a scanner which directly images a given scene) is that increased resolution may be obtained by suppression of background "noise" in final signal processing.

Finally, image tubes, operating in the visible and reflectance infrared portion of the spectrum, are becoming increasingly important. Examples of image tube systems are vidicons, image orthicons, and image isocons, the vidicons being of greater importance at present. The first Earth Resources Technology Satellite (ERTS-1) utilized a vidicon system as part of its sensor complement. The ERTS camera system operates by simultaneously shuttering three return-beam vidicon cameras. Each camera senses a separate spectral band within the range 0.48 u to 0.83 u. Once an area has been scanned by the camera, the resultant image is stored on the photosensitive surface of the camera tube where it is scanned by an electron beam to produce a video signal output. These signals may then be either stored directly on tape-recording devices or transmitted in real time to ground receiving stations (where they may be stored on magnetic tape). One area which should be touched on with respect to video systems is the use of low-light-level illumination television systems (LLTV), which utilize special optics to obtain night imagery without the aid of flash equipment. The potential of this type of system is being explored; and the system itself has been employed by the military and law enforcement officials, as well as by researchers interested in the natural environment.

Thermal Infrared

The infrared portion of the electromagnetic spectrum may be divided into three parts: (1) the near or reflective infrared, 0.7 um to 1.5 um (in this area, film emulsions are sensitive to directly reflected energy); (2) middle infrared, 1.5 um to 5.5 um (here scanners are used to measure both emitted and reflected radiation); and, (3) far infrared (5.5 um to 1,000 um). Thermal infrared sensors, then, generally image emitted radiation, although reflected radiation may also be recorded. During daylight hours, approximately equal amounts of reflected and emitted solar energy are returned to an earth-oriented sensor in the spectral region between 3.0 um and 4.5 um. An infrared detector operating in this region may record phenomena related to reflectance.

The earth is essentially a black body with its radiant energy peak at 300°K. As such, the earth is an excellent energy source for a passive sensing device operating in the far-infrared wavelengths. All objects above absolute zero which absorb the sun's radiant energy tend to increase in temperature and reemit the energy, basically in the infrared portion of the spectrum. This emittance can be defined as radiant energy per second per centimeter squared. According to Stefan-Boltzmann law for a black body, the total emissive power or radiant energy is exactly proportional to the fourth power of its absolute temperature. However, since there is no such thing as a true black body, emissivity is generally given as the ratio w/w_b, where w is the emittance of a real body and w_b is the emittance of a black body at exactly the same temperature. Since the thermal sensors do not depend wholly upon reflected energy for image formation, those systems provide both day and night surveillance capabilities. Operating in a scanning mode, thermal infrared systems also provide the important real-time data acquisition capability. As mentioned previously, atmospheric absorption by H_2O, CO_2, O_2, and O_3 limits the ability of sensors to obtain imagery in the thermal infrared portion of the spectrum. This absorption necessitates the use of atmospheric windows* (e.g., 3.5 um to 5.5 um and 8 um to 14 um) in order to obtain high-quality imagery.

An optical-mechanical scanner,such as the one described above, is the most frequently used imaging device that will sense in what is generally referred to as the thermal infrared portion of the electromagnetic spectrum. Photographic emulsions are not sensitive to energy at wavelengths in the thermal infrared region. Optical-mechanical scanners use a detector that consists of a coating of some infrared-sensitive material, such as indium antimonide, or mercury-doped, copper-doped or gold-doped germanium, on the end of an electrical conductor. Because this material occupies an extremely small area, it is then feasible, in an airborne system, to cool a detector with liquid nitrogen for sensing at wavelengths of from 3 to 6 u and with liquid helium for longer wavelengths.

Figure 2-15 is a thermal infrared image, taken with an 8-to-14-um RS-14 radiometer at approximately 10:30 a.m. local time on June 27, 1969, in conjunction with the Bomex experiments. It includes the ocean, a portion of the urban area of Bridgetown, Barbados, and adjacent rural lands. The portion of Bridgetown along the coastline occupies a low coastal ridge, while the agricultural fields are, in the main, either plowed or fallow (Pease et al., 1970).

Passive Microwave

Both radar and passive microwave systems operate in the microwave portion of the electromagnetic spectrum from 0.1 cm to 100 cm. Atmospheric attenuation here is negligible. However, because there is a trade-off between wavelength and spatial resolution at a given aperture or antenna size, passive microwave systems generally operate in the shorter wavelength portion of the microwave spectrum. In this region there is some attenuation caused principally by water vapor and atmospheric oxygen. Passive microwave systems, then, operate in the same spectral region as very short wavelength radars. They differ from radars, however, in that they make use of the natural radiation emitted from objects rather than artificial illumination. The major properties of objects that determine the character of their microwave radiation are (1) emittance; (2) transmittance; (3) reflectance; and (4) temperature. Although microwave systems image essentially emitted radiation, as do thermal infrared devices, passive microwave imagery is more linearly a function of temperature than is infrared imagery. Microwave radiance, or rather what is often called the brightness temperature of objects apparent on microwave imagery, more closely approximates a black-body curve than thermal infrared imagery. Although passive microwave systems exhibit day-or-night operational capability, a drawback is their relatively low spatial resolution. Although systems may be designed with resolution to suit specific tasks, this is costly, and there is a practical limit on the design and installation of an antenna for a given system. Selection of wavelengths for operation and antenna size (the longer the antenna the better the resolution)

---

* Windows are wavelength bands within which the atmosphere offers relatively high transmission of electromagnetic energy.

Figure 2-15. Thermal infrared image of Bridgetown, Barbados and adjacent rural lands (Courtesy National Aeronautics and Space Administration).

would be a function of the need to detect and map a given object of phenomenon. Since spatial resolution is inversely proportional to wavelength (for a given aperture or antenna size), resolution requirements dictate operation at the shortest wavelengths possible, generally on the order of 8 mm (National Academy of Sciences, 1970).

Imaging microwave radiometers have been developed, which utilize a narrow-beam antenna attached to a mechanical scanning device. This device continuously moves the antenna through a designated angular range in a plane transverse to the aircraft flight path. The antenna beam covers a narrow strip on the ground in the transverse direction. The forward motion of the aircraft provides the means of developing a given scan line on an image strip. Figure 2-16 is a passive microwave image of an urban area (Coalinga) and surrounding rural setting in the Central Valley of California. This image was taken from an altitude of 2,500 feet by the Naval Weapons Center, China Lake. In general, gray tones are associated with cropped fields, black tones with dry bare soil, and whitish tones with wet bare soil and built-up areas.

Electronic scanning systems presently being developed and tested have major advantages: no movable mechanical parts, fast scanning capabilities, and computer control on phase and amplitude of each element. These systems are currently being designed using solid-state generators. Their amplitude and phase are controlled with simple electronic units. The major problem is primarily cost (American Geological Institute, 1968).

Radar

Radar is an active remote sensing system which operates in the microwave portion of the EM spectrum. As such, its imaging capability is dependent upon the return from the target of energy supplied by the radar system itself. The nature of energy returned to the radar sensor is dependent upon both the properties of the transmitted electromagnetic energy and the properties of the surface phenomena that are being sensed. Properties of the electromagnetic energy include (1) wavelength, (2) polarization, and (3) direction. The properties of surface phenomena that must be considered are (1) dielectric and conducting properties, (2) surface roughness in wavelength units, (3) physical resonances, (4) surface slopes, (5) subsurface effects, and(6) scattering area (National Academy of Sciences, 1970).

Some imaging radar systems are side-looking; that is, they scan a path to one side of the aircraft's flight path. The name "side-looking airborne radar" (SLAR) is often used in designating these systems. These systems offer day-or-night and, for certain systems, virtually an all-weather capability. Radar also has the ability to cover large areas on a single image and does so in a short time. With respect to ground resolution, radars are to some extent wavelength and slant range dependent (see Figure 2-17). Ground resolution is also a function of beam width. However, this is adjustable by varying the antenna size on a "brute force" system or adjusting the synthetic aperture on a synthetic-aperture system (Moore, 1965). Synthetic-aperture radars direct a narrow beam of energy at right angles to the flight path of the aircraft. A pulse of energy is transmitted from the radar antenna, and the relative intensity of the reflections from objects being sensed produces an image. On the next transmitted pulse, the aircraft has moved forward a small distance and a slightly different

Figure 2-16. Passive microwave image of Coalinga and adjacent rural area in the Central Valley, California (Courtesy Naval Weapons Center, China Lake).

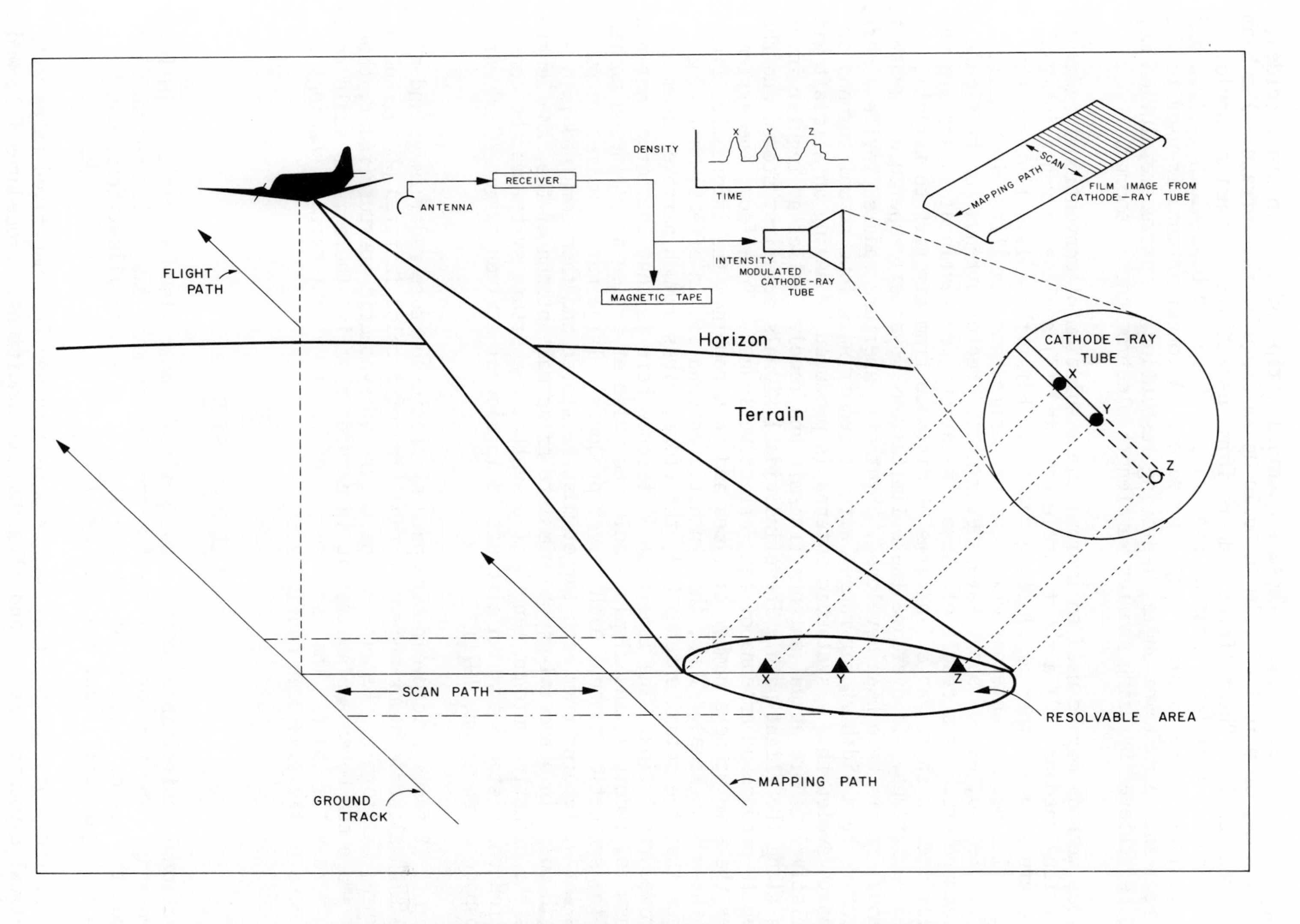

Figure 2-17. Diagram of side-looking airborne radar (SLAR) system.

strip of terrain is imaged. These sequential strips of terrain are recorded, side by side, on a roll of film to build up an image of the terrain. The beam of conventional or "brute force" radars forms essentially a constant angle. Resolution is, therefore, best at near ranges where the beam width is less and progressively worse as slant range increases. A longer antenna is used to focus the beam into a narrower angle, improving resolution. Improved resolution may also be achieved by using shorter wavelength electromagnetic energy.

Various methods may be used to improve the resolution of conventional radars: (1) a long antenna, (2) a short wavelength, and (3) a close-in range interval. There are also a number of limiting factors. First there is a limit to the practical length of antennas which can be carried and stabilized in the aircraft. Second, use of short wavelengths means greater attenuation by clouds and atmosphere. As a result of these limitations, conventional radars are primarily used in short-range (in terms of distance from aircraft to target), low-level operations. To overcome these limitations, synthetic-aperture (synthetic-antenna) radars have been developed. Synthetic-aperture radars provide a narrow, effective beam width at far ranges without requiring a long actual antenna or a short wavelength. A synthetic antenna is produced by having an aircraft with a relatively short actual antenna transmit and receive pulses at regular intervals along the flight path. These individual signals are first stored and then added to produce an antenna of long effective length. In effect, the system scans the same scene a number of times and then combines the information from all these scan lines. Thus, the synthetic antenna is, in effect, many times longer that the actual antenna and, therefore, gives a much narrower beam and improved resolution. The important difference here is that the actual antenna transmits, receives, and displays only one pulse at a time as a line on an image. For the synthetic antenna, each target produces a large number of return pulses. This set of returns from each target must be stored and then combined into a single pulse in a special way to simulate an actual antenna of the same length. Thus the effective antenna length of a synthetic-aperture system may be considered the distance that an aircraft is in view of a given target (Goodyear Aerospace Corporation, 1971).

Figure 2-18 shows a Goodyear Aerospace synthetic-aperture radar image and a NASA high-altitude black-and-white rendition of a color infrared photograph of Ventura, California. Because of the nature of synthetic-aperture radar, the SLAR image can be made plannimetric in nature; that is, there is no scale variation across the image. The pseudoscopic effect (apparent terrain shading) is produced by the side-scan configuration.

IMAGE PROCESSING

Operational control in a remote sensing mission must also be practiced in image processing. The type or quality of processing in many cases dictates whether or not the imagery will be of any use at all. A simple illustration can be seen in Figure 2-19 (Lent and Thorley, 1969).

Both of the photos of the test panels were obtained from negatives taken with identical exposure settings and illumination conditions. Procedures followed in printing the photos were also identical; only the development time was varied to produce the differences which are apparent in them. The change in development time has caused a shift in film gammas. (Gamma is a measure of the extent

Figure 2-18. Comparison of synthetic-aperture radar image and a black-and-white rendition of a color infrared photograph for the Oxnard Plain, California (Courtesy Goodyear Aerospace and the National Aeronautics and Space Administration).

Figure 2-19. The above test panel photo illustrations were produced from negatives obtained with identical exposure settings and illumination conditions. Printing procedures were identical, but development time was varied to produce the changes in density ranges apparent between the two test panels. The alteration in development time has caused shifts in film gammas.

of development and the contrast of the photographic material.) The ability to alter film gamma can be used to advantage when particular contrast ranges are required, but to correct for gamma variation between multiband images can lead to wrong conclusions.

At this point, a philosophical digression must be made. Although it is now possible to obtain imagery using a large number of sensors operating in almost all portions of the EM spectrum, the question still remains as to whether or not a signature key (compilation of representative photographic densities) made for one area at one time can be valid for another area at another time. There is a clear need for accurate recording and calibrating of sensors, environmental parameters, and data parameters if a multiband/multispectral concept is to be properly applied. With all the variables which exist and need to be measured in the atmosphere, in ground-truth material, in systems parameters, etc., repeatable photographic density results may never be achieved fully. Hence, there is a need for improving the reliability of such data.

IMAGE INTERPRETATION

Although somewhat beyond the scope of this discussion of imaging with photographic and nonphotographic sensor systems, some general comments on the interpretation of data produced by these systems is presented here. Image interpretation is defined here as the act of examining photographs and/or images for the purposes of identifying objects and phenomena and judging their significance. In carrying out this task, an interpreter may use many more types of information than those recorded on the images he is to interpret. These data are often grouped under headings such as collateral, or ground truth, and/or on-site verification. They may come from many sources: literature, laboratory measurement and analysis, field work, and ground and/or aerial photography. Acquisition of these types of ancillary data may vary significantly between remote sensing projects in relation to the spatial, temporal and cost constraints defined by a given image acquisition and interpretation program.

Supportive collateral data are often available in the form of maps and other records in tabular or graphic form. Examples include statistics such as meteorological or land use data collected by various individuals as well as government agencies. A review of these existing source materials--maps and atlases, reports related to the proposed project, existing classification schemes (conventional photointerpretation keys, land use, soil, or vegetation classifications, etc.)--aids not only in the interpretation of remotely sensed data, but may also produce a better definition of the scope, objectives, and problems associated with a given project.

Laboratory measurements and analyses are a continuing function of system design. These tasks enable the user of remotely sensed data to understand existing systems configurations, problems inherent to specific sensors, as well as the ongoing update and refinement necessary to provide adequate, consistent, detailed information. As previously stated, for example, the tone or color hue of an object recorded on a remotely sensed image is largely a function of the amount or intensity of energy reflected or emitted by that object within specific spectral bands, and is referred to as a "spectral signature." Spectral signatures may be obtained and catalogued in the laboratory or field, and subsequently compared with remote sensing data to assist in image interpretation.

In remote sensing today, the term "ground truth" is most commonly (and not improperly) equated with field survey; i.e., the observing, noting, recording, and often mapping the important elements of a given area. The amount of field work required for a given remote sensing project varies and is, in general, dependent upon the following considerations: (1) image quality, including scale, resolution, and information to be interpreted; (2) type of analysis or interpretation involved; (3) accuracy requirements for both boundary delineations and classification; (4) the experience of the interpreter and his knowledge of the sensor, area, and subject to be interpreted; (5) terrain conditions and area accessibility (for various reasons many areas may not be accessible for field work); and (6) the existence of other source material.

Field work often involves sampling for the verification of questionable interpretations and error corrections. In such cases it becomes important to consider how best to sample, and then to design a sampling strategy to fit the problem. Elaborate multi-stage sampling design are presently being used in conjunction with aerial surveys to provide accurate estimates of various environmental parameters.

While it is true that many types of remote sensing projects require field surveys prior, during, and after initial data acquisition,visual observations, notations, and specific field measurements as required by project objectives may not be sufficient. In most field surveys, especially those associated with remote sensing operations, it is appropriate to record systematically observations on terrestrial or low altitude aerial photographs. Such photographs are useful as: a permanent record of visual observations; a base for future notations and measurements; and documentation for reports of the field survey data.

The acquisition and analysis of the data described above should be viewed as an important element in remote sensing. As such, it must be realized that these data have their own variance, and, like a remotely sensed image, are subject to interpretation. Furthermore, collateral data play a dual role in the integral process of remote sensing interpretation and analysis: first, to assist in the interpretation and analysis process; and second, to verify interpretations and analysis. Just as data acquisition must be thoroughly considered and planned, so, too, must be the nature, amount, timing, and method of acquisition and integration of these ancillary data into a given remote sensing data acquisition program.*

Once imagery and the ancillary information described above have been assembled, image interpretation should proceed methodically, from general considerations to specific details; from known to unknown features (Stone, 1956). Methodical evaluation of the information content of a given image by proceedings from known to unknown features is standard scientific procedure. However, proceeding from general to specific considerations is valid as long as the general (regional) pattern does not bias the interpretation of specifics. Specific (local) considerations may often provide the detailed evidence to confirm a broader regional pattern (Olson, 1969). In an overall interpretation of a given area on an image, it may be best to proceed methodically, one topic at a time, such as landforms, vegetation, hydrology, transportation. It is important to remember, however, that features falling into these abstract categorizations are often broadly interrelated. The specific goals of the project should be used as a guide to which the procedural steps (methodical, known to unknown, general to specific, and topic by topic) will produce optimum information extraction. To imply that all steps need or should be followed in every interpretation is, as Olson has said, "an unwarranted channelization of the infinite variation that the photo-interpreter encounters" (Olson, 1969).

Although images may vary, photographic interpretation techniques apply to all images regardless of the type of sensor that produced them or the nature of the electromagnetic energy recorded. Interpretation is based upon an analysis of the specific properties of images. These properties are: (1) shape, (2) size, (3) tone, (4) texture, (5) pattern, (6) shadow, (7) site, and (8) association. The interpretation of any image involves the integration of one or more, and preferably all, of these elements in a deductive process which allows the interpreter to correctly identify objects and/or phenomena in the area under consideration and asess their significance.

Today, image processing systems are being developed which aid the image analyst

---

* For further information on this topic the reader is directed to the following references: Lintz, 1969; Friedman, 1968; and Wilson, 1968.

in his interpretation tasks. Technically, an image processor may be either a human, machine, or hybrid integrating the best aspects of man and machine. Single and multi-image processors* may obtain basic cueing from either tone variations, such as shape and texture, or tone values. More sophisticated systems integrate both cueing types into output decisions. First-order, second-order, and third-order systems may be defined as obtaining basic cueing from (1) tone variations, (2) tone values; and (3) combinations of tonal variations and tone values, respectively (Dalke, 1968).

Single-image first-order techniques are plentiful, including (1) line following, (2) fourier plane filtering, (3) edge enhancement, (4) scanning masks, (5) character-recognition techniques, and (6) multiaperture array scanning. These single-image techniques may be expanded to multi-image processors by applying them to each image in turn and compiling all information obtained in the processor output.

An example of a simple second-order technique involves a grayscale-level selection on a single image. A point is accepted or rejected as being in a certain category only if its optical density lies in the accepted region. This can be directly expanded to the multi-image problem by accpeting a point only if its optical density lies in specified density ranges on every one of the input images. Specific examples of second-order systems are (1) optical combiners, (2) electronic additive-color combiners, and (3) photographic-level selection. Second-order systems, therefore, exploit spectral characteristics of the data, a kind of information which is ignored by first-order systems.

Third-order systems utilize both types of cueing, color photography and reflectance infrared photography being examples of this type of system. Strictly speaking, color photography is a third-order type of data collection, rather than processing. The third-order processor, in general, is the human image interpreter. A true third-order processor would integrate shape, texture, and spectral information into an output format suitable for analysis without the need of interpretation (Estes, 1969). An expanded discussion of image processing and analysis techniques may be found in Chapter 3.

This chapter presents the parameters involved and factors important for a basic understanding of imaging with photographic and nonphotographic sensor systems. Multiband/multispectral scanning may enhance the detection and identification of objects by utilizing contrast ratios that may exist in very narrow bands of the EM spectrum. Polarization, differential absorption and reflectance may also facilitate information extraction and ease of interpretation. This concept may or may not depend to some extent upon the use of sophisticated data reduction techniques. Based on optical density readings from a number of selected spectral channels, tonal signatures of various conditions of a terrain feature and phenomena could be investigated and, hopefully with more data, automatically identified. Finally, it should be stressed that, although there are many sophisticated remote sensing techniques available, there is still a place for the individual with a small camera in a light aircraft. An image of an area, regardless of the quality, at least provides a record of a given scene and its associated phenomena at a given point in time.

---

* "Processor" is used here to denote either human or machine interpretation systems.

REFERENCES

American Geological Institute, 1968, AGI Short Course Lecture Notes, American Geological Institute, Washington, D.C.

American Society of Photogrammetry, Photointerpretation Subcommittee I, 1963, "Basic Matter and Energy Relationships Involved in Remote Reconnaissance," *Photogrammetric Engineering*, 29(5):761-799.

American Society of Photogrammetry, 1966, *Manual of Photogrammetry*, 3d ed., George Banta Company, Menasha, Wis., vols. I and II.

Avera, H. Q., et al., 1966, *Feasibility of Multiband Photographic Reconnaissance*, SID 66-301, North American Aviation, Space and Information Systems Division, Downey, Calif.

Carmen, P. D., and R. A. F. Carruthers, 1951, "Brightness of Fine Detail in Aerial Photography," *Journal Optical Society of America*, 161(41):305-310.

Colwell, R. N., 1968, *Manual of Multiband Photography*, NASA Grant No. 05-003-080, National Aeronautics and Space Administration, Washington, D.C.

Dalke, G. W., et al., 1968, *Multi-Image Correlation Systems Study for MGI*, Phase II Technical Report, Center for Research in Engineering Science, University of Kansas, Lawrence.

Estes, J. E., 1969, *Geographic Applications of Multi-Image Correlation Remote Sensing Techniques*, Ph.D. dissertation, University of California, Los Angeles, University Microfilms, Ann Arbor, Mich.

Friedman, J. D., 1968, "Role of Ground Monitoring in Infrared Imagery Surveys," paper presented at Thirty-fourth Annual Meeting of American Society of Photogrammetry, March 10-15, Washington, D.C.

Goodyear Aerospace Corporation, 1971, *Basic Concepts of Synthetic Aperture Radar*, Goodyear Aerospace Corporation, Litchfield Park, Ariz.

Hall, H. J., and H. K. Howell, Eds., *Photographic Considerations for Aerospace*, 2d ed., Itek Corporation, Lexington, Mass.

Jensen, Niels, 1968, *Optical and Photographic Reconnaissance Systems*, John Wiley & Sons, Inc., New York.

Lent, J. D., and G. A. Thorley, 1969, "Some Observations on the Use of Multiband Spectral Reconnaissance in the Inventory of Wildland Resources," *Remote Sensing of Environment*, 1(1):31-45.

Limperis, T., 1964, "Target and Background Signature Study," *Third Symposium on Remote Sensing of Environment*, University of Michigan, Institute of Science and Technology, Ann Arbor, pp. 423-433.

Lintz, J., Jr., 1969, "A Primer on Ground Truth," in *Remote Sensing of Environment: Lecture Notes*, Engineering 807.4, Short Course, University of California at Los Angeles, August 4-15.

Molineaux, C. E., 1964, "Aerial Reconnaissance of Surface Features with the Multiband Spectral System," *Third Symposium on Remote Sensing of Environment*, University of Michigan, Institute of Science and Technology, Ann Arbor, pp. 299-321.

Moore, R. K., 1965, *Radar as a Sensor*, CRES Report No. 61-7, University of Kansas, Center for Research in Engineering Sciences, Lawrence.

Myers, V. I., et al., 1966, "Remote Sensing in Soil and Water Conservation Research," *Fourth Symposium on Remote Sensing of Environment*, University of Michigan, Institute of Science and Technology, Ann Arbor, pp. 801-814.

National Academy of Sciences, 1970, *Remote Sensing: With Special Reference to Forestry and Agriculture*, National Academy of Sciences, Washington, D.C.

Nunnally, N. R., 1969, *Introduction to Remote Sensing: The Physics of Electromagnetic Radiation*, USGS Contract No. 14-08-001-10921, Association of American Geographers, Washington, D.C.

Olson, C. E., Jr., 1969, "What is Photographic Interpretation?" *Proceedings of Summer Short Course in Remote Sensing*, University of Michigan, Ann Arbor.

Orr, D. G., 1968, "Multiband Color Photography," *Manual of Color Aerial Photography*, Appendix I, Part 1, American Society of Photogrammetry, Falls Church, Va.

Parker, D. C., and M. F. Wolf, 1965, "Remote Sensing," *International Science and Technology*, No. 43, pp. 20-31.

Pease, Robert W., et al., 1970, *Mapping Terrestrial Radiation Emission with the RS-14 Scanner*, Technical Report III, USDI Contract No. 14-08-001-11914, University of California, Riverside.

Rumney, G. R., 1968, *Climatology and the World's Climates*, New York, Macmillan Company.

Steiner, D., and T. Guterman, 1966, *Russian Data on Spectral Reflectance of Soil Vegetation and Rock Types*, Final Technical Report, Contract No. DA 91-591-EUC 3863/01-652-0106, Department of Geography, University of Zurich, Zurich, Switzerland.

Stone, K. H., 1956, "Air Photo Interpretation Procedures," *Photogrammetric Engineering*, vol. 22:123-32.

Strahler, A. N., and A. H. Strahler, 1973, *Environmental Geoscience: Interaction Between Natural Systems and Man*, Hamilton Publishing Company, Santa Barbara.

Strandberg, C., 1967, *Aerial Discovery Manual*, John Wiley & Sons, Inc., New York.

Wilson, J. E., 1968, "Ground Truth Procedures for Aiding Interpretation of Remote Sensor Data," paper presented at Thirty-fourth Annual Meeting of American Society of Photogrammetry, March 10-15, Washington, D.C.

Van Riper, J. E., 1971, *Man's Physical World*, McGraw-Hill Book Company, New York.

Yost, E. F., and S. Wenderoth, 1967, "Multispectral Color Aerial Photography," *Photogrammetric Engineering*, 33(9):1020-1033.

Quantitative Data Extraction and Analysis of Remote Sensor Images

David S. Simonett*
Earth Satellite Corporation

The volume of data generated by remote sensing systems rapidly is exceeding the capability of trained image interpreters to reduce the data into needed information. The Earth Resources Technology Satellite alone generates numerous images of 10,000 square mile areas in a single year. Sophisticated computer interpretation techniques are considered as one possible solution to this problem. The preceding chapter discussed various elements of traditional human photo-interpretation. In this chapter, Simonett treats statistical and computer techniques for extracting quantitative information from remote sensing data. Comparisons are made between simple and complex procedures for data extraction. The conceptual and pragmatic considerations involved in the various procedures for enhancing, processing, and outputting data are discussed and evaluated. Chapters 2 and 3 provide the background information on technological aspects of remote sensing, from which framework it will be possible for the reader to understand more fully the earth science applications that follow in succeeding chapters.

In analyzing remote sensor images, we seek to derive both data and information from the images. These should be expressed in numerical or quantitative terms insofar as feasible: Only when numbers are associated with data and information can rigorous and repeatable measurements be made and quantitative hypotheses tested. Obtaining numbers from images can be achived in many ways, ranging in complexity from a man tallying vegetation classes in rectangular cells on an image to computer statistical pattern recognition studies using multispectral scanners.

The first objective in quantitative analysis of remote sensor images is to identify points, lines, and areas without ambiguity or to develop probabilistic statements about points, lines, and areas. Whether complete freedom from

* The author wishes to acknowledge the criticisms he received on this manuscript from Messrs. Charles Sheffield and Michael Hord of Earth Satellite Corporation.

ambiguity (identification) is necessary or possible will vary from case to case. Complete identification is not usually feasible, and probabilistic statements are required giving the accuracy levels of the determination. Along with the identification or probable identification of an object, we are concerned with enumeration or counting the numbers of things in classes (points, lines, areas --e.g., houses, roads, and crops of different types) and with mensuration, the determination of lengths, sizes, and areas.

The relative skill and speed in achieving these objectives will vary with circumstances. Generally, man is skillful ("man is the best 200-pound nonlinear computer in existence") but for certain tasks relatively slow in analyzing a large number of images. On the other hand, vast amounts of data completely indigestible to a man can be handled quickly by a computer, but the computer may be less accurate than an interpreter. The advantages and shortcomings of each (man and machine) have led most recent researchers to move toward fully interactive systems for image analysis. Such systems involve real-time decision making with man as an essential part of the system. Fully interactive systems involve man, analog display (television, photo printers, etc.), and analog and digital computers. Examples of interactive systems are described in Marshall and Kriegler (1971), Peterson et al. (1969), Estes and Senger (1971), Eppler et al. (1971), Weber and Polcyn (1971), and Hoffer and Goodrick (1971).

ELEMENTS OF PATTERN RECOGNITION

Analysis of an image is an exercise in pattern recognition. The recognition of patterns and the delineation of boundaries between homogeneous classes on an image (water, bare ground, vegetation type, geologic structures, urban housing quality, snow, etc.) is something which an experienced scientist does very well on a single black-and-white or color image. He recognizes different classes and patterns through use of many contextual and inferential clues in the photograph. These include spatial relationships of tone, texture, and the size, shape, and geometry of objects as well as the spectral information in the color photography. His field and interpretation experience and his knowledge of particular scientific disciplines are brought to bear on establishing the classes and the boundaries between them.

Man's recognition of patterns in three-dimensional real space as given in the example above involves his processing and compacting masses of data, then extracting useful information and classifying it into meaningful classes. However, pattern recognition in quantitative analysis also includes "statistical space"--as well as real space--in which the "pattern" is a vector in an n-dimensional space. An example would be the use of a 12-channel scanner for which each point on the ground has a grayscale value on each of 12 images. These 12 grayscale values may be "imagined" as providing a location in 12-dimensional "statistical space" for that point. The pattern recognition system seeks to partition or place boundaries in the n-dimensional space so that each region of it can be assigned to a class of patterns. There is thus an analogy--though imperfect--between the two-dimensional pattern recognition carried out by man (three-dimensional if stereoscopy is employed) when he makes identification and erects boundaries on a photograph and the n-dimensional statistical pattern recognition achieved by a computer when it seeks clusters and erects boundaries in "statistical space."

Viglione points out that the "key to pattern recognition is invariance." He continues:

> For example, in photographic image analysis, it is desirable that the classification assigned to an object or pattern of interest be independent of the position of that pattern in the field, the aspect at which it is viewed, the background against which it is seen, partial obscuration of that pattern, minor changes within the pattern class, and changes in the illumination or background noise. It is not too difficult to provide any one of these invariances. To provide all of the desired invariances with a practical amount of hardware, however, requires that the decision mechanism extract the essence (my emphasis) of the patterns to be identified (Viglione, 1970).

In passing, it must be said that an interpreter does all these things routinely and without much thought about the uniqueness of his capacity. Pattern recognition also involves the comparison of information derived from new data with that taken from known sample patterns or paradigms. For man, the paradigm is highly experientially based and consists of the sum of many experiences in field work and image interpretation over decades. For machines, the number of sample patterns is naturally much smaller. However, for limited problems a succession of patterns can be fed into the computer, and it can adaptively improve its knowledge of the sample characteristics through use of a learning algorithm. The output from man or machine is thus a decision on the nature of an unknown pattern in comparison with known patterns.

The concept of pattern recognition as given above can be extended also to include the various ways of enhancing (or preprocessing) imagery as well as the extraction of and analysis of "patterns" in the information extracted from the image. Indeed, the analytical tools and procedures used in working with photographs are themselves subsets of the general field of pattern recognition. In the following pages, comparisons will be made between simple (usually manual) and complex (usually machine) procedures for enhancing, processing, rendering decisions on, and outputting data. The conceptual and pragmatic relationships between procedures will be outlined. The similarities between and transformations of data arising from the different kinds of processing will also be discussed in such a way that the reader will see the connections between the various methods of quantification, and between traditional and newer procedures.

STEPS IN PATTERN RECOGNITION

There are five principal steps in pattern recognition in images: (1) input of the initial patterns, (2) preprocessing of patterns, (3) feature extraction, (4) decision/classification function, and (5) output of the classification.

Only the first and fifth steps are reasonably discrete. Steps 2, 3, and 4 overlap to greater or lesser extent depending on the problem being studied and the processes used. The sequence of these steps is, however, generally a proper ordering of the events in an analysis. They may now be examined in turn.

The input pattern may consist of a single black-and-white photograph to be analyzed by a photo interpreter. The same photograph could also be digitized line by line with a scanner for computer analysis. A color photograph to be analyzed by an interpreter is also an input pattern. It in turn may be scanned sequentially with blue, green, and red filters so that the three-dimensional color vectors in congruent geometry are recorded for digital processing. The input pattern might consist of a large number of channels from a multispectral scanner. In this case, the dimensionality of the data would be very high. Photo interpretation would not be feasible and the data could conveniently be handled only through computer processing.

Images obtained at different times also would be an input pattern. In this instance, in order to make comparisons between the images on a small area basis, they would have to be brought to the same exact geometry through optical or digital rectification, itself a preprocessing function, before processing manipulations could take place.

A densitometer trace across an image is also an input pattern. (A densitometer trace records the variations in transmittance of a constant light source passing through a series of points on an image). An input pattern could even be as simple an item as a line drawn across an image on which are marked the widths of crowns of trees. Though these items vary greatly in their dimensionality in real space, statistical space, and in time, all are input patterns capable of preprocessing analysis.

....<u>preprocessing function</u> or enhancement includes such procedures as removal of distortions (both geometric and photometric), scale change, translation, rotation, "noise" removal, image sharpening, grayscale-level slicing, filtering, color combination, and so on. A simple procedure such as printing a photograph with a different gamma (contrast) to expand the grayscale, or edge enhancement by reprinting through a positive and negative film sandwich of the same scene is an example. Preprocessing also involves functions of some complexity such as obtaining the two-dimensional Fourier transform of an image. This requires sophisticated optical equipment or digital programs to perform satisfactorily. In all cases, however, the preprocessing seeks (1) to produce a high level of invariance in the data; (2) to reduce its dimensionality; (3) to emphasize particular characteristics of the data; (4) to put it in a more convenient format; (5) to reduce noise, both random and systematic; and (6) to restore degraded images. A great variety of mathematical transformations may be applied somewhat unknowingly by the analyst when he makes various edge and/or other enhancements of the images using simple methods.

....<u>feature-extraction</u>....in pattern recognition involves determination of features through the syntax or the logic of the problem or through statistical manipulation of the data. Syntactically and logically derived features are very difficult to describe and define for computers, since each is a special case in itself. However, for the human they represent the sum of interpretation, field, and intellectual experience and may be generalized as "argument-in-context." Highly experienced scientists make judgments in photo interpretation which are based upon convergence of evidence, utilizing contextual and other clues in the imagery to improve identification. This capacity of man is substantially beyond that of analog and digital systems at this time and only when the latter are allied with man in a fully interactive (man plus analog plus digital) system can the experience and judgment of the scientist be brought to bear on the problem in conjunction with the speed and "number-crunching" capacity of computers.

The statistically designed features used during the feature-extraction phase include the familiar techniques of multivariate analysis, discriminant function analysis, and clustering analysis. In this feature-extraction phase, therefore, a real dichotomy emerges between man using a great number of "arguments in context" and convergence-of-evidence clues, which he does well and the machine rather ineptly, and the implementation of statistical algorithms, which the man does very slowly if at all and which the machine does superbly. It is important to note, however, that it is difficult to ensure that the statistical algorithms and convergence-of-evidence procedures converge on the same answer both in degree and kind. It would be remarkable if they readily did so, for their decision models and philosophical foundations are so dissimilar.

The function of the feature detector is thus to reformat and extract the essence of the pattern from input information (after preprocessing) so that is can be most readily classified and decisions can be rendered on a larger bulk of data from the same milieu.

The fourth step in the pattern recognition process is that is <u>classification and decision</u>. In this phase, items (features) present in the data are grouped into appropriate classes, and decisions are made probabilistically (and in some cases deterministically) on the class into which a given item will be placed. Two examples will suffice:

(1) A photo interpreter decides after inspecting many photographs that he can distinguish seven classes of neighborhood and housing quality on color infrared photographs (see Mullens, 1969). He then places boundaries around neighborhoods on the photographs.
(2) In computer analysis of 12-channel multispectral-scanner data, feature extraction and data compaction are performed using principal-components analysis. This is now employed as input to a clustering algorithm which seeks the naturally occurring clusters in 12-dimensional "statistical space" into which the data fall. (In passing, it should be stressed that these "natural" clusters vary with the algorithm and metric employed, and the only real test of their suitability for a particular problem is to check manually item by item for aberrant classifications. A man makes this judgment.)

The fifth and final step in the pattern recognition process is that of <u>classification output</u> in a variety of forms. Output includes such diverse forms as (1) hand-prepared overlays to an aerial photograph, (2) overlays corrected to fit the scale of a map, (3) an alpha-numeric output from a line printer attached to a computer, (4) a black-and-white photographically reproduced output derived from a computer terminal, (5) a display on a color television unit, (6) a tabular array organized by the interpreter or printed by the computer. The result achieved from following these steps would then require verification. This is an essential concluding phase to all research.

In discussing each of these steps in the following pages, selected examples will be drawn from the literature of different ways of handling and manipulating data, and tables will also be given comparing simple (usually manual) and complex (usually machine) methods.

In order to keep the sources, if not the numbers, of publications to a minimum for ease in outside reading, I have very deliberately confined the bulk of references to five sources containing articles published through mid-1972:

(1) *The Proceedings of the Seventh International Symposium on Remote Sensing of Environment*, volumes 1 to 3, held at the University of Michigan May 17 to 21, 1971; (2) papers appearing since 1969 in *Remote Sensing of Environment: An Interdisciplinary Journal*, published by American Elsevier Press; (3) papers since 1964 in *Photogrammetric Engineering*, published by the American Society of Photogrammetry; (4) the book *Remote Sensing of Earth Resources* edited by F. Shahrokhi (1972); and (5) papers later than 1964 in *Photogrammetria*, published by the International Society of Photogrammetry. There is thus some bias in this list. Each of the various steps in the pattern recognition process may now be looked at in more detail and applications drawn from this selective literature list will be examined.

INPUT PATTERNS

The principal input patterns and their characteristics which influence analysis and processing are briefly outlined below:

Photographs Obtained with Framing Cameras

Photographic emulsions give a continuous image, subject only to grain noise. The quality of both lenses and films is now such that very high resolution and/or geometric fidelity may be obtained with photographs. When obtained with framing cameras, such photographs image an area at a single instant and have point perspective--that is, all points on the ground and/or its inverted image pass through a single point. Being central-perspective projections they give true stereoscopy for viewing in three dimensions and, with appropriate geodetic ground control, enable very accurate maps and orthophotos (fitted to particular projections) to be made. Only framing mapping-quality cameras and photographs have these qualities. Thus, where the final output of image analysis is required to be geometrically very accurate, framing cameras must be used.

The types of photographs most commonly used, in decreasing order, are (1) conventional black-and-white (panoramic film employing a "minus blue," yellow filter to cut haze), (2) conventional three-layer color, (3) three-layer color infrared, and (4) multiband black-and-white photographs. The radiometric quality of a framing camera varies with the lens design both in respect to absolute radiant intensity across the field of view of the lens and with respect to wavelength. Illumination falls off from the center of the lens at approximately cos 40, where 0 is the lens semiangle. Spectral selectivity is a peculiarity of individual lenses.

Other Photographic Images

A variety of other photographic systems exist but are very much less common than the framing mapping camera photograph. Each may be used with conventional black-and-white, color, or color infrared film. None are used to obtain multiband photography. The two major systems are strip (or Sonne) type cameras, exposed line by line as the film is pulled past a slit, and panoramic cameras in which a high resolution lens rotates to scan a swath. Thus two types of line-perspective images (rather than point perspective) are obtained, with higher resolution than usually obtained from mapping cameras, but at the sacrifice of geometric fidelity: in addition to across-image distortions, the along-track image is continually subject to aircraft pitch, roll, and yaw. Because they are obtained with different lenses than framing cameras, radiometric quality varies across the image in a different way.

Images Produced by Sampling

Unlike photographs obtained with lenses, which are continuous-tone images, other devices for recording electromagnetic radiation employ a sampling process; and the input images are thus sampled images ab initio. These devices rely on the incoming radiation to activate discrete elements which are then read out and transmitted as in a television system or are photographed or are recorded on magnetic tape.

Sampled images include images made with all the following devices or systems:

(1) Vidicon image tube -- Used in TIROS meteorological satellites.
(2) Return beam vidicon -- The RBV used on ERTS is a multiband scene-framing system with three channels. The data are telemetered directly or are tape-recorded and later telemetered to receiving stations.
(3) Image dissector camera -- Used in NIMBUS meteorological satellites.
(4) Image orthicon tube -- Used in commercial television.
(5) Solid-state camera -- Similar to a Sonne-type strip camera except that film is replaced by a linear array of photo-conductive detectors. Square arrays up to 500 by 500 have been prepared. Under development.
(6) Optical mechanical scanner -- May be single- or multiple-channel through use of a diffraction grating. Detectors used are sensitive to specific wavelengths. May be recorded on film through modulation of a cathode-ray tube or a glow tube, now very commonly recorded directly in analog form on magnetic tape in congruent geometry. A four-channel system is being used on ERTS-1. ERTS-1 data are either telemetered directly or after tape-recording.
(7) Real-aperture radar -- Usually recorded on film through modulation of a cathode ray tube; may be recorded on magnetic tape.
(8) Synthetic-aperture radar -- Both optical and digitally processed images may be recorded on film or magnetic tape. Optically processed film recording is the most common.

All sampled images are subject to greater or lesser degree to significant problems of low geometric fidelity. Distinct low-frequency, middle-frequency, and high-frequency distortions arise from the optics and electronics of the framing systems. Scanning systems such as optical-mechanical scanners and side-looking radars have in addition continuous variations in along- and across-track scales, coupled with complex line-perspective, rather than point-perspective geometry. Finally, there are point-to-point radiometric distortions varying in degree and kind with the system employed.

From this brief account, it is clear that the character of the images used in analysis in a system in which quantitative data is required will markedly influence the amount and kind of preprocessing required.

Line-Trace Data

An appreciable number of remote sensing instruments record not image data but rather line-trace data, produced through one or more devices recording at a single angle as the aircraft or space vehicle moves forward. These devices sacrifice image format and usually ground spatial resolution to achieve significant gains in radiometric resolution (albedo and thermal emission), in spectral resolution (reducing the bandwidth of spectral channels by sacrificing spatial resolution), or in angular resolution (where the same object sensed at several angles may be identified more securely than at a single angle, e.g., in microwave radiometry and radar scatterometry).

These line-trace data are also sampled data in each case, being sampled in the time/space domain. They may be recorded on a chart, film, or magnetic tape or may be telemetered directly to a receiving station.

Other forms of line-trace data include the product of certain steps in preprocessing. These include microdensitometer traces, waveform analyzer output, line-scan modulation on a cathode-ray tube (CRT), --- and so on. For the purposes of further analysis, these can also be considered input data.

References which describe images and line-trace output are widely scattered in the literature. The best single sources are the eight Symposia on Remote Sensing held at the University of Michigan since the early 1960s. See also Steiner et al. (1972).

PREPROCESSING

Many preprocessing functions may be implemented using special techniques with film, with optical and electronic analog systems, and with digital systems.

Since the input data come in a variety of formats (film, analog magnetic tape, digital magnetic tape, paper tape, line chart recorder output, and so on), the first step in computer formatting is frequently that of digitizing film onto magnetic tape by scanning the image, or of conversion from analog to digital tape so that the data is computer-compatible.

The preprocessing may be designed to achieve one or more of the following purposes: (1) to enable qualitative judgments to be made or to improve qualitative judgments concerning the data; (2) to eliminate geometric or radiometric distortions in the image, thus improving the quality of the quantitative manipulations to be performed; (3) to emphasize or enhance data; (4) to restore certain features not present in the original film or data; and (5) to simplify, or condense, data (data compression).

Image Geometry Preprocessing

Since imagery and line-trace input come in a variety of scales and geometries, an investigator is faced with the problem of reconciling these geometries so that different images or data may be overlaid for comparison. If he lacks suitable equipment for high-quality rectification, he may live with data with a variety of scales and distortions or develop laborious manual procedures so that he can analyze the material effectively.

It is common, for example, to have available aerial photographs of an area of different dates, scales, and quality. In most instances, it would be financially out of the question--if a large area is involved--to attempt absolute geometric congruencing of this imagery. However, with very high altitude or space photography, the nearly orthographic view obtained in narrow field-of-view cameras, together with the very large area encompassed in a single frame may warrant either analog or digital image modification or orthophoto production to ensure congruency in images.

If multiple images are to be processed in either an analog or digital computer and point decisions are to be made using statistical pattern recognition methods, the images or data must be in point geometric congruence already (as it usually is with the output from a single flight with a multispectral scanner) or they must be brought to point congruence through matching images to a reference image or a reference map or orthophoto. This is an exceedingly difficult task (indeed, in many instances, it is infeasible) for images of different type or date unless the following requirements are at least substantially met:

(1) The area imaged is flat or at most gently undulating, and/or
(2) The images are obtained with very narrow field-of-view systems, and/or
(3) The images are obtained from very high flying aircraft or spacecraft (in which case even moderate relief may be tolerated; the image displacement on ERTS imagery of a mountain 3,000 feet high is less than a resolution cell across at the edge of the imagery), and/or
(4) The images are produced by framing cameras and orthophotos can be produced.

Very specifically this indicates one of the principal advantages of spacecraft images, namely, that time-differing images may be brought to acceptable congruence much easier and at distinctly less cost per unit area than aircraft images of any type, if the space images are rectified in a central facility employing first-order equipment.

Optical, electronic, and digital rectification are possible. In general, optical rectification is best and cheapest. Electronic and digital image matching are plagued by electronic distortions in the first case and by the cost of the processing in the latter.

If exact point-to-point correspondence is not required, simple optical and moderately expensive electronic and digital congruence may readily be obtained. Most workers studying area-extensive targets find that, in general change detection studies, where exact correspondence is not necessary, some departures from congruence can be tolerated. References which discuss these matters in some detail include Steiner et al. (1972); Bakis et al. (1971; also in earlier papers not cited here), who discuss digital congruencing with the fast Fourier transform. *The Manual of Photogrammetry*, published by the American Society of Photogrammetry, is a standard reference for optical and electronic rectification systems.

Radiometric Correction of Images

Radiometric corrections of images are intended to eliminate or at least reduce the effects of the following variations in image density to ensure a high level of spatial invariance with respect to scene radiance (reflectance or emisssion): (1) fall-off in light intensity away from the center of a photographic lens; (2) fore-lighting and back-lighting in a photograph (looking into and away from the sun); (3) systematic variations along a sensor flight path arising from changes in scene illumination, developing and printing procedures, etc.;(4) Scan-line (across-track) viewing angle variations in multispectral scanners; (5) Antenna pattern and across-track variations in radar images; (6) High-frequency across-track variations in sampled images arising from weak phosphors in the CRT and similar items; and (7) Nonflat response with image tubes.

The procedure of radiometric correction is frequently termed normalization of an image. Many methods have been used; not all achieve correction equally well. Some work well with a single image. Others are needed in addition to achieve normalization between two images of the same scene or on a long flight path. Variations in scene radiance arising from random topographic relief are normally not removed by these procedures.

The procedures used include

(1) Use of an antivignetting (neutral density) filter on a lens in which the density off-axis varies as the inverse of the vignetting function. If an antivignetting filter is not used on the camera or other components, then under low illumination levels the outer part of the photo is shifted to the toe of the film-sensitivity curve. Compensation may be achieved in printing by placing a neutral density sheet over the negative.

(2) Ratioing between photographic layers on a color film or between channels on a multispectral scanner analog or digital image (Brooner and Simonett, 1971; Maurer, 1971; Crane, 1971; Smedes et al., 1971). The following are among the options available: ratio a channel to the sum of all channels, ratio adjacent channels, ratio the difference and the sum of adjacent channels.

(3) Scan-line normalization. This includes procedures to eliminate or reduce fore-lighting and back-lighting, antenna pattern and other across-track variations in radar images, radiometric distortions from changing viewing angle in multispectral scanners. Point-densitometer readings may be manually adjusted with respect to position on an image (for radar antenna pattern see Simonett et al, 1967) or an unsharp (defocused) low-density positive may be sandwiched with a negative to correct the final positive. Algorithms have been developed by Crane (1971) at Michigan, and others have been developed at Purdue (Hoffer and Goodrick, 1971).

(4) Normalization or calibration of image tubes which have a nonflat response across the image may also be achieved to eliminate this effect by use either of a low-density additive sandwich in film processing or by point digital correction by scanning an image of a completely spectrally flat scene in the laboratory or in nature (uniform grey reflectance card or snow).

(5) Other techniques include subtraction of path radiance by subtracting the darkest object in a scene from all others (Crane, 1971), and equal-interval quantizing (Brooner, Haralick and Dinstein, 1971) of photographs or of multispectral images subject to along-track variability.

Image-Enhancement Procedures

The principal image-enhancement procedures are those of density slicing including contouring, edge enhancement, change detection through image addition, subtraction and averaging, and contrast stretching. These can be achieved in black-and-white through use of positive and negative sandwiches of images and by use of optical color combiners or be electronic or digital processing output and/or display. A simple equivalent usually exists for either complex analog and digital procedures. However, although simple procedures can almost always be found that will do cheaply the main functions of the digital computer, this is possible only when the exact sequence of operations to be performed is known. The computer has the advantage of flexibility of approach.

Density Slicing. A slice or segment of the grayscale may be selected to emphasize a given feature: e.g., water on a near-infrared black-and-white photograph. Since water absorbs infrared radiation, it is normally the blackest item on a near-infrared photograph. Through exposure control, one may photographically clip out all gray tones lighter than those for water. One would thus obtain a simple dichotomy: water, black--everything else, white. At a cost of much time and patience in a photographic laboratory, photographic density slices may be obtained of any portion or width of a grayscale. It is not an easy procedure by any means, but it is feasible with Agfa Contour film with which equidensity slicing may be obtained (Ranz and Schneider, 1971).

Variable grayscale position and width slicing can be readily implemented with an electronic system by placing the transparency of the photograph on the face of a cathode-ray tube (CRT) and scanning it, thereby converting the image densities to voltages. The voltage levels desired are then selected and displayed on a CRT, black-and-white or color television monitor or printed on a film writer. Frazee, Myers, and Westin (1971), for example, used density slicing and a color display in a test of mapping soil conditions in South Dakota. Equidensity slicing may be achieved on a color photograph in any one or more of the color layers with a Vario-chromograph color scanner (Helbig, 1972).

With a digital system, any level or levels of gray may be selected and output on a line printer, on a flat-bed or drum plotter, or directly onto a photographic film writer.

What are some of the advantages and disadvantages of each of these procedures? If an investigator needs to density-slice occasionally, or he has very limited funds, clearly he should use the photographic procedure himself or pay to have it done, unless it is possible to have a service organization digitize an image for him or process it with electronic analog equipment. Much time is consumed in fiddling with photographic density slicing, and it is not easily reproducible time after time. It is inherently difficult to calibrate photographic reproduction and to retain calibration. An analog system involving cathode ray tubes or image tubes may well cost thousands of dollars, and, while offering great flexibility and speed, it may be difficult to calibrate.

For a digital computer system, the film must be scanned and digitized. Programs must be written and algorithms developed. While these are relatively simple programs, none are trivial; and the integration of a complete input-output system is a major task. Once set up, it also is reproducible, very flexible, easily calibrated, and rapid. The level of quantization employed in digitization, however, markedly affects the fineness of slicing and can introduce quantization noise or "spurious contouring" in an image. The easiest way to understand quantization "noise" is to consider a single photograph and the frequency distribution of grayscales for all points on the photograph. Figure 3-1 shows such a frequency distribution. In order to show the grayscale density slice in the figure, the image would need to be quantized to 16 levels of gray, or 4 bits

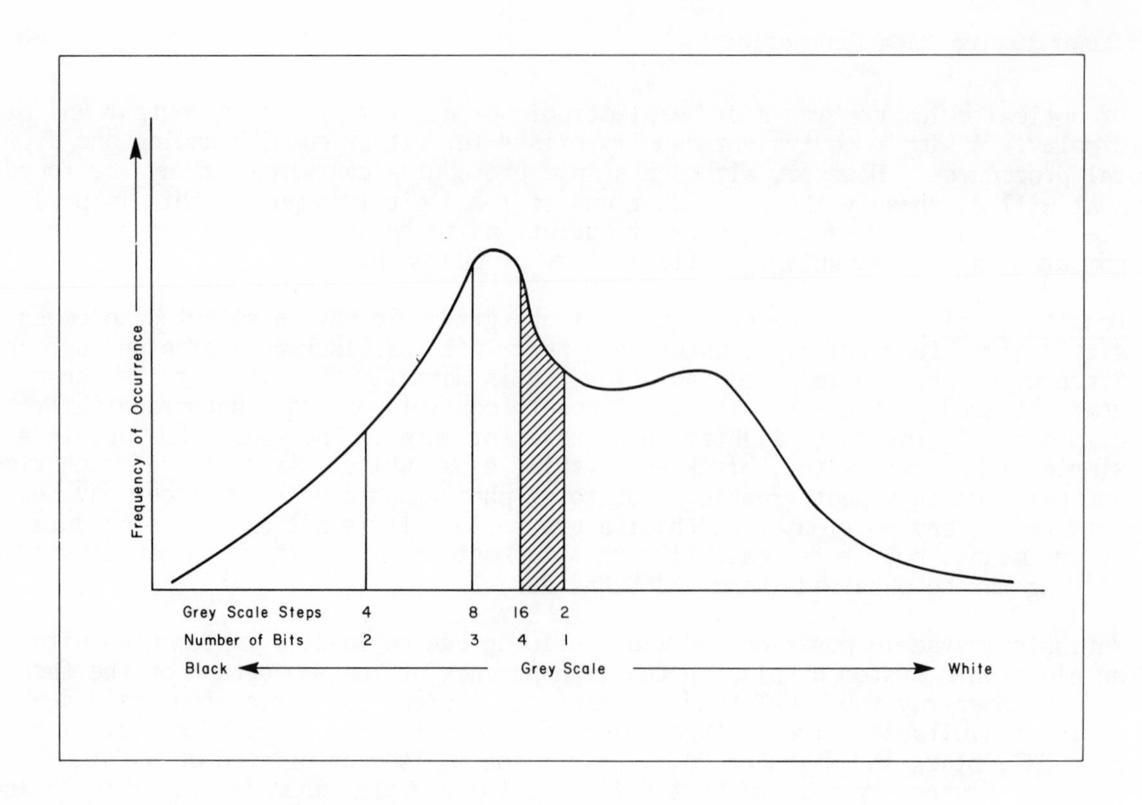

Figure 3-1. Frequency of occurrence of selected grey scale values on an aerial photograph.

(N bits gives 2^N gray levels). Normally, most images when analyzed in computers are not quantized to more than 64 levels of gray (6 bits) although occasionally it may be lifted as high as 1024 levels (10 bits). The narrower the slice of grayscale desired for emphasis, the higher the quantization level required. Digitization to a one-bit level produces a binary output (black or white). A high level of quantization is expensive to achieve and each further digital operation thereafter is expensive because of the large amount of redundant data present. Quantization noise or spurious contouring arises when too few or too many levels are used. Large steps in grayscale do not match the continuous grayscale of a photograph very satisfactorily. Too many steps tend to contour within natural categories in an image, and this can be very misleading.

Edge Enhancement. Edge enhancement is an important preprocessing step in that it can be used to "sharpen" an image by restoration of high-frequency components and to emphasize certain preferred edges or all edges to aid interpretation. These could include all edges with sharp density gradients, more subtle gradients, or edges aligned in a given direction.

There are various ways of emphasizing edges photographically. One simple method is to sandwich a positive and negative image together and displace one with respect to the other slightly. All edges at right angles to the direction of displacement will be emphasized as white lines at the leading edge and black lines at the trailing edge in the resulting photograph exposed through the sandwich;

this is a directional derivative. However, edges of equal sharpness lying parallel to the direction of photo displacement will not be emphasized. However, if one wished to emphasize all edges independent of direction this procedure is not satisfactory. To achieve invariance with respect to edge enhancement (remember that invariance is a desirable attribute we seek in pattern recognition studies), it is necessary to mount the positive and negative sandwich on a rotating disc with an exposure light mounted off-axis some distance above the photos. As the disc rotates, the light shines differentially through the two images and enhances all edges irrespective of direction. However, in this case the enhancement will differ depending upon the gradient of the edge. A steep gradient between a very dark and light area will produce a different edge than one with a low gradient, depending upon the angle at which the light is mounted off the axis of rotation of the disc. The greater the degree of off-axis mounting the shallower the gradient which is emphasized. This procedure is somewhat selective with respect to the sharpness of the edge between areas. A lineament of interest to a geologist may or may not be emphasized by such a procedure. Thus the enhancement procedure may emphasize noise as well as information for the interpreter. Another procedure is to sandwich an unsharp positive and a sharp negative and print through both.

The electronic analog of the displacement of two films with respect to one another along a line is to differentiate the image along the scan lines of a CRT. This suffers from the same advantages and disadvantages of the optical system plus normally a distinct loss in resolution in going from the photograph through the CRT and then finally onto a television display. To achieve the electronic equivalent of invariance of edge enhancement with respect to direction, a spiral scan or its equivalent is required.

A more complex optical procedure is to take the Fourier transform of an image using a collimated light source or laser and to filter out all but the high-frequency components (leaving either some or all direction of the high-frequency or edge components) with a mask be reconstituting the image.

Similar procedures may be employed digitally. In the digitalization process, the pixel-by-pixel digitization takes place in a sequential scan in a raster format comparable with that of a CRT. Thus, there is already built into the system preferred orientation from the scanning direction. This needs to be removed before edge enhancement proceeds. The steps involved then are development of algorithms for removing scan-line noise, for directional derivative edge enhancement, and for handling direction/invariant enhancement. In the second instance, the algorithm takes the first derivative in a given direction. In the third instance, it involves the use of functions which are neutral with respect to orientation, such as a rotation invariant second-derivative operator, i.e., a Laplacian or a Fourier Transform.

A commonly quoted example of edge enhancement is that of emphasizing lineaments in a photograph for fracture trace mapping. This is not a trivial problem in any of its parts. Geologists differ among themselves in interpretation of lineaments where others believe none exist. Consequently, we have no stable base against which to evaluate the performance of either an analog or digital system because the comparison is with an interpretation which is both conceptually and experimentally biased.

This does not mean that excellent fracture analyses cannot be done by a competent geologist or that the results obtained from it are not useful in general geological mapping and in studies of economic geology. They are. What it does say is that one is not comparing machine results with an absolute. A lineament mapped by a geologist may have many changes in grayscale and in other characteristics along the lineament. The machine will emphasize these differences as well as those which are directly related to the lineament. It also may not emphasize features inferentially related to the lineament which the geologist also uses to make his decisions. As a result, the machine will produce a high level of noise in its edge enhancement-lineation detection procedure. However, whatever it does is reproducible and consistent, which man frequently is not. The edge-enhancement procedure also cuts down the volume of data to be inspected as well as giving emphasis to some, but not all, of the data required.

Change Detection. An interesting preprocessing function is that of detecting change from one image to another. In this instance, one is seeking change of interest to the observer. Such change is embedded in a large amount of extraneous change, or clutter. Consider, for example, an observer interested in detecting significant changes in field acreage from one time to another. In addition to the change in acreage which he desires, there will also be much irrelevant change such as that in crop or soil condition. Change-detection preprocessing functions that are easy to implement are all of high ambiguity. The interpreter normally has to intervene to make judgments on what is ambiguous and what is useful information. Automated change detection is still very difficult. Manual or interactive man-machine change detection will be with us for some time to come.

Typical procedures used in change detection are those of flicker, that is, alternately presenting the first and then the second image to the observer at a rate of about ten frames per second. At this rate, areas where change has taken place appear to jump while areas of no change remain stable on the image. Flickering can be done readily with a very simple stereoscope set-up and two light sources with the light alternately blinking on and off behind the two images. It can also be implemented in an analog system using CRT tubes or in digital and fully interactive systems.

Another common process used for detecting change is that of "subtracting" (actually ratioing) one image from another. This may be done photographically by using a positive transparency of one image and a negative of the other and printing a new photograph through both. Areas of no change will be medium gray. Areas of change will differ in light or dark tones. However, the sign of the change with respect to one photograph will not be displayed. The same procedure can be very easily implemented with an electronic system or in a digital system. Whether done with simple optical equipment (preceded by orthophoto generation) or with the more complex electronic and digital systems, the principal difficulty remains that change detection, while intrinsically a very attractive idea for studying the environment, proves not to be readily tractable to preprocessing either by simple methods or by electronic or digital systems: Winnowing the information from the noise and achieving substantial data compaction through preprocessing is still in an early stage of development. It should come as no surprise therefore that most of the change-detection steps are still carried out manually.

Change detection will be a significant item in the ERTS (Earth Resources Technology Satellite) experiments sponsored by NASA. Those changes which involve very high environmental contrasts, such as major road and airport construction, are relatively easy to implement because the magnitude of the change and the grayscale variation involved is so great that ambiguities are kept to a minimum. However, less extreme changes will require considerable photo-interpretation time for analysis. However, preprocessed images showing areas of change are a valuable adjunct to the unpreprocessed images. When the original and preprocessed images are used together a more complete interpretation may be made by the interpreter.

Contrast Stretching. Contrast stretching is a widely employed image preprocessing function, used to make subtle grayscale differences, not readily detectable with the naked eye, more obvious for interpretation. Any image of low contrast or any portion of the grayscale of an image may be enhanced by this procedure.

Images of low contrast, for which stretching is appropriate, may arise from various means. Certain scenes may be of inherently low contrast in a given wavelength, or a contrasting scene may be viewed throught a hazy atmosphere.

A common technique to improve contrast is to produce new negatives and positives through repeated processing with high-gamma film. A log-etronic processer may also be used for stretching. The greatest control in stretching is maintained in digital processing. Low-contrast ERTS frames may be contrast stretched before color combination in order to enhance the color contrast.

Image Smoothing

Image smoothing can be readily done with an analog system either by defocusing a camera or CRT blurring of spotsize. Brown (1972) points out smoothing and reduction of signal variance is better done digitally than with analog systems. He employed a ten-line smoothing function which could not be achieved with analog equipment, to match the smoothing function to the signal and therefore to discriminate against noise.

Other Options

The preceding examples of preprocessing options are only portions of the options available. Other options include thresholding (Steiner et al., 1972), optical and electronic color combination of images (Peterson et al., 1969; Steiner et al., 1972; Estes and Senger, 1971; Lent and Thorley, 1969), digital image sharpening with Laplacian operators (Steiner et al., 1972), quantification of textures using auto correlation functions, nearest-neighbour algorithms and dichotomous keys, Fourier transforms, variance of the signal, number of edges per unit distance, and microdensitometer traces either raw or after analyses such as power spectral analysis, etc. (Kaizer, 1955; Haralick and Anderson, 1971; Brown, 1972; Brooner, Haralick, and Dinstein, 1971; Simonett and Brown, 1965).

FEATURE EXTRACTION

Quantitative feature extraction involves four principal aspects: (1) the development of a logic, structure, or syntax for isolating significant variables for analysis; (2) the preparation of quantitative measurements; (3) the determination of the characteristics of the variables; and (4) the collapsing of data so that only the essential point or essence of the data structure is carried forward into the following step of decision/classification. Each of these steps is briefly examined.

The logical or syntactical step involves structuring the design of the experiment and the measurements to be obtained. Thus, considerations such as what will be measured and why, how data will be sampled and aggregated, the number of variables to be used (e.g., specifying the number of channels in the multispectral scanner), the form in which the measurements will be carried forward to the next step in the analysis, methods of data compaction, and so on, are all relevant.

The development of the logic is iterative. Thus, both measurements and reasons are examined. Trial runs are made to find the most economical way of abstracting the necessary information without unnecessary processing. A data-compaction step--such principal components analysis--may also be run on a sample of the data to get a handle on its internal structure. First, this phase of feature extraction is to be thought of as an iterative process of refining judgements on the most suitable procedure to be used. In order to help in this process, histograms, covariance matrixes, means, standard deviations, and scatter diagrams are commonly prepared for subsets of the data. An example from outside the field of remote sensing will help to make the procedure clear.

A significant process in urbanizing the western world is the gradual radial expansion of cities, leaving a ring of somewhat blighted land immediately surrounding the central business district. Population densities are only moderate in the central business district, rise into and slightly beyond the blighted area, and then decline toward the outer edge of the city, around the edges of which new suburban development and satellite cities may cause a rise again in population densities. You are given the assignment of finding relationships between income and social composition of the community as a function of radial distance from the central business district and as a subsidiary function of the sector of the city. At the same time, you are asked to make comparisons between these data and the location by size and type of public open space in the form of park and recreation space. The reasoning behind this is to develop a model for better location of public resources to those areas which both on an income (mobility) and open-space supply basis are the most poorly served in the community. Given this problem, one immediately confronts issues such as which variables should be used, are all quantitative, can parametric statistics be used to work with the data, or must some nonparametric statistics be used; may the data be collapsed; what problems will there be in maintaining internal consistency in the data from one portion of the city to another, and so on. Preliminary runs on a small sample of the data would normally be carried out in order not to invest time in an untested procedure.

In remote sensing, this same process may be thought of in both qualitative and quantitative terms. A qualitative example would be the production of a photogeologic map, a landscape-region map or a photo-vegetation map before going into the field. In the absence of accessory field data, the analyst uses experience and judgment to produce his map, in the expectation that it will be revised after field work. In forest studies, some more overtly quantitative procedures may be used with images. The height of a tree (variable 1, measurement 1), its tone (variable 2, measurement 2), its size (variable 3, measurement 3), and its texture as a mass (variable 4, measurement 4) are commonly used as a basis for discrimination between species.

If one or more of these variables are not functional in a particular case they would simply be excluded in order to cut down unnecessary work. Similarly, in working with multispectral scanner the output from the multiple images would be looked at for small samples.

Steiner (1970) emphasizes the similarity between the photo-interpretation process and the extraction of the essence of data through the feature extraction processing in the following words:

New observations, not contained in the original data set, can be allocated in exactly the same way, by making use of the previously determined discriminant functions. It should be noted, therefore, that automated aerial or space surveys do not differ from the basic principles of conventional photo interpretation, i.e., the selection of a sample of subjects of known identity, the establishment of a key based on this sample, and the application of the key information to classify all other objects in the study area whose identity is not known as yet. For the mathematical solution the discriminant functions represent the key, and the comparison of the classification of sample subjects as produced by the analysis with the true identity of these subjects provides a statistical estimate for the overall accuracy of the survey.

In this quotation, Steiner was describing the use of linear discriminant functions with time sequential data for identification of crops.

The measurements of the data, as noted above, represent the variables used in the analysis. The variables may be uncorrected grayscale, (from a photograph, color band or multispectral channel) or a normalized variable. In most remote sensing applications, the principal variables used in each channel will be tone (grayscale), texture (some measure of the spatial organization and variability of grayscale), and, for manual or semiautomatic processes with aerial photographs, height measurements from stereoscopic photo pairs.

The measurements involve problems of resolution (the finer the resolution the more variable the probability density function for an area-extensive target) and the resolution in grayscale (the number of detectable shades of grey to which the eye, the analog equipment, or the digital equipment is sensitive). These items all have to be considered in the analysis.

The search for the essence of the data structure arises from the need to be parsimonious. Just as it is not necessary to have 50 variables to account for the bulk of variation in any dependent variable so too it is not necessary to use every channel of a multispectral scanner or all the data that are collected through time in a multiple photographic sequence. In short, we are searching for key indicators of the relationship in question; and we discard extraneous or highly cross-correlated data, collapsing measurements (variables) to that minimum which is substantially orthogonal in feature space.

There are many ways in which the essence of a problem can be distilled. In photo interpretation it may be the discovery that at one key time of the year a virtually 100 percent discrimination between two entities can be made, using a single channel, whereas at other times of the year even three or more channels may be unsatisfactory. Similarly, with a multispectral scanner, it may be the discovery that to discriminate one crop from all others may require as few as two channels and that the addition of extra channels achieves no gain.

To summarize, the feature-extraction process thus is to be viewed as a procedure whereby the internal and external structure of the problem and the internal structure of the data are both evaluated and judgments are rendered on the minimum information needed by time, channel, or some other factor in order to achieve identification accuracies which will be acceptable for the problem at hand.

Quantitative Measurements of Image Grayscale and Image Color

In the development of dichotomous keys it is common to use gross steps in grayscale--light, medium, dark--as part of the classification key. However, this may be done more precisely through use of a grayscale density wedge against which the individual values on a photography may be compared.

Since it is both inaccurate and time-consuming to visually transfer subtle gray tones from the density wedge to the interior of a frame, it is rare to go beyond a three-step sequence of grayscale in developing keys, and most quantitative grayscale information from photographs is obtained with microdensitometers.

Instruments for simple point densitometry or for full x-y scanning are available. Spot and scanning microdensitometers often are equipped with color filters, for use with color photography. Congruent point registry of the three bands of a color film to analog or digital tape may be obtained. Even point densitometry, however, may be used to build up statistics suitable for feature extraction. Some examples follow of the use of densitometry for feature extraction.

Feature extraction may consist merely of identifying the within-class variance from a densitometer trace. Thus, Pestrong (1969) used traces across images in coastal wetlands on multiband photographs to separate plant communities and to profile channel depth in inaccessible sites.

To produce analog contour maps of continuously varying functions, scanning microdensitometers (isodensitracing) are frequently used: examples include temperature contouring in water and of soil (Myers et al., 1970), bathymetry (water depth displayed in color), edge and thickness of sediment plumes and outfall sites (James and Burgess, 1970).

In forestry, microdensitometry has been used for numerous studies: Ciesla, Drake, and Wilmore (1972) used the cyan layer of false-color photography to test for the significance (t-test) between three plots sprayed against the forest tent caterpillar. LeSchalk (1972) prepared power spectrum analysis of forest types; wave forms were treated as a time series.

Smedes et al. (1971) used color infrared film for Yellowstone National Park to prepare scanning three-color microdensitomery for maximum likelihood function terrain type identification. Anuta et al. (1971) also used a scanning microdensitometer to digitize Apollo multispectral imagery. After spatial registration, they used divergent analysis (pairwise separability between classes).

Brooner and Simonett (1971) and Brooner, Haralick and Dinstein (1971), used point densitometry on color images of crops in eastern Kansas and the Imperial Valley of California respectively. They used Bayesian approaches, following normalization of the images.

Examples of Statistical Feature Extraction

The most useful basic review of this area is found in Chapter 3, "Automatic Processing and Classification of Remote Sensing Data," by D. Steiner et al. (1972), in *Geographical Data Handling*, volume 1, edited by R. F. Tomlinson (1972), pages 354-485. This is an extended and very logical account of the area of digital feature extraction and classification procedures. A full discussion is also given of the various preprocessing techniques. The chapter will require some background in mathematics and statistics for students wishing to make use of this material.

Feature Extraction with Training Sets: Multispectral Scanner

Feature extraction with the multispectral scanner commonly employs training sets. A training set is a subsample, the identification of which is completely known. It is used to generate subpopulation statistics in order that decision rules in the following step may be implemented most efficiently. The feature selection process, being preceded by sampling, is contingent for its utility on the quality of the sampling: the size of the sample, its spatial distribution, and efficiency are all involved. The problem is to establish the probability distributions in n-dimensional space (n equals the number of channels of the multispectral scanner being used); these are then used to erect decision rules to apply to the prediction data set. In general, the probability distributions are empirically derived at the time of the aircraft flight by obtaining ground-truth data. They may also be known a priori from previously obtained data which can be prepared in a table look-up procedure. (See Eppler, Helmke, and Evans, 1971).

A number of data-display techniques are used with multispectral scanner data to facilitate feature extraction: histograms for each category and by channel; matrices of correlation and covariance. The training-set data are usually used with parametric discriminants: Bayesian probabilities or maximum likelihood functions. Thresholding is commonly used with both. Thresholding is simply a process of assignment to a discard class of items unlike the sample, rather than lumping them with classes of the training set.

Because of the very large amount of computational time involved in using the maximum likelihood ratio, many alternative procedures are being tested. Crane and Richardson (1972) note that while it is possible to reduce the number of data through sampling (see the problems of sampling mentioned later) it is also possible to save time with the decision rule itself. The decision rule in common use is "based on two assumptions: (1) that the data are gaussian (normal); and (2) that training data for each class adequately represent the entire class. With these two assumptions the maximum likelihood decision rule becomes a quadratic rule. This rule requires a large number of multiplications for each decision especially when many channels of data and many classes are used." They found a linear decision rule compared favorably in accuracy and was 50 times faster than the maximum likelihood function: "In choosing a subset of channels for processing, the linear method is especially promising. The reason is quite simple: there are many subsets of channels that provide near-optimum recognition performance for the training data. Thus, even though linear methods might occasionally choose a different subset than would the quadratic, the difference in performance is likely to be negligible."

Bond and Atkinson (1972) also have developed very fast nonparametric procedures. Linear discriminant functions achieved satisfactory results with multiclass/multiband data as long as the order of class separability was observed during the classification process. Their algorithm took 5 minutes for one area compared with 70 minutes for 6 channels and 5 hours using 12 channels with the maximum likelihood function. Savings such as these are important in making the computer more available in the future for working with multispectral scanner data. If the costs can be brought down two orders of magnitude below those currently obtaining with the LARSYS 2 programs (Purdue University programs) there will be very widespread use of the computer in analyzing ERTS and future spacecraft multispectral systems. There is every reason to believe that savings of this order are feasible and that real-time processing with analog computers will be feasible and relatively inexpensive.

Other studies giving increased speed or very satisfactory prediction results include those by Su, Jayroe, and Cummings (1972)--a composite sequential clustering algorithm; by Richardson et al. (1971)--an elliptical boundary condition model; and by Eppler, Helmke, and Evans (1971), who developed a table look-up procedure 30 times faster than the maximum likelihood function and broadly as accurate.

Other statistical methods for extracting features include linear discriminant functions, polynomial discriminant functions, potential functions (the n-dimensional potential exerted by a point in space), and nonparametric partitioning. An extended discussion is found in Fu (1971) and in Steiner et al. (1972).

Steiner (1970) used linear discriminant function analysis to extract the features for crop identification. With 11 crops and 13 variables (times of observation), 100 percent identification was possible. Time was sliced so fine as to be almost differentiated: probably comparable accuracy could be achieved with a dichotomous key and manual interpretation. The principal value of this paper was its emphasis on time as a discriminant.

Steiner and Maurer (1969) achieved high identification accuracies with stereo height of crops with linear discriminant analysis. It is much more complex to implement height measurements than simple density measurements, and there is not much likelihood that this procedure will be widely used. They tangled with the perennial problem of equal probability and weighted probabilities for predicting from a training set to a prediction set. Equal probability assumes equal likelihood of all crops in the prediction set. Weighted probability assumes that the distribution of crops within the prediction set is the same as that in the training set. In large areas where the proportions of different crops are the same, this is a better assumption than equal probability and might be used in predicting over large areas of spring wheat.

One of the few papers investigating the relationship between size of training sets and the accuracy of results is that by Roth and Baumgardner (1971). They investigated the relation between soil color and organic matter, employing the coefficient of determination for one channel and for six channels, for sample sizes of 1, 9, 25, and 144. The best single channel improved from an r^2 of 0.42 to 0.46, the best six from 0.61 to 0.72 in going from 1 to 144 cases: very limited regional sampling would be adequate for this type of solution. However, most situations require much higher sampling rates.

The general question of sampling rates over large areas is of considerable importance now that many workers are studying ERTS imagery. (see Fu, Landgrebe, and Philips, 1969; Hoffer and Goodrick, 1971).

Hoffer and Goodrick showed for aggregated classes (bare soil, water, green vegetation) that training samples selected from a very small area can be extrapolated over considerable distances (97 percent accuracy for soil, 100 percent for water, and 99 percent for green vegetation). Since time is a valuable discriminant function (Steiner, 1970), this suggests that multidate ERTS imagery and gross categories should achieve good discrimination over large distances. An important point made by Hoffer and Goodrick was that although there was significant shift in the spectral data there was no shift in accuracy because there were only those three classes present in the area they studied. This result should be viewed with some caution becuase there will be problems of thresholding in more complex environments where large areas do not fit simply into the bare-soil or green-vegetation categories. Their study also showed that simple distance decay functions will not be found with crops and that very careful scrutiny will have to be made of the way decay functions are organized spatially.

A paper by Higgins and Deutsch (1972) on the effects of picture operations in the Fourier domain is important in that it shows the types of errors in the spatial domain which are introduced by different sampling rates in different areas. The more complex and more finely segmented the individual scene (e.g., fields in Southeast Asia) the more difficulty is encountered in row and column sampling to reduce data volume: sampling is a common procedure with the multispectral scanner. The paper indicates some of the problems encountered as one moves from one environment to another in terms of the likely accuracy of results and shows that spatial domain sampling--depending on the area--introduces both high- and low-frequency noise in the data.

Analog Computer Processing

Weber and Polcyn (1971) describe analog computer processing at the University of Michigan with SPARC (Spectral Analysis and Recognition Computer). This system is 100 times faster than a digital system alone. They use digital preprocessing to implement elimination of scan-angle effects, shadowing, and nonuniform response. Average pair probability of misclassification (APPM) is used for feature extraction (Nalepka, 1970).

The General Electric Company also has developed an analog system for high-speed statistical decision. Two of the systems (GEMS) have been produced. One is located in Valley Forge, Pennsylvania. The other became operational in Daytona Beach, Florida, in June 1973. Extraction of texture-related information has not yet been developed with these analog computers. Digital systems are flexible, but costly of processing time. Analog systems are special purpose and fast in processing, but at the sacrifice of flexibility. Each new capacity or operation demands new hard-wired components.

Feature Extraction Through Use of Clustering Algorithms

In areas for which training sets are not available, feature extraction can be derived through using a clustering algorithm.

This is similar to photo interpretation in an unknown region where an interpreter places lines around regions which appear photographically similar. The process of mapping natural landscape types is a manual clustering routine with single photographs or images.

Turner (1972) points out that "despite the existence now of a large body of literature on cluster analysis there is no unanimity on a universally based criterion although there is some consensus on the best criteria for certain types of data." He states that, when data can be considered a sample from a continuous multivariate normal distribution, the generalized variance (the determinant of the pooled within-group variance-covariance matrix) seems to have wide applicability. He also notes that, where data are sampled from discrete distributions or where there are mixed data from both distribution types, most criteria suggested are based upon Euclidian distance measures. In his study, he uses a technique influenced by one developed by Tryon and Bailey (1970). This technique is the well-known one of setting up trial group centroids "iterative condensation on centroids" and each point is then assigned to that group to which it had the smallest Euclidian distance. The process is repeated iteratively until no change occurs.

In analyzing the procedures and dilemmas in both training set and clustering approaches of feature extraction, it has been found that: both work well with small data sets but the dimensionality and cost of processing is substantial for large areas. Spatial-spectral clustering classification philosophies have been developed using a one-pass clustering procedure akin to that used by Nagy et al. (1971). He used a distance function measure (maximum of the absolute values of the differences between the spectral components), with a spatial contiguity constraint. He weighted the spatial portion of the analysis initially more strongly than the spectral using a two-dimensional spatial correlation function.

Another useful review paper dealing with the problems of clustering and training sets in feature selection is that by Nagy et al. (1971). They developed clustering with spatial contiguity constraints, which is similar to procedures in use for some years by geographers. They observed problems of overlapping of statistical and real classes like those observed by Haralick, Caspell, and Simonett (1970).

Fu (1971) and Steiner et al. (1972) discuss in some detail the various similarity, minimum distance, minimum variation, mode seeking, iterative discriminant analysis, and feature space transformations used in clustering. The most commonly used clustering measures are those of Euclidian distance, similarity ratios, normalized correlations, minimum distance to the mean, minimum of least squares, iterative determination of centroid locations, principal components analysis, canonical discrimnant functions, and separability measures.

Even after any of these clustering routines has been applied it is frequently necessary to manually inspect the data in order to find peculiar or adverse inclusions.

As implied in the earlier discussion, there are many problems in the use of training sets: How adequately do training sets represent the data to be used for prediction? Over what distances from a training set may the training be extrapolated with any confidence? What is the most appropriate and time-saving statistical technique for use with training data? What happens in situations where training data are obtained at very unsuitable times to achieve maximum discrimination? Comparable and indeed even more serious problems arise with clustering algorithms. These problems may be illustrated by referring again to the process of delineation of natural landscapes on images. Workers who engage in delineating natural or homogeneous landscapes know that this may be done very easily in some locations. As one moves into new areas, it is frequently very difficult to decide where a boundary lies and where a new class should be erected. Thus, the natural clustering one engages in is at the mercy of the size of the area over which one carries out the analysis. In a similar fashion, clustering algorithms are at the mercy of the geographical space over which they are used. The literature is full of pretentious claims for the efficiency of one or another algorithm in comparison with other approaches; in fact, we are still at too early a stage in analysis of clustering routines to know how to separate out matters of indeterminancy and open-endedness and their relations to the spatial and multispectral dimensionalities of the data.

Studies on Texture

Feature extraction of texture is typically employed in developing photo-interpretation keys. Three to five texture steps may be used. The equivalent of this process in analog technique is to use the variance of the signal in a chart strip recorder. Nunnally (1969) used microdensitometer plots to help group natural landscape classes on radar images of Tennessee. Morain and Simonett (1967) used probability density functions from a CRT and pulse-height analyzer to indicate textural differences on radar images of plant communities.

Feature extraction of texture is expanding to a significant degree with digital systems, for it is now realized that texture may be added to multispectral data to significantly improve identification. A useful general analysis in this area is given by Ramapriyan (1972) in his article on spatial frequency analysis of multispectral data. He uses the discrete Fourier transform as also does Palgen (1970). Since the variance of the signal in the amplitude domain is related to texture in the image, most measures utilize some aspect of signal variance. Among the earliest of such measures is contrast frequency (Rosenfeldt, 1962), the average number of times a specified departure from the average density occurs in a selected portion of the picture. This will be recognized as one simplification of the spatial probability density function.

Matrices of spatial gray tone dependence have been used by Haralick (1971) for analysis of texture. The elements of the matrix are the relevant frequencies with which selected gray tones occur in neighboring pixels of defined angular relationships and distances. Haralick defined scalar functions of these matrices including the angular second moment inverse difference, the angular second moment, and correlation between neighboring gray tones. Since these features are direction dependent they are not invariant with respect to angular rotation, but they may be made invariant by summing over four directions to perform feature extraction. Similar problems of lack of invariance require summing over all directions when the Fourier Transform is used. Other techniques, developed by

Hord and Gramenopoulos (1971), are those of thresholded derivative densities and geometric analysis of the signal to noise ratio in the Fourier Transform plane. These techniques were refined by them (1973) through the prior regionalization, or partitioning, of the format and followed by application of the algorithms to samples from each region.

Woolnough (1972) used microdensitometry to evaluate the textural components of muskeg and obtained 92 percent identification with a simple texture measure derived from the microdensitometer data. Maurer (1971) measured the textures of crop fields using a precise scanning microscope photometer and employed a nearest-neighbor probability training and prediction procedure.

DECISION/CLASSIFICATION FUNCTION

After the feature-extraction step is completed (for a subset of the data) the decision rules for discrimination between categories--developed during the feature-extraction phase--are used to place new data into one or another category, or they are placed into a thresholded, nonidentified class.

In qualitative analysis, the decision rules are judgmentally based. They are developed as a series of rules and procedures for handling difficult cases of overlapping categories. In making a land-use map, for example, the development of decision rules is, like the preceeding feature-extraction phase, an iterative process. In the first instance, broad classifications are set up based on the principal classes which are observed in the imagery. An example of this would be the major land-use mapping scheme using aerial photographs developed by Anderson, Hardy, and Roach (1972) and used by the U.S. Geological Survey, Geography Applications Program (GAP), in their land-use mapping. The broad land-use classes so established serve to define the first broad level of interpretation and decision rules. Thereafter, as mapping proceeds, case after case is encountered involving slight variations. Judgments are made and the decisions reached are codified into practice. Thus, in the process of mapping in the Central Atlantic Regional Ecological Test Site (CARETS), GAP has developed an intensive set of documented decision rules necessary to implement in that area the broad categories developed during the "feature-extraction" process by Anderson and his colleagues.

In qualitative mapping such as vegetation and geological mapping, it is rare indeed for the decision rules to be formally structured. Most qualitative interpretation with remote sensing imagery is very much a catch-as-catch-can process, in which after the fact it is very difficult for another interpreter to reconstruct the same material. The highly judgmental basis of the decision rules erected is well shown in comparisons of maps produced by different workers. Thus, one geologist confronted with evidence of faulting may link a group of faults along a line broken by sedimentary fill across valleys, into a single extensive fault. Another more cautious geologist may well leave the same faults as isolated elements and not integrate them into the single larger feature. In another example, two workers mapping natural plant communities may perceive a complex mixed area in quite dissimilar fashion. One may decide to erect a new class composed of a complex mixture of two or more entities, while, even at the same scale of mapping, another worker may prefer to maintain the discrete categories. Thus, continuing problems of lumping and splitting occur when qualitative judgments are made.

Imperfect and qualitative though these judgments are, they are nonetheless decisions; rules for the implementation of these decisions could be structured if necessary. Very frequently, rules are not structured, because most scientists do not wish to subject themselves to the mental discipline required to codify their practices. Another reason is that the amount of time required for codification is very great: the diversity of natural landscapes and systems is so substantial that many boggle at the work involved and retreat.

Where statistical procedures are used, however, the decision rules must be specifically thought through in order that the computer or analog device may implement them on the remaining data. The decision and classification rules then for machine implementation are by definition quantitative and statistical, whereas those used for the human interpreter are judgmental and substantially qualitative--only occasionally are they strictly quantitative.

The decision rules used in quantitative procedures with the computer involve thresholding and choice of decision boundaries.

Selection of a thresholding level is used to produce a null class into which all nonidentified items may be placed. The function of thresholding may best be described by example. If no thresholding is used, then all items presented for classification must be assigned to one or another of the established classes that are developed in the feature-extraction phase. It is rare for all items in an area to be desirable parts of a classification. Thus, using no thresholding produces a large number of errors of commission. Conversely, a high level of thresholding will reject or omit many items which should be classified into one of the selected categories. Thus, the level of thresholding used dictates the proportion of errors of omission and comission. Depending on the problem at hand, it may be desirable to have no thresholding, severe thresholding, or some intermediate level. The choice of the intermediate level--or indeed any level--is dictated by the requirements of the problem and by the distribution in statistical space of the data. The position usually chosen is designed to yield a minimum sum of errors of omission and comission. Examples of thresholding are to be found in every use with the multispectral scanner. The thresholding problem may be treated as part of the general problem of erecting decision surfaces between clouds of data in n-dimensional space, to which we now may turn.

In the feature-extraction process, a variety of statistical procedures may be used in order to find the ones most efficient in errecting boundaries between the delineated classes (using a training set) or the naturally occurring classes (using a clustering algorithm). Different statistical procedures commonly produce results of broadly comparable accuracy. However, they are not all equally parsimonious of computer time. The decision rules then simply are the codification of the location of the boundary values in n-dimensional space between one class and another. In order to reduce the cost of classifying very large data sets simplified procedures such as table look up and the use of one or another of the linear approximations which are simpler and less demanding of computer time than the maximum likelihood function may be used.

OUTPUT OF CLASSIFICATION

As noted earlier, the output from the classification may be given in a variety of forms. The three principal classes of output are tabular, graphical, and map formats. These may be obtained from either manual or computer and analog systems.

Tabular Output. Numerous tabular output forms are possible. A common output is an accuracy of identification matrix giving correct identifications on the diagonals, errors of commission on one axis and errors on omission on the other. This could be derived as the direct result of a point-by-point tabulation of photo interpretation results: (1) from the overlay of a newly interpreted map placed over a previous map and then using a point counting grid, or (2) from cell-by-cell tabulation and comparison in a computer. Directly tabular data is not easily produced from analog equipment, but may be when the equipment is attached to the computer so that the computer outputs the data. Tables may be readily prepared with the computer.

In tabulating errors of omission and commission, this output collapses the fifth and six steps together. This is a common procedure where it is possible to readily verify the results at the time of output.

Graphical Output. Histograms of the frequency of occurrence of a single identified category in the area may be prepared manually. Any comparable graphical plot may be easily produced with the computer, or be readily displayed on a cathode ray tube. It would be photographed to give a permanent record.

Map Output. An interpreted map is probably the most common form of output. This could be either a qualitative, a mixed qualitative - quantitative, or a quantitative map based upon tabulation of statistics.

The list of maps is as endless as the genius of man to devise: single value and multiple category maps; isarithmic (contouring continuous functions); dasymetric (discrete identification of non-continuous distributions); use of absolute values, percentages, ratios, change from one time to another, point and line as well as area formats.

Monochromatic and color television displays are common methods of presenting the final output map, either from an analog or a digital identification system. An alphanumeric output from a digital system is widely employed using a line printer. Several such outputs may be photographed as separation plates and later combined photographically, or in printing, to give a color map. Some installations may have film write-out devices, which use discrete gray steps to map with considerable accuracy the various categories. The geometric fidelity of film write-out devices is now so high that a hybrid digital analog system can produce very accurate output maps. Others may use plotters of various types.

An extended analysis is given in *Geographical Data Handling* (editor, R. F. Tomlinson, 1972, pp. 891-1123) referred to earlier. In this publication details will be found of numerous output devices: printers, plotters, cathode ray tubes, film write out devices, color displays, 3D units, and other equipment used for output. These systems may be used in various ways for graphical and map output.

Verification of Results

Verification of results in a study can be a very informal or a highly structured procedure. A distinct advantage of the more quantitative and structured forms of data extraction in remote sensing is that quantitative verification of results is explicit and frequently carried out by the author. The processes in qualitative mapping or quasi-quantitative mapping, as traditionally carried out by geographers, biologists and geologists, is a much more informal procedure. It is based as much as anything on time (somebody else discovers errors in one's work), reputation (geologist X is known to be a more careful worker than geologist Y), or a qualitative insert map may be placed on a larger map indicating the quality of the data sources and judgments used to prepare the major map. The great advantage of the computer, and the quantitative straightjacket it places around us, is that it forces investigators to face squarely the uncertainties in their output and to examine conscientiously the errors of various types in their work. This attitude is now beginning to permeate much of the previously qualitative work by natural scientists, and a more explicit attempt is being made to quantify results.

REFERENCES

Anderson, J. R., E. E. Hardy, and J. T. Roach, 1972, "A Land Use Classification System for Use with Remote-Sensor Data," *Geological Survey Circular 671*, U.S. Geological Survey, pp. 1-16.

Anuta, P. E., S. J. Kristof, D. W. Levandowski, T. L. Phillips, and R. B. MacDonald, 1971, "Crop, Soil, and Geological Mapping from Digitized Multispectral Satellite Photography," *Proceedings of the Seventh International Symposium on Remote Sensing of Environment*, vol. III, University of Michigan, Institute of Science and Technology, Ann Arbor, pp. 1983-2016.

Bakis, R., M. A. Wesley, and P. M. Will, 1971, "Digital Correction of Geometric and Radiometric Errors in ERTS Data," *Proceedings of the Seventh International Symposium on Remote Sensing of Environment*, vol. II, University of Michigan, Institute of Science and Technology, Ann Arbor, pp. 1427-1436.

Bond, A. D., and R. J. Atkinson, 1972, "An Integrated Feature Selection and Supervised Learning Scheme for Fast Computer Classification of Multispectral Data," in R. Shahrokhi, Ed., *Remote Sensing of Earth Resources*, vol. I, University of Tennessee, Tullahoma, pp. 645-672.

Brooner, W. G., R. M. Haralick, and Its'hak Dinstein, 1971, "Spectral Parameters Affecting Automated Image Interpretation Using Bayestian Probability Techniques," *Proceedings of the Seventh International Symposium on Remote Sensing of Environment*, vol. III, University of Michigan, Institute of Science and Technology, Ann Arbor, pp. 1929-1949.

Brooner, W. G., and D. S. Simonett, 1971, "Crop Discrimination with Color Infrared Photography," *Remote Sensing of Environment*, 2(1):21-35.

Brown, W. L., 1972, "Reducing Variance in Remotely Sensed Multispectral Data--A Pragmatic Approach," in F. Shahrokhi, Ed., *Remote Sensing of Earth Resources*, vol. I, University of Tennessee, Tullahoma, pp. 525-537.

Brown, W. L., F. C. Polcyn, and S. R. Stewart, 1971, "A Method for Calculating Water Depth, Attenuation Coefficients and Bottom Reflectance Characteristics," *Proceedings of the Seventh International Symposium on Remote Sensing of Environment*, vol. I, University of Michigan, Institute of Science and Technology, Ann Arbor, pp. 663-682.

Ciesla, W. M., L. E. Drake, and D. H. Wilmore, 1972, "Color Photos,Aerial Sprays and the Forest Tent Caterpillar," *Photogrammetric Engineering*, 38(8):867-873.

Crane, R. B., 1971, "Preprocessing Techniques to Reduce Atmospheric and Sensor Variability in Multispectral Scanner Data," *Proceedings of the Seventh International Symposium on Remote Sensing of Environment*, vol. II, University of Michigan, Institute of Science and Technology, Ann Arbor, pp. 1345-1355.

Crane, R. B., and W. Richardson, 1972, "Rapid Processing of Multispectral Scanner Data Using Linear Techniques," *Remote Sensing of Earth Resources*, vol. I, F. Shahrokhi, Ed., University of Tennessee, Tullahoma, pp. 581-595.

Eppler, W. G., C. A. Helmke, and R. H. Evans, 1971, "Table Look-up Approach to Pattern Recognition," *Proceedings of the Seventh International Symposium on Remote Sensing of Environment*, vol. II, University of Michigan, Institute of Science and Technology, Ann Arbor, pp. 1415-1425.

Eppler, W. G., D. L. Loe, and E. L. Wilson, 1971, "Interactive Displays/Graphics Systems for Remote Sensor Data Analysis," *Proceedings of the Seventh International Symposium on Remote Sensing of Environment*, vol. II, University of Michigan, Institute of Science and Technology, Ann Arbor, pp. 1293-1306.

Estes, J., and L. W. Senger, 1971, "An Electronic Multi-Image Processor, *Photogrammetric Engineering*, 37(6):577-586.

Frazee, C. J., V. I. Myers, and F. C. Westin, 1971, "Remote Sensing for Detection of Soil Limitations in Agricultural Areas," *Proceedings of the Seventh International Symposium on Remote Sensing of Environment*, vol I, University of Michigan, Institute of Science and Technology, Ann Arbor, pp. 327-343.

Fu, K. S., 1971, *On the Applications of Pattern Recognition Techniques to Remote Sensing Problems*, Technical Report EE 71-13, School of Electrical Engineering, Purdue University, Lafayette, Indiana.

Fu, K. S., D. A Landgrebe, and T. L. Phillips, 1969, "Information Processing of Remotely Sensed Agricultural Data," *Proceedings I.E.E.E.*, 57(4):639-653.

Haralick, R. M., 1971, "On a Texture-Content Feature Extraction Algorithm for Remotely Sensed Imagery," *Proceedings of the I.E.E.E. Conference on Decision and Control*, pp. 650-657.

Haralick, R. M., F. Caspall, and D. S. Simonett, 1970, "Using Radar Imagery for Crop Discrimination: A Statistical and Conditional Probability Study," *Remote Sensing of Environment*, 1(1):131-142.

Haralick, R. M., and D. E. Anderson, 1971, *Texture-Tone Study with Application to Digitized Imagery*, Technical Report 182-2, University of Kansas, Remote Sensing Laboratory, Lawrence, pp. 1-146.

Helbig, M. S., 1972, "Investigation of Color Detail, Color Analysis and False-Color Representation in Satellite Photographs," in F. Shahrokhi, Ed., *Remote Sensing of Earth Resources*, vol. I, University of Tennessee, Tullahoma, pp. 274-292.

Higgins, J. L., and E. S. Deutsch, 1972, "The Effects of Picture Operations in the Fourier Domain and Vice Versa," in F. Shahrokhi, *Remote Sensing of Earth Resources*, vol. I, University of Tennessee, Tullahoma, pp. 460-480.

Hoffer, R. M., and F. E. Goodrick, 1971, "Variables in Automatic Classification over Extended Remote Sensing Test Sites," *Proceedings of the Seventh International Symposium on Remote Sensing of Environment*, vol. III, University of Michigan, Institute of Science and Technology, Ann Arbor, pp. 1967-1981.

Hord, R. M., and N. Gramenopoulos, 1971, "Automatic Terrain Classification From Photography," *Processing SPIE Symposium on Remote Sensing of Earth Resources and the Environment*, Palo Alto, California.

Hord, R. M. and N. Gramenopoulos, 1973, "Boundary Detection and Regionalized Terrain Classification from Photography," Electronic Industry Association Committee on Automatic Imagery Pattern Recognition, Washington, D.C., Symposium.

James, W., and F. J. Burgess. 1970, "Ocean Outfall Depression," *Photogrammetric Engineering*, 36(12):1241-1250.

Kaizer, M., 1955, *A Quantification of Textures on Aerial Photographs*, Technical Note 121, AD 69484, Boston University Research Laboratories, pp. 1-33.

Lent, J. D., and G. A. Thorley, 1969, "Some Observations on the Use of Multiband Spectral Reconnaissance for the Invention of Wildland Resources," *Remote Sensing of Environment*, 1(1):31-46.

Marshall, R. E., and F. J. Kriegler, 1971, "An Operational Multispectral Surveys System," *Proceedings of the Seventh International Symposium on Remote Sensing of Environment*, vol. III, University of Michigan, Institute of Science and Technology, Ann Arbor, pp. 2169-2191.

Maurer, H., 1971, "Measurement of Textures of Crop Fields with the Zeiss-Scanning-Microscope-Photometer 05," *Proceedings of the Seventh International Symposium on Remote Sensing of Envirorment*, vol. III, University of Michigan, Institute of Science and Technology, Ann Arbor, pp. 2329-2342.

Morain, S. A., and D. S. Simonett, 1967, "K-Band Radar in Vegetation Mapping," *Photogrammetric Engineering*, vol. 33, pp. 730-740.

Mullens, R. H., 1969, "Analysis of Urban Residential Environments Using Color Infrared Aerial Photography: An Examination of Socioeconomic Variables and Physical Characteristics of Selected Areas in Los Angeles Basin," in *Studies in Remote Sensing of Southern California and Related Environments*, Technical Report 4, U.S. Department of the Interior, Contract 14-08-0001-10674.

Myers, V. I., et al., 1970, "Soil, Water, and Plant Relations," chapter 6 in *Remote Sensing*, National Academy of Sciences, pp. 253-297.

Nagy, E., G. Shelton, and J. Tolaba, "Procedural Questions in Signature Analysis," *Proceedings of the Seventh International Symposium on Remote Sensing of Environment,* vol. II, University of Michigan, Institute of Science and Technology, Ann Arbor, pp. 1387-1401.

Nalepka, R., 1970, "Investigation of Multispectral Discrimination Techniques," Report No. 2264-12-F, Willow Run Laboratories, *Institute of Science and Technology,* University of Michigan, Ann Arbor.

Nunnally, N. R., 1969, "Integrated Landscape Analysis with Radar Imagery," *Remote Sensing of Environment,* 1(1):1-6.

Palgen, J. J. O., 1970, "Applicability of Pattern Recognition Techniques to the Analysis of Urban Quality from Satellites," *Pattern Recognition,* 2:255-260.

Pestrong, R., 1969, "Multiband Photos for a Tidal March," *Photogrammetric Engineering,* 35(5):453-470.

Peterson, R. M., G. R. Cochrane, S. A. Morain, and D. S. Simonett, 1969, "A Multisensor Study of Plant Community Densities and Boundaries at Horsefly Mountain, Oregon," *Remote Sensing in Biology,* P. L. Johnson, Ed., University of Georgia Press, pp. 63-94.

Ramapriyan, H. K., 1972, "Spatial Frequency Analysis of Multispectral Data," in F. Shahrokhi, Ed., *Remote Sensing of Earth Resources,* vol. I, University of Tennessee, Tullahoma, pp. 621-644.

Ranz, E., and S. Schneider, 1971, "Progress in the Application of Agfacontour Equidensity Film for Geo-Scientific Photo Interpretation," *Proceedings of the Seventh International Symposium on Remote Sensing of Environment,* vol. III, University of Michigan, Institute of Science and Technology, Ann Arbor, pp. 779-790.

Richardson, A. J., R. J. Torline, and W. A. Allen, 1971, "Computer Identification of Ground Pattern from Aerial Photographs," *Proceedings of the Seventh International Symposium on Remote Sensing of Environment,* vol. II, University of Michigan, Institute of Science and Technology, Ann Arbor, pp. 1357-1376.

Rosenfeld, A., 1962, "Automatic Recognition of Basic Terrain Types from Aerial Photographs," *Photogrammetric Engineering,* 28(2):115-132.

Roth, C. B., and M. F. Baumgardner, 1971, "Correlation Studies with Ground Truth and Multispectral Data: Effect of Size of Training Field," *Proceedings of the Seventh International Symposium on Remote Sensing of Environment,* vol. II, University of Michigan, Institute of Science and Technology, Ann Arbor, pp. 1403-1414.

Simonett, D. S., and D. A. Brown, 1965, "Possible Uses of Radar on Spacecraft in Contributing to Antarctic Mapping, Crevasse, Sea Ice, and Mass Budget Studies," *CRES Technical Report 61-4,* Center for Research in Engineering Science, the University of Kansas, Lawrence, pp. 1-18.

Simonett, D. S., J. Eagleman, A. Erhard, D. Rhodes, and D. Schwarz, 1967, "The Potential of Radar as a Remote Sensor of Agricultural Crops: 1. A Study with K-Band Imagery in Western Kansas," *CRES Technical Report 21-61*, Center for Research in Engineering Science, the University of Kansas, Lawrence, pp. 1-24.

Smedes, H. W., 1971, "Automatic Computer Mapping of Terrain," *Proceedings of the International Workshop on Earth Resources Survey Systems*, vol. II, University of Michigan, Ann Arbor, pp. 344-406.

Smedes, H. W., H. J. Linnerud, L. B. Woolaver, and S. J. Hawks, 1971, "Digital Computer Mapping of Terrain by Clustering Techniques Using Color Film as a Three-Band Sensor," *Proceedings of the Seventh International Symposium on Remote Sensing of Environment*, vol. III, University of Michigan, Institute of Science and Technology, Ann Arbor, pp. 2073-2094.

Steiner, D., 1970, "Time Dimension for Crop Surveys from Space," *Photogrammetric Engineering*, 36(2):187-194.

Steiner, D., et al., 1972, "Automatic Processing and Classification of Remote Sensing Data," Chapter 3 in R. F. Tomlinson, Ed., *Geographical Data Handling*, Symposium Edition, Second Symposium on Geographical Information Systems, I.G.U., Ottawa, August.

Steiner, D., and H. Maurer, 1969, "The Use of Stereo-Height as a Discriminating Variable for Crop Classification on Aerial Photographs," *Photogrammetria*, 24: 223-241.

Su, M. Y., R. R. Jayroe, and R. E. Cummings, 1972, "Unsupervised Classification of Earth Resources Data," in F. Shahrokhi, Ed., *Remote Sensing of Earth Resources*, vol. I, University of Tennessee, Tullahoma, pp. 673-694.

Tryon, R. C., and D. E. Bailey, 1970, *Cluster Analysis*, McGraw-Hill Book Co., New York.

Turner, B. J., 1972, "Cluster Analysis of Multispectral Scanner Remote Sensor Data," in F. Shahrokhi, Ed., *Remote Sensing of Earth Resources*, vol. I, University of Tennessee, Tullahoma, pp. 538-549.

Viglione, S. S., 1970, "Applications of Pattern Recognition Technology," Chapter 4 in *Adaptive, Learning, and Pattern Recognition Systems*, Academic Press, Inc., New York.

Weber, F. P., and F. C. Polcyn, 1971, "Remote Sensing with Optical-Mechanical Line Scanners to Detect Stress in Forests," *Proceedings of the Thiry-seventh Annual Meeting of the American Society of Photogrammetry*, Washington, D.C., pp. 123-152.

Woolnough, D. F., 1972, "Automatic Recognition of Muskeg from Aerial Photographs," *Photogrammetria*, 28(1):17-25.

Remote Sensing of Natural Resources

Robert D. Rudd
University of Denver

The natural environment represents a complex set of interrelationships among phenomena such as flora, fauna, landforms, geologic structure, atmospherics, etc. These phenomena interact to form ecosystems at various scales that define the surface and subsurface character of the earth. From man's viewpoint, these phenomena not only constitute the nature of earth habitats and physical setting for human lifestyles, but are the renewable and nonrenewable finite resource base for human activity. Remote sensing is envisaged as a data source for inventorying, monitoring, and gaining new insights into the complexity of the natural environment. Specific attention is focused in this chapter on an overview of remote sensing research in the lithosphere, atmosphere, hydrosphere, and biosphere. Fuller treatments are accorded geology-geomorphology and vegetation in subsequent chapters, since these are the components of the natural environment that have received the greatest attention in remote sensing research.

For a long time man's investigation of his natural environment was prompted by curiosity. To be sure, some inquiry had direct economic considerations as its motive, but much was fundamentally oriented simply toward a better understanding of the physical setting. Increasingly over the past several decades, however, an element of necessity has manifested itself. As man's numbers have increased and tentative efforts to control the increase have met with little success, concerned attempts to evaluate and reevaluate his resource base have been made. Despite the inadequacy of these assessments, a sobering awareness of the finiteness of resources, even the air we breathe, has emerged. In addition, we see piecemeal evidence of our ability to alter the environment ever more completely and more rapidly. The effects, in any total sense, are little known. The need for a more ordered use is very clear, however. We also are reminded periodically of the modest understanding and lack of control we have of natural forces, as atmospheric and tectonic activity continue to take their toll of life and property. A prerequisite to effective action on any of these matters is an improved data base. We need more complete and detailed observation of natural phenomena, in order to be able to monitor the environment more thoroughly, detect change, and more carefully inventory our resource base.

Although our knowledge about the physical environment has increased impressively in recent times, the increase has served to produce a greater awareness of how spotty the information we have really is. Despite existence of continental or world maps of vegetation with few or no blank spaces, the nature of the categories mapped and the scale of the maps reveal that they are generalizations. Enormous areas on most continents lack detailed, accurate vegetation maps. Similarly, although the areal geology of some parts of the world has been mapped in great detail, other areas are known only superficially. Moreover, mapping of the known parts extends over several generations, along with substantial differences in procedure, theory, and equipment. The circulation of the earth's atmosphere and the world's water balance are markedly affected by proportional changes in the areal extent of ice and water in the Arctic. During summer melt, great changes in albedo can occur relatively rapidly, and the mean areal extent of ice is believed to fluctuate 10 percent or more. Yet we have only the sketchiest picture of the temporal and spatial variations of snow cover north of the Arctic circle (Campbell, 1971). A glance at a map of weather stations in the 48 coterminous states, or in some European nations, is reassuring, albeit misleading. The causes of weather variation are global. A world map of continental weather stations is discouraging, and one showing only the oceans is something else! To be sure, there are ship and aircraft reports from ocean areas, but these are far fewer than from land stations in spite of the world's preponderately watery surface. Upper-air data are especially sparse; only recently the entire tropical Pacific was represented by eight rawinsonde stations (Cooley, 1971). Great strides in energy-mass budget studies and modeling offer encouraging prospects for hydrology and meteorology advancements, but such studies require types of data that have only recently begun to be collected. Our data base of the natural environment is indeed inadequate.

The application of remote sensing techniques to such problems may make possible a form of quantum jump in data acquisition. Although they will operate in conjunction with, rather than in place of, more conventional procedures, they indicate a potential that is startling. But the task of gathering the required data is immense. Basically there is the need simply for current spatial coverage. The type and scale of imagery which is satisfactory for one task, however, will be unsatisfactory for many others. Some studies in fact indicate that the most effective, as well as most efficient, analysis requires several scales and complementary forms of data. Add to this the need for greater temporal coverage (seasonal, daily, etc.), and potential data quantity needs begin to assume astronomical proportions. Such quantities of data will be welcome, but as they become available their utilization will pose a challenge. The computer and other forms of electronics have been turned to with encouraging success in appropriate circumstances (see Chapter 3). Automated scanning devices are capable of recognition of some features where signature parameters can be adequately employed, or tapes can be read and print-out maps have been produced of a variety of subjects. For the present, however, automated analysis may best serve in a role similar to one that small-scale imagery can play especially well, that of indicating where closer inspection is needed to permit the interpreter to maximize his contribution. Combination of the speed of automated analysis and the superior flexibility of the skilled human interpreter could make manageable the flood of data which we need and which is in prospect.

Regardless of the degree of success achieved with automation techniques, the spatial and temporal dimensions of the task ahead will require the effort of a substantial number of scientists. Aside from those whose specialty is the hardware used to collect the data, representatives of all of the sciences, especially the earth sciences, will be needed. There are several aspects of this work that should have special appeal for geographers. Much of the work to be done will involve the inventory of extensive areas and will employ small-scale imagery. Small-scale images of the earth's surface should be at least as familiar to geographers as to other earth scientists. The imagery will depict the several aspects of environment as they exist in nature: interrelated. The significance of interrelationships among the several components of the environment, and the environment and man, in a spatial context is a familiar theme to most geographers. Finally, areal inventory of physical features involves typology, classification, regionalization, and cartographic expression, topics on which geographers have written at great length. The point is not whether geographers are better equipped than others to do such work; it is simply that they should have the background to also contribute. Some already have, as have representatives of most other disciplines, and the preliminary phase of an exhaustive survey of the earth's resources with the aid of remote sensing is under way. In many of the cases cited below, only an indication of potential is offered, and some of them will be found later to have been misleading. Remote sensing application to most fields is in the embryonic stage. The studies referred to range over most of the natural sciences, although coverage is far from complete. Their purpose is to indicate the variety of applications these techniques may serve.

The Lithosphere

Depending on how one defines it, remote sensing in some form has been used by earth scientists for a long time. Geologists, for example, employ seismographs, Geiger counters, and magnetometers routinely. Even in the somewhat more restricted use of the term "remote sensing" employed in this volume, the long-standing importance of the conventional air photo is well enough documented that it need not be elaborated here. As the newer or more sophisticated sensors and imagery forms became available, students of surface form, structure, and lithology began testing their utility. The all-weather, day-or-night capability of imaging radar made it an obvious choice for aerial mapping of some areas which had frustrated earlier attempts owing to inclement weather. Perhaps one of the best-known efforts was the one in Panama (MacDonald, 1969), and the revision of then current but inaccurate maps of parts of that area was the focus of many articles and news briefs. While imaging radar is not without its shortcomings, this success holds promise for the many parts of the world where, for similar reasons, maps of uncertain quality now constitute the only maps.

As the first conventional photos taken by astronauts became available, students of landforms and structure were among the most delighted with the choice of targets. The same climatological factors, which made many of them so photogenically cloudless, contributed to the dearth of masking vegetation and overburden, leaving structures and major lithologic differences boldly exposed. But perhaps more important was the fact that the entire structure, as well as it relation to adjoining areas, was there on one image. There was no need for concern about the cause for tonal differences from place to place, such as those which obscure relationships on most conventional photo mosaics. To the student of world structural patterns, the shortcomings of scale in a satellite photo of the Pamirs may be compensated by improved access to the area.

The study of structural relationships has benefited in several ways from the use of remote sensing. Orbital imagery depicting extensive areas on a single photo enhances the detection and tracing of discontinuous features. Some features, seemingly unimportant or simply puzzling when viewed in a limited perspective, fall into place in a broader view--in fact, may contribute to it. Study of Apollo 9 photos taken over Ethiopia revealed the presence of a large exposure of basement rocks in an area previously mapped as being basalt. In addition, a number of large shear faults unidentifiable as such on aerial photos were detectable. Analysis of the structural relations of the area in the light of the new information provides the basis for a new hypothesis of plate tectonics in the Red Sea region (Bannert, 1971).

The striking visibility of faults and joints, orthogonal (or nearly so) to the look-direction of imaging radar, is attested to in numerous studies. A study employing X-band radar notes that other lineaments, such as bedding or layering, and contacts between dissimilar lithologic units also are detectable (Page, 1969). The fact that some radar imagery exhibits nongeologic lineaments as well or better, notably tree lines and cultural features (Wise, 1967), only reemphasizes the basic need for ground checks in all remote sensing. That radiometric temperature differences among rock units and the surface materials can be used to identify structures is illustrated by a study describing the discovery of a faulted plunging anticline, undetectable on conventional photography or in the field. "We could have walked across the anticline without recognizing it, for there were no conspicuous lithologic or topographic patterns" (Sabins, 1969). Radiometric temperature differences between the various materials at night were apparently greater than daytime differences in light reflectance (Figures 4-1 and 4-2).

Differences in infrared (IR) radiance of some rocks and minerals in the 3-to-5-um and 8-to-14-um bands offer possibilities for the use of IR scanners in mineral exploration and areal geology mapping as well as structure detection. With the day-or-night capability of IR sensing, studies of both situations have been made to see what differences appear. In a number of instances, early-morning imagery has been found especially useful in distinguishing between similar rock types, for example, limestone and dolomite (Rowan et al., 1969). At other times of day, distinction between the two was more difficult or impossible at this site. Some discrimination among gross rock type classes (i.e., sedimentary versus igneous) based on radar imagery has been reported, but commonly some surrogate such as surface-form characteristics, visible on conventional photography, constitutes the basis. The use of a Fraunhofer line discriminator (Hemphill, 1969) to detect solar-excited luminescing minerals, of emissivity minima in thermal IR bands (Vincent and Thomson, 1971), and laser-induced luminescence (active Fraunhofer line discriminators) for materials that do not ordinarily luminesce (Gross and Hyatt, 1971) have been suggested also as aids to rock-type and mineral identification. In fact, the task is a difficult one, and most efforts are still in the pioneering stage. Gross distinctions based on more conventional signature parameters can be used, however, and will aid in surveys of little-known areas and to identify major rock-unit boundaries until more research has pinpointed signatures and limiting conditions.

A chief problem with mapping areal geology by remote sensing is the presence of vegetation and overburden which masks or contributes to the lithologic sensor signal. This "noise," unwanted ordinarily by the geologist, is useful to the student of vegetation or soils. Some geologists, however, have found that there are situations in which what appeared to be a liability can be made an

Figure 4-1. Conventional photography (left) and thermal IR scanner imagery of the same area in California. (The two were not obtained in the same year, however.) After Sabins, 1969.

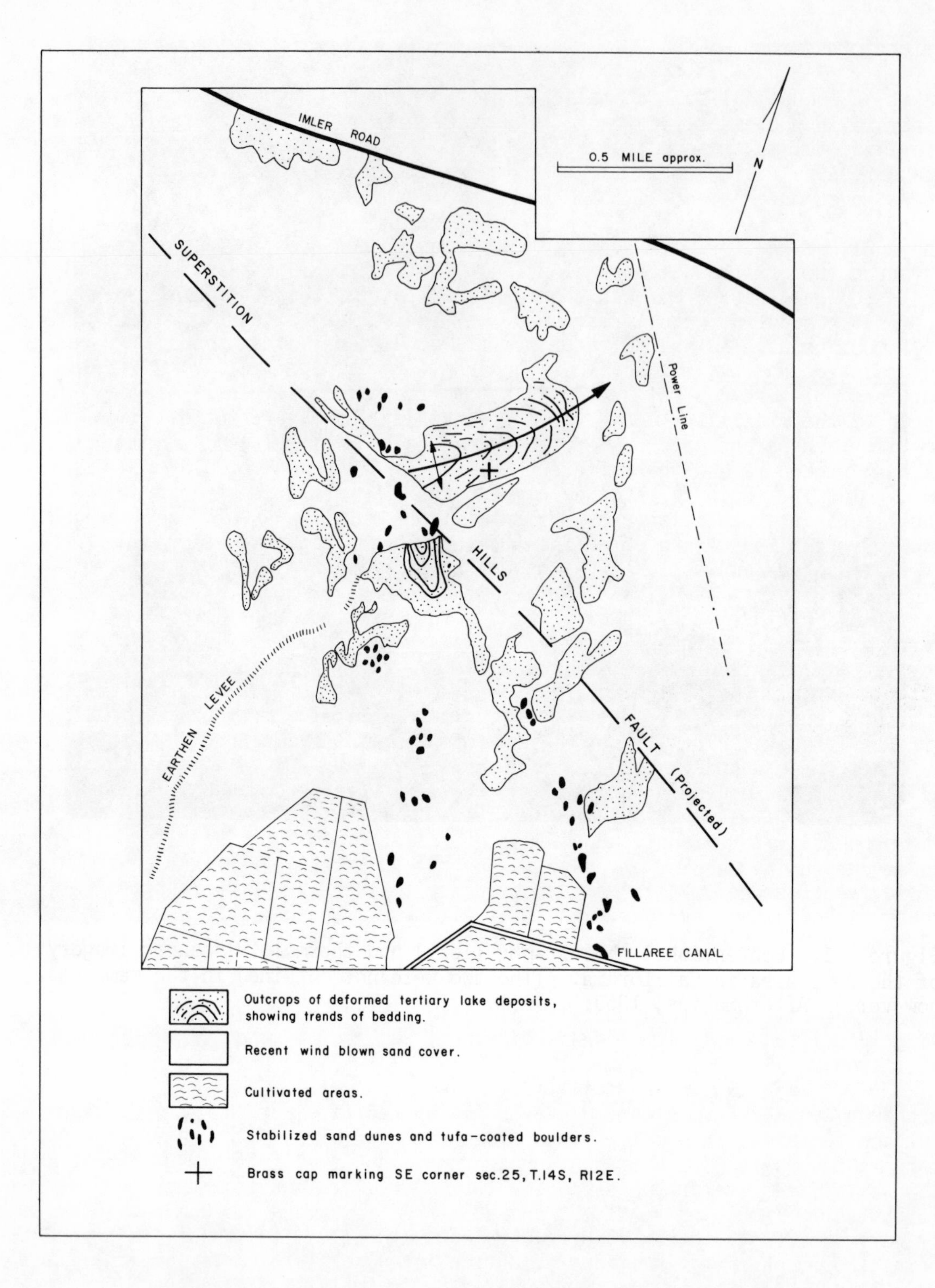

Figure 4-2. Geologic interpretation of IR scanner imagery in Figure 4-1. After Sabins, 1969, p. 402.

asset. Geochemical soil anomalies, believed due to unusual concentrations of minerals in the underlying bedrock, have been found to be detectable by spectroradiometer in the spectral reflectance data from trees growing on the site (Canney, 1969). The trees then become indicators (geobotanical indicators) of zones which have potential for mineral exploration.

The application of remote sensing techniques to the study of soils per se also is advancing. Although conventional air photos have long been fundamental to soil studies, they have their shortcomings. Direct observation of the soil is commonly prevented by the presence of vegetation, and often the vegetation itself must be used as an indicator of soil conditions; other surrogates, such as drainage density, surface form, and photo tones, are indicators of soil texture and moisture conditions. In a study (Frazee et al., 1971) seeking evidence of the proximity to the surface of a clay pan layer, optical densities on film transparencies (tonal differences) have been isolated by a density-slicing procedure and the different density levels coded to color for display on a color TV. Such color enhancement points up subtle tonal differences which facilitate interpretation. Experiments with several bands of long-wavelength radar systems indicate a potential for texture and moisture discrimination in vegetated areas as well as areas of essentially bare soil. The strength of signal return in a given band varies with grain size, and a multiband analysis utilizing multifrequency radar returns may suggest the spatial pattern of texture variation (Morain and Campbell, 1972). The possibility of greater accuracy in determination of soil-surface moisture conditions through the use of a polarimeter also is indicated (Stockhoff and Frost, 1971). Polarization of reflected sunlight is known to be a sensitive indicator of surface-soil moisture. Although the utility of such information to agriculture is perhaps most evident, those who have tried to map soils utilizing hue as a parameter will be aware of how useful a knowledge of the soil wetness could be.

The propensity for visual enhancement of relief by imaging radar is well known to anyone who has looked at radar imagery of an irregular surface. Students of surface form have utilized this property to identify landform provinces, categorize drainage systems, and infer lithology from differences in texture signatures. Success in automated computer mapping of terrain types through the digital processing of multispectral scanner imagery has been achieved in a 12-square-mile area flown at 6,000 feet. Bedrock exposures, talus, vegetated rock rubble, glacial kame terrace, glacial till, forest, bog, water, and shadows were identified with better than 80 percent accuracy by the system (Smedes et al., 1969).

Although weather-satellite imagery is not appropriate for the study of many surface features, it should not be discounted for all. Such imagery may not compare favorably with astronaut photography, but that from NIMBUS, ESSA, and ITOS satellites is markedly superior to imagery obtained from the TIROS series in the early 1960s. Some NIMBUS and ESSA AVCS (advanced vidicon camera system) imagery depicts the earth's surface remarkably well. Studies of drainage patterns, geomorphic province identification, structural features, and the like, have been based on such imagery (Sabatini et al., 1971). As a trade for resolution quality, continuous coverage is offered, prompting studies seeking evidence of change. Indication of soil erosion; coastal sedimentation; changes in directional orientation and spatial distribution of sand dune fields; and, with the infrared data from some satellites, monitoring of volcanic activity are examples of some of the studies that have used weather-satellite information. Others include monitoring lake conditions, identifying natural vegetation macro boundaries, comparative terrain classifications, changes in coastal morphology, and numerous types of oceanographic studies.

The Atmosphere

Applications of remote sensing techniques to studies of the atmosphere are so numerous, and the practice so relatively long-standing, that this topic requires different treatment. Although all the data available are not being used with greatest effectiveness yet and some sensing systems are still experimental, routine operational use of some remotely sensed atmospheric information has been with us for a number of years now. Five families of U.S. meteorological satellites have been launched, and each family includes several members.

TIROS-1 was launched in 1960 and provided the first global cloud-cover photos, although some cloud-cover pictures were obtained from Explorer 6 in 1959. There were ten members of the TIROS family, the last being launched in 1965. These satellites, in addition to providing data for research and some application to weather analysis, established the feasibility of an operational weather-satellite system whose principal purpose would be to supply data for weather-service daily needs. The ESSA series which followed serves that purpose; ESSA-1 was launched in 1966 and ESSA-8 and ESSA-9 in 1968 and 1969, respectively. ESSA satellites, called TOS satellites (for TIROS operational system), operate in pairs; one has AVCS (advanced vidicon camera system) equipment and the other APT (automatic picture transmission) capability. AVCS equipment collects and stores global data, transmitting the data on command to a few U.S. receiving stations. The APT system transmits continuously and may be received by anyone having the relatively inexpensive receivers (Vermillion, 1968); more than 500 such receivers in some 90 countries and trust territories avail themselves of these data. AVCS imagery typically has resolution superior to that of APT imagery. The ESSA satellites have a polar orbit and thus can scan the entire globe.

In January 1970, NASA (National Aeronautics and Space Administration) launched the prototype of a new series, ITOS-1 (Improved TIROS Operational Satellite). It had a circular, near-polar orbit at an altitude of 790 nautical miles. The orbit was sun-synchronous, and the satellite furnished day-and-night full global coverage daily. NOAA-1 (National Oceanic and Atmospheric Administration), the first operational satellite of this type, was launched in December of that year. The ITOS satellite, in addition to several TV cameras, has several radiometers, one of which provides IR data in real time. These DRIR (direct readout infrared) data can be displayed on a photofacsimile recorder as an IR image of the area shown. IR data also may be stored on board for later transmission to the ground. The capability of the scanner plus orbital motion afford IR total earth coverage in 12 hours (Rao et al., 1971). Although the ITOS spacecraft encountered difficulties in 1971, this new series promises substantial advances in data quality.

There are two other families of U.S. weather satellites, NIMBUS and ATS (the U.S.S.R. also has operational weather satellites, the METEOR series being analogous to our ESSA series). NIMBUS satellites are NASA research satellites as opposed to NESS (National Environmental Satellite Service) satellites, such as ESSA and NOAA, which are operational satellites providing data for such NOAA subelements as the Environmental Data Service. While information obtained from early NIMBUS satellites was useful in the development of subsequent operational weather satellites, NIMBUS-3 had a specific meteorological research assignment: to obtain data for the determination of the earth's heat budget and atmospheric structure. NIMBUS-1 was launched in August of 1964, NIMBUS-4 in 1970, and NIMBUS-5 in 1972.

NIMBUS satellites, being experimental and research satellites, carry more sensor systems than operational weather satellites; NIMBUS-4 has ten. A listing of the sensors on that satellite may be instructive as an example. The image dissector camera system (IDCS) provides photo imagery of the earth similar to that produced by the APT or AVCS cameras in other satellites. The temperature humidity infrared radiometer (THIR) constitutes a double package, since the scanner operates in two channels. One provides cloud-top or earth-surface temperatures, the other water-vapor-content data for the upper troposphere and stratosphere. A satellite infrared spectrometer (SIRS) obtains radiation data for use in determining vertical temperature structure and water-vapor content for the atmosphere. The monitor of ultraviolet solar radiation (MUSE) measures variation in solar flux, solar flux being a cause for ozone formation and heating of the stratosphere. The filter wedge spectrometer (FWS) monitors the vertical water-vapor content in the atmosphere under the orbital path, while the backscatter ultraviolet spectrometer (BUV) monitors the global distribution of ozone for energy-balance and mass-exchange studies. The infrared interferometer spectrometer (IRIS) measures radiation from the earth-atmosphere system for computation of atmospheric and surface temperatures. The interrogation, recording, and location system (IRLS) constitutes a completely different type of sensor. It interrogates position fixes and collects geophysical data from a variety of types of stationary or moving instrumented platforms throughout the world, including constant-level balloons. These data are then retransmitted from the satellite to command and data acquisition stations on earth. Lastly, the selective chopper radiometer (SCR) obtains the temperature of six layers of the atmosphere to provide a more complete atmospheric structure model. The satellite has direct readout capability of IDCS data, and some IR data. Earlier NIMBUS models had fewer sensors, but even NIMBUS-1 had four (Sabatini et al., 1971).

The Applications Technology Satellites (ATS) are also NASA research and development satellites, but these are geostationary satellites positioned more than 20,000 miles from earth--that is, they will remain over the same geographical location with only minor correction commands being occasionally necessary. ATS satellites employ spin scan cloud cameras to obtain an image of the full earth disc (Figure 4-3). ATS-1 provides black-and-white imagery, while ATS-3 provides color imagery (ATS-2 malfunctioned). The imagery from these satellites has very low resolution (2 nautical miles at the satellite subpoint for ATS-3), but it has two notable meteorological uses: upper-air wind calculations based on cloud movements and monitoring of storm development as evidenced by cloud patterns. The satellite scans the full earth disc in about 25 minutes, and combining a number of these images makes it possible to obtain an animated view of cloud movement and storm-system development. Although the satellite normally is geostationary, it is capable of being moved for improved vision of a particular portion of the earth. In 1971, it was positioned for the most favorable view of the midcontinental United States during the severe storm period of the spring, and then was moved toward hurricane areas for late summer and early fall (U.S. Executive Office(President's Report), 1972).

NASA ATS III MSSCC 18 NOV 67 153255Z SSP 49.16°W 0.03°S ALT 22240.59 SM

Figure 4-3.

The purpose of the foregoing descriptions is to emphasize the variety and quantity of weather-satellite remote sensing data which exist. TIROS-1 alone provided almost 23,000 photos; and, while the resolution on the imagery of the earliest satellites is admittedly poor, there are tens of thousands of images from ESSA and NIMBUS satellites, not to mention the thousands of hours of THIR, IRIS, SIRS, BUV, etcl, data from NIMBUS satellites (Table 4-1). Resolution on weather-satellite imagery cannot be expected to match that of astronaut photography; it was never intended to and it comes from higher altitudes. Those who have seen only a few, and perhaps poor, samples may be misled about its possibilities. Some of the ESSA and NIMBUS AVCS imagery shows major surface features well; NIMBUS-1, which failed to achieve the intended circular orbit, produced AVCS imagery at perigee with 330-meter resolution. To attempt to use this imagery for detailed mapping or study would be to misuse it; however, high-latitude coverage and repetitive-temporal consideration constitute trade-offs for resolution.

It is interesting to see how the factor of resolution as a problem can be diminished in some circumstances. In a study in which relative change in sun-reflected radiation over Los Angeles, as measured by ATS-3 green-channel data, was compared with ground-based reflectometer measurements of sampled particulate matter and horizontal visibility data, a strong correlation was observed (McLellan, 1971). ATS-3 was 35,000 kilometers from Los Angeles at the time. Resolution requirements need to be considered carefully (as discussed in Chapter 2), since various factors such as great linear dimension, intuitive association possibilities, and sharp tonal contrast may offset resolution limitations per se. Thermal phenomena associated with vulcanism, smaller than the normal resolution element of a system, are commonly detectable on IR imagery, for example.

The nature of atmospheric studies employing weather-satellite data may seem to be covered by the identification of sensors some of the satellites carry. In fact, much of the data/imagery has multiple utility, and additional uses continually are being found. For example, NIMBUS and ESSA imagery provide a basis for monitoring areal extent of snow cover, although the intended target for the camera is cloud cover. Combination of snow-cover areal data and ground reports of water equivalent provides the basis for improved river and flood forecasts. The basic goal of the remote sensing programs in meteorology, however, is nothing less than making the data coverage of the atmosphere, and of anything which affects it, as complete as is humanly possible. Operating with phenomena for which scale considerations range from a few hundreds of meters to thousands of kilometers (Cooley, 1971) and needing to have knowledge not only of the entire atmosphere but also the surface below it as well as extraterrestrial influences, it is clear that establishing more and more conventional weather stations will never do the job. Remote sensors which provide areal rather than point coverage of various parameters are especially appealing in this connection. Also appealing are the continuous real-time capability and the ability to sense at the top, in the middle, or at the bottom of the atmosphere that remote sensors and their platforms promise.

The size and importance of the task ahead in atmospheric science was recognized some time ago; United Nations resolutions in 1961 and 1962 were the basis for the creation of the World Weather Program (WWP) (Zavos, 1971). The World Weather Watch, the operational portion of WWP, was implemented in 1968, and the second four-year phase began in 1972. A related research effort was launched as the Global Atmospheric Research Program (GARP), a major international cooperative

TABLE 4-1. NIMBUS DATA COLLECTION FIGURES

NIMBUS 1	(Launch - 28 August 1964)
AVCS	11,600 pictures
APT	2,000 pictures
HRIR	100 hours
NIMBUS 2	**(Launch - 15 May 1966)**
AVCS	114,003 pictures
APT	148,810 pictures
HRIR	2,190 hours
MRIR	1,313 hours
DRIR	1,370 hours
NIMBUS 3	**(Launch - 14 April 1969) (Data through 25 September 1970)**
IDCS	41,494 pictures
HRIR	5,684 hours
MRIR	3,268 hours
DRID	72,075 pictures
DRIR	12,745 hours
IRIS	1,738 hours
SIRS	8,389 hours
MUSE	8,521 hours
IRLS	21,190 data frames
NIMBUS 4	**(Launch - 8 April 1970) (Data through 28 February 1971)**
IDCS	30,656 pictures
THIR (11.5 um)	4,819 hours
THIR (6.7 um)	2,801 hours
DRID	Selected Coverage
DRIR	Selected Coverage
IRIS	6,372 hours
SIRS	6,684 hours
MUSE	6,784 hours
BUV	6,627 hours
FWS	1,316 hours
SCR	6,784 hours
IRLS	22,027 data frames

SOURCE: After Sabatini et al., 1971.

effort to achieve long-range (14-day) weather forecasting, with remote sensing input as an important component. Progress in the organization of effort and the launching of satellites with sensors designed to fill the gaps in our knowledge are impressive but may be misleading. The greater part of the task of achieving satisfactory operational capability remains to be done. Conventional sources will continue to supply most of the upper-air data through 1975, for example. Satellites and sensors have malfunctioned; understanding of the data is incomplete; utilization of some of the data awaits the development of automation techniques; tests of data from some sensors are few or preliminary --and so on. There is no shortage of research opportunities for those who would like to apply remote sensing techniques to atmospheric studies--and data are available in quantity and variety.

The Hydrosphere

The interrelatedness of the physical elements of the environment is illustrated nowhere better than in investigations of the earth's water resource. Oceanographic studies of sea-surface temperature have utility for meteorological global-mass and energy-budget studies, as do hydrologic studies of surface-soil moisture and snow pack. Accordingly, in this section topics will be treated that could have been included in other sections just as appropriately. Hydrology is, in fact, commonly treated as an aspect of geology.

Regional water-storage inventories benefit from repetitive imagery which reveals seasonal or longer-term fluctuations of lake surface areal extent. In locations difficult of access or where lakes are quite numerous, conventional methods for assessing change often provide information of uncertain quality with resultant limitations on the use of the data. Substantial changes of the areal extent of water surface in a large region affects the water budget and results in differences in the amount of modification of air masses passing over the region. Some of the occasional lack of success with numerical weather forecasts is believed due in part to inaccuracies in surface-water and soil-moisture data employed. Changes in standing water levels throughout a region are likely to be reflected in subsequent stream flow, and therefore in flood or water-shortage prognostications. Several categories of remote sensor imagery are capable of providing information on such changes.

Infrared imagery as a detector of thermal pollution has received much publicity, but less well known is its utility in detecting underwater springs. Useful in understanding fluctuations in lake regimes, such information also can be related to groundwater levels and to circulation patterns within the water body. Remote sensor imagery has been used to locate freshwater springs just offshore of saltwater coasts, too.

Weather-satellite imagery is being used to monitor ice conditions in the Great Lakes and other large lakes. In addition to its utility to various of man's activities on the lakes, such information, again, is valuable to numerical meteorological predictions.

Snow-cover surveillance and water equivalence of snowpack are important inputs for water management and flood prediction. Point data samples have long been used for estimates of snowpack water equivalence, but snow cover is typically uneven and areal data should provide a basis for better estimates. Several studies suggest that remote sensing can provide such data. Microwave brightness temperatures are found to have a direct relationship to the water equivalent of dry snow (Meier and Edgerton, 1969). In a study which utilized sodium iodide (NaI) scintillation crystals (Deal et al., 1971), water equivalents were estimated from the reduction of radiation from the underlying surface. A study of snowfield mapping with K-Band radar (Waite and MacDonald, 1969) indicates the possibility of refining water-equivalent estimates in that the areal extent of old snow can be mapped right through a new layer of snow.

Numerous applications of remote sensing to oceanography have been identified; wave and current action, temperature surveys, and pollution detection are examples. Because of the vastness of the sea, the possibility of using satellite data is especially appealing and many studies have this focus. Ocean-swell wavelengths have been obtained by the application of Fourier optical analyzer techniques to Apollo 7 photography (Noble, 1970). Sun glint, usually an unwanted feature on a photograph, has been used to estimate sea-surface wind speeds from weather satellite photos. Sun-glint patterns were found to be divisible into categories of ocean surface roughness (Strong and Ruff, 1970). Weather-satellite infrared imagery has been used for a number of years to study warm and cold surface ocean currents. The more sophisticated IR sensors on the ITOS satellite have made it possible to distinguish between the Gulf Stream, shelf, and slope waters along the U.S. east coast (Rao et al., 1971). In fact, the accuracy with which sea-surface temperatures are being obtained by remote sensing rivals oceanographic mercury thermometry at the surface. Total heatflow measurements from the sea surface by an airborne (not spacecraft) infrared radiometer system has produced temperature data with an accuracy approaching 0.01°C (McAlister, 1969). Airborne remote sensors have been found to have other oceanographic application. IR radiometry has been used to detect preferred fish concentration zones owing to water temperature conditions; radar scatterometer and passive microwave data provide a basis for determining sea state with applications in ship routing; and passive microwave data have been used to detect salinity differences in areas of estuary outflow.

While the use of conventional aerial photography in water pollution detection has been found to have its limitations (Welch, 1971), remote sensing in the ultraviolet, infrared, and microwave portions of the spectrum have been shown to have utility, notably in the location and quantity assessment of oil spill. The Federal Water Quality Administration's 1969 estimate of 7,000 oil spills in U.S. waters annually and the growing number of supertankers in the world augur well for increased use of this capability.

Reference was made earlier to the inadequacy of our knowledge of conditions in the Arctic. Enough is known from the few studies that have been made that the necessity for more complete information is evident (Campbell, 1971). In comparison with the Antarctic region, the Arctic is an area of frequent and rapid change. Melt of surface snow over the plateau of Antarctica is modest and affects the albedo little; in the Arctic, leads (linear open water areas) and polynyas (nonlinear openings) change in areal extent and location frequently and often with great rapidity. It is thought that such changes are the chief causes of albedo changes in the area. Sea ice in the Arctic is comparatively thin, averaging about 3 meters, and it moves about considerably. Rates of motion as high as 50 kilometers per day have been observed, and individual floes have been tracked along paths that cover tens of thousands of kilometers over a period of years. Preliminary studies of Arctic ice indicate that ice masses of different age act in different ways (Biache et al., 1971) and that a knowledge of spatial variation of ice age would be helpful in attempts to predict change. Some studies suggest that the heat and water flux of the entire Arctic Ocean into the atmosphere is mostly determined by the open water areas, yet little is known of the development and change such areas undergo. Families of polynyas, some with dimensions of 10 kilometers by 70 kilometers, have been observed to appear and disappear within a few days' time.

Projects such as AIDJEX (Arctic Ice Dynamics Joint Experiment), formed in 1970 by Americans and Canadians, are being expanded to include other nations and more tasks. The problems of study of the Arctic are made especially difficult by the extended periods of darkness and the probability that many of the changes which occur do so during periods of dense cloudiness. Microwave sensing, both active and passive, can overcome these obstacles, however; and these sensors are capable of identifying ice openings, distinguishing between ice-mass ages, and providing other needed data. The potential utility of sequential satellite data for such studies will be self-evident.

The Biosphere

Although the title of this section may be only slightly more presumptuous than the others, some admission of its limitations seems appropriate. Man, a rather important element in the biosphere, is referred to only incidentally; and even reference to his agricultural pursuits is left for subsequent chapters. Actually, the mantle of natural (or nearly so) vegetation provides the focus here in a glimpse of remote sensing applications to the study of life forms, although some mention of wildlife is made.

As with so many of the natural sciences, aerial photography was established early as a basic tool for the study of rangeland and forests and remains so today. When infrared film began to become routinely available, its use in such studies revealed the value of examining vegetation with wavelengths beyond the visible part of the spectrum. Species identification and indications of plant stress were among the early study topics aided by the use of photographic IR, notably with color IR. Gradually the use of more and more of the spectrum or more detailed use of parts of it (Colwell, 1961, 1968) became incorporated into studies of the forest resource. Radar, so highly touted for its ability to reveal structure and surface form through intervening vegetation, also is capable of providing imagery that will depict broad vegetation classes (Morain and Simonett, 1967) (Figure 4-4). While difficulties in discriminating between within-vegetation-class units are encountered on single-band radar imagery, it is suggested that multiband multipolarization imagery may provide such discrimination (Simonett, 1970). The use of color IR aerial photography to identify tree-stress problem areas offers hope of remedying the almost annual occurrence of substantial loss that occurs in locations difficult of access and in the midst of forests with great areal extent. Realization of the location and extent of the problem early enough should make it possible to reduce total loss by timely remedial action. The use of thermal IR scanners by the U.S. Forest Service has been found beneficial in several ways. Smoldering small fires which could become large fires if ignored are susceptible to detection by thermal scanners. Alternately, during the height of activity of an extensive fire when smoke obscures the scene thoroughly, a scanner flown over the fire area will penetrate the smoke and identify the outline of the area that is ablaze (National Academy of Sciences, 1970).

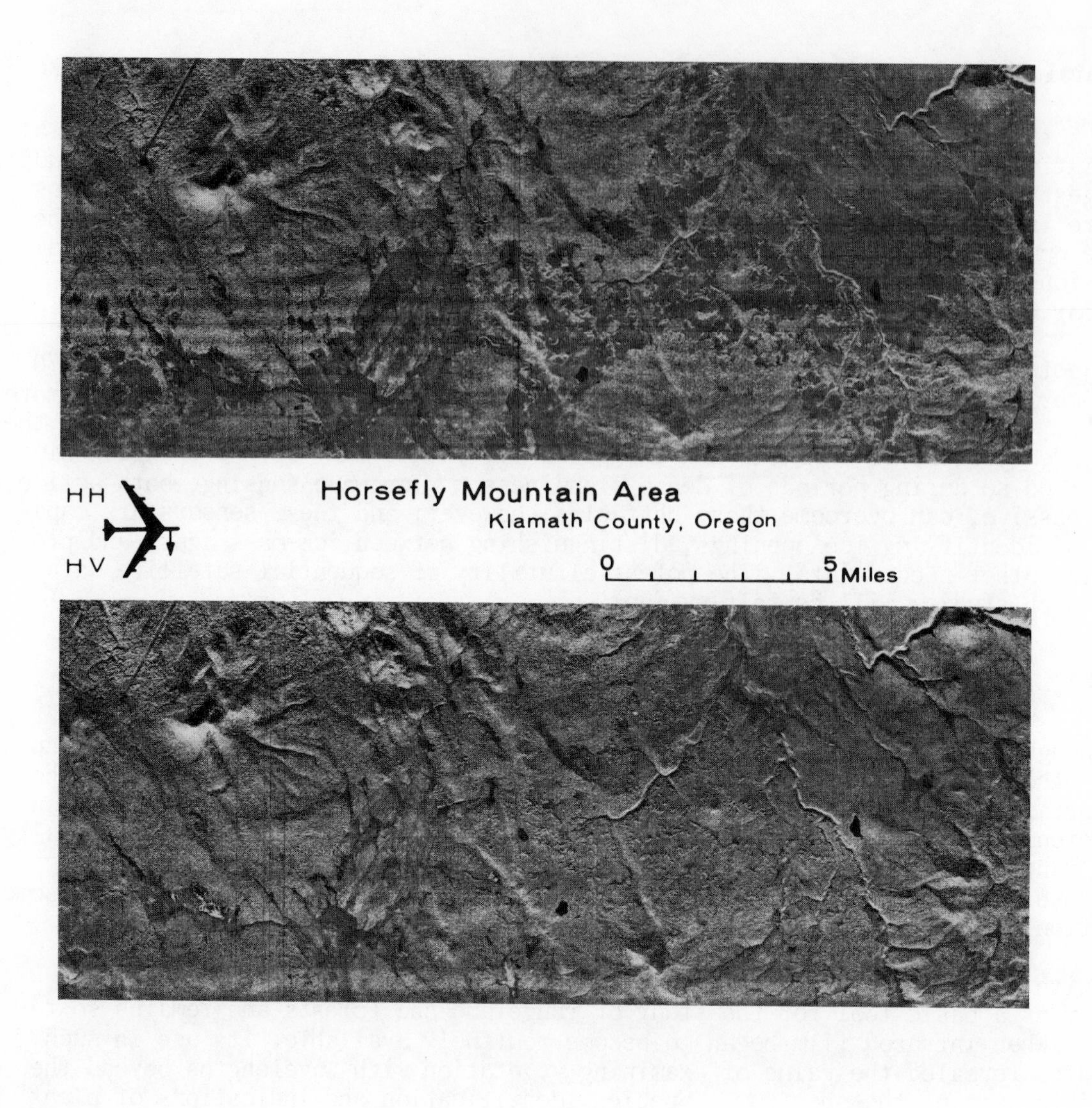

Figure 4-4. Indications of vegetation patterns on K-band radar imagery. Notice contrasts associated with different polarization. After Morain and Simonett, 1967.

Forests cover an estimated one-third of the world's continents. The possibility of using satellite imagery for the assessment of this resource and subsequent efforts to monitor it thus has obvious appeal. Since species identification, even on large-scale aerial photos, often becomes a problem, the utility of orbital-scale imagery for inventory is immediately questionable. Two points deserve consideration here: (1) detailed species mapping from orbital imagery is unreasonable but broad-gauge mapping is not; and, (2) the degree of success of any such mapping is strongly affected by the nature of the imagery. In a study of the application of Apollo 9 color IR imagery to a forestry mapping problem, a considerable amount of general information was obtained (Aldrich, 1971). The area in forest as opposed to other land use was identifiable, areas of deciduous trees were separable from those with evergreens, and some mixed stands were identifiable as such. The timing of the photography was helpful; it was March, and neither deciduous trees nor agricultural fields had much foliage. Separation of forested from nonforested land, or deciduous from evergreen,may not seem very sophisticated information, but it is basic information which we do not have for much of the world's forested area. Moreover, until we have it, we lack a basis for monitoring change in the forest resource base. The utility of satellite imagery is enhanced by its sequential character. Not only can imagery for a desired time of year be selected from such coverage, but also the changes which occur with the progress of the season become valuable additional information. Indeed, many forms of natural vegetation would be identifiable as a result of accompanying phenological changes that would not be in a single temporal posture.

In the United States there are more than a billion acres of rangeland, suitable for grazing livestock or for wildlife, but not presently adaptable for crop production. The task of inventory and monitoring of this resource also can be made easier with remote sensing. Space and aerial photos can provide information, at different levels of detail, necessary for decisions on use and management (Poulton et al., 1969). On much of the area in question, individual plants are substantially smaller than trees and they collectively cover far less of the surface; yet satellite imagery can be useful here, too. Although requiring some special treatments, range-resource analysis can employ many of the same concepts used by forestry and agriculture, and temporal considerations are especially important. But satellite imagery is not likely to be used alone in range studies or any others. Orbital imagery, aircraft imagery, and sample ground studies will be used in complementary fashion, each where its effectiveness is greatest. The United States has, as a part of its International Biological Program, a grassland biome program, a major ecosystem analysis of the functioning of natural grasslands (Miller and Pearson, 1971). The productivity of a grassland and its modification by herbivores are basic desirable data; and standing crop biomass is the indicator of productivity. The tedious hand operation of sampling biomass by weighing dried hand clippings may be reduced by utilizing remote sensing techniques. As a result of the establishment of the fact that, within a given grass type, a measurable relationship exists between aboveground plant biomass and percent cover, percent-cover maps could be converted into standing-crop biomass maps. Remote sensing should be able to contribute substantially to the creation of percent-cover maps with inputs at several scales for the different phases of the effort.

Finally, remote sensing is being applied to a limited extent in wildlife census efforts. Although much of the effort is yet in the experimental stage, salmon spawning pools have been photographed with various film-filter combinations for fish counts, thermal IR nighttime imagery of animals has been flown, migratory bird numbers at flyway resting stops have been sampled, automated pond counts from scanner imagery have been employed in setting hunting quotas, and at least one state wildlife agency has hired a commercial remote sensing firm to provide deer population sample data. There are even a few elk wandering about in Wyoming with monitoring devices about their necks that can be detected by polar orbiting satellites. But perhaps the most bizarre remote sensing-faunal relationship is the suspected correlation between certain radar "angles" and unusually dense mosquito swarms (Frost, 1971). The potential applications for such data are as yet uncertain.

REFERENCES

Aldrich, R. C., 1971, "Space Photos for Land Use and Forestry," *Photogrammetric Engineering*, 37(4):389-401.

Bannert, D., 1971, "Plate Drift in the Red Sea Region Analyzed from Space Photographs," *Proceedings of the Seventh International Symposium on Remote Sensing of Environment*, vol. II, University of Michigan, Ann Arbor, pp. 1261-2171.

Biache, A., C. A. Bay, and R. Bradie, 1971, "Remote Sensing of the Arctic Ice Environment," *Proceedings of the Seventh International Symposium on Remote Sensing of Environment*, vol. I, University of Michigan, Ann Arbor, pp. 523-561.

Campbell, W. J., 1971, "The Remote Sensing Needs of Arctic Geophysics," *Proceedings of the Seventh International Symposium on Remote Sensing of Environment*, vol. II, University of Michigan, Ann Arbor, pp. 937-940.

Canney, F. C., 1969, "Remote Detection of Geochemical Soil Anomalies," *Second Annual Earth Resources Aircraft Program Status Review*, NASA/MSC, Houston, Tex., vol. I, pp. 7-1 - 7-8.

Colwell, R. N., 1961, "Some Practical Applications of Multiband Spectral Reconnaissance," *American Scientist*, 49(1):9-36.

Colwell, R. N., 1968, "Remote Sensing of Natural Resources," *Scientific American*, 218(1):54-69.

Cooley, D. S., 1971, "Applications of Remote Sensing to Operational Weather Forecasting," *Proceedings of the Seventh International Symposium on Remote Sensing of Environment*, vol. II, University of Michigan, Ann Arbor, pp. 941-949.

Deal, L. J., J. F. Doyle, Z. G. Burson, and A. E. Fritzsche, 1971, "Environmental Radiation Surveys and Snow Mass Predictions from Aircraft," *Proceedings of the Seventh International Symposium on Remote Sensing of Environment*, vol. III, University of Michigan, Ann Arbor, pp. 2193-2216.

Frazee, C. J., V. I. Myers, and F. C. Westin, 1971, "Remote Sensing for Detection of Soil Limitations in Agricultural Areas," *Proceedings of the Seventh International Symposium on Remote Sensing of Environment*, vol. I, University of Michigan, Ann Arbor, pp. 327-343.

Frost, E. L., 1971, "Correlated Radar and Trapping Studies of Insect Swarming over Atlantic Coastal Lowlands," *Proceedings of the Seventh International Symposium on Remote Sensing of Environment*, vol. III, University of Michigan, Ann Arbor, pp. 1905-1915.

Gross, H. G., and H. A. Hyatt, 1971, "Luminescence Induced by UV and Visible Lasers for the Remote Active Sensing of Materials from Ground, Air and Space," *Proceedings of the Seventh International Symposium on Remote Sensing of Environment*, vol. II, University of Michigan, Ann Arbor, pp. 869-888.

Hemphill, W. R., 1969, "Geologic Applications Program--Summary of Recent Progress and Plans," *Second Annual Earth Resources Aircraft Program Status Review*, NASA/MSC, Houston, Tex., vol. I, pp. 1-1 - 1-4.

MacDonald, H. C., 1969, "Geologic Evaluation of Radar Imagery from Darien Province, Panama," *Modern Geology*, 1(1):1-64.

McAlister, E. D., 1969, "Sea-Surface Temperature and Heat Flow--BOMEX," *Second Annual Earth Resources Aircraft Program Status Review*, NASA/MSC, Houston, Tex., vol. III, pp. 49-1 - 49-16.

McLellan, A., 1971, "Atmospheric Pollution Detection by Satellite Remote Sensing," *Proceedings of the Seventh International Symposium on Remote Sensing of Environment*, vol. I, University of Michigan, Ann Arbor, pp. 563-584.

Meier, M., and A. T. Edgerton, 1969, "Snow and Ice Sensing with Passive Microwave and Ground Truth Instrumentation: Recent Results, South Cascade Glacier," *Second Annual Earth Resources Aircraft Program Status Review*, NASA/MSC, Houston, Tex., vol. III, pp. 43-1 - 43-13.

Miller, L. E., and R. L. Pearson, 1971, "Areal Mapping Program of the IBP Grassland Biome: Remote Sensing of the Productivity of the Shortgrass Prairie as Input into Biosystem Models," *Proceedings of the Seventh International Symposium on Remote Sensing of Environment*, vol. I, University of Michigan, Ann Arbor, pp. 165-205.

Morain, S. A., and J. B. Campbell, 1972, "Soil Mapping from Radar Imagery: Theory and Preliminary Applications," unpublished manuscript.

Morain, S. A., and D. S. Simonett, 1967, "K-Band Radar in Vegetation Mapping," *Photogrammetric Engineering*, 33(7):730-740.

National Academy of Sciences, 1970, "Applications of Remote Sensing in Agriculture and Forestry," in *Remote Sensing with Special Reference to Agriculture and Forestry*, National Academy of Sciences, Washington, D. C., Chapter 4.

Noble, V. E., 1970, "Ocean Swell Measurements from Satellite Photographs," *Remote Sensing of Environment*, 1(3):151-154.

Page, L. R., 1969, "Geologic Analysis of the X-Band Radar Mosaics of Massachusetts," *Second Annual Earth Resources Aircraft Program Status Review*, NASA/MSC, Houston, Tex., vol. I, pp. 4-1 - 4-19.

Poulton, C. E., R. S. Driscoll, and B. J. Schrumpf, 1969, "Range Resource Inventory from Space and Supporting Aircraft Photography," *Second Annual Earth Resources Aircraft Program Status Review*, NASA/MSC, Houston, Tex., vol. II, pp. 20-1 - 20-28.

Rao, P. K., A. E. Strong, and R. Koffler, 1971, "Sea Surface Temperature Mapping off the Eastern United States Using NASA's ITOS Satellite," *Proceedings of the Seventh International Symposium on Remote Sensing of Environment*, vol. I, University of Michigan, Ann Arbor, pp. 683-691.

Rowan, L. C., T. W. Offield, K. Watson, R. D. Watson, and P. J. Cannon, 1969, "Thermal Infrared Investigations, Mill Creek Area, Oklahoma," *Second Annual Earth Resources Aircraft Program Status Review*, NASA/MSC, Houston, Tex., vol.I, pp. 5-1 - 5-25.

Sabatini, R. R., G. A. Rabcheosky, and J. E. Sissala, 1971, *Nimbus Earth Resources Observations*, Technical Report 2, under Contract No. NAS 5-21617, NASA, GSFC, Greenbelt.

Sabins, F. F., Jr., 1969, "Thermal IR Imagery and Its Application to Structural Mapping in Southern California," *Geological Society of America Bulletin*, 80(Mr): 397-404.

Simonett, D. S., 1970, "Remote Sensing with Imaging Radar: A Review," *Geoforum*, 2:61-73.

Smedes, H. W., K. L. Pierce, M. G. Tanguay, and R. M. Hoffer, 1969, "Digital Computer Terrain Mapping from Multispectral Data, and Evaluation of Proposed Earth Resources Technology Satellite (ERTS) Data Channels, Yellowstone National Park: Preliminary Report," *Second Annual Earth Resources Aircraft Program Status Review*, NASA/MSC, Houston, Tex., vol. I, pp. 3-1 - 3-37.

Stockhoff, E. H., and R. T. Frost, 1971, "Polarization of Light Scattered from Moist Soils," *Proceedings of the Seventh International Symposium on Remote Sensing of Environment*, vol. I, University of Michigan, Ann Arbor, pp. 345-364.

Strong, A. E., and I. S. Ruff, 1970, "Utilizing Satellite-Observed Solar Reflections from the Sea Surface as an Indicator of Surface Wind Speeds," *Remote Sensing of Environment*, 1(3):181-185.

United States Executive Office of the President, National Aeronautics and Space Council, 1971, *Aeronautics and Space Report of the President, 1971 Activities*, Government Printing Office, Washington, D.C.

Vermillion, C. H., 1968, *Constructing Inexpensive Automatic Picture-Transmission Ground Stations*, NASA Office of Technological Utilization, Washington, D.C.

Vincent, R. K., and F. J. Thomson, 1971, "Discrimination of Basic Silicate Rocks by Recognition Maps Processed from Aerial Infrared Data, *Proceedings of the Seventh International Symposium on Remote Sensing of Environment*, vol. I, University of Michigan, Ann Arbor, pp. 247-268.

Waite, W. P., and H. C. MacDonald, 1969, "Snowfield Mapping with K-Band Radar," *Second Annual Earth Resources Aircraft Program Status Review*, NASA/MSC, Houston, Tex., vol. III, pp. 46-1 - 46-22.

Welch, R., 1971, "Remote Sensing for Water Pollution Control," *Photogrammetric Engineering,* 37(12):1285-1286.

Wise, D. U., 1967, "A Radar Geology and Pseudo-Geology Cross Section," *Photogrammetric Engineering,* 33(7):752-761.

Zavos, B., 1971, "Applications of Remote Sensing to the World Weather Watch and the Global Atmospheric Research Program," *Proceedings of the Seventh International Symposium on Remote Sensing of Environment,* University of Michigan, Ann Arbor, Michigan, vol. I, pp. 207-219.

5

Geomorphic-Geologic Mapping From Remote Sensors

Anthony J. Lewis
Louisiana State University

The subsurface and surface features of the earth, geology-geomorphology, give character to areas at regional and local scales. A variety of processes, both natural and man-induced, work to keep these phenomena in a state of dynamic equilibrium. The importance of these features and processes to man lies in areas such as mineral exploration, site selection for particular land uses, evaluation of disaster potential, and aesthetic appreciation. Remote sensing provides a means for describing, delimiting, inventorying, and monitoring such phenomena; new perspectives may also be obtained. This chapter examines remote sensing research in geology-geomorphology with respect to sensor and platform data capabilities, regional and local data acquisition, and the qualitative and quantitative nature of the data obtained.

Photogeology, the collection of qualitative and quantitative geologic-geomorphic information, had its beginnings before the development of thermal infrared, radar, or other remote sensor systems acquiring data from different parts of the electromagnetic (EM) spectrum. Although most geologic-geomorphic remote sensing data are still gathered by means of conventional aerial cameras using standard black-and-white film, the more exotic, technologically sophisticated sensors are assuming increasing importance.

The use of aerial photographs has expanded beyond conventional black-and-white (B-W) photography. Today, color, color infrared (CIR), black-and-white infrared (B-WIR), and multiband photography are in use. Other variations from the conventional 1:20,000 vertical (B-W) photographic format are small-scale, high-altitude photography, continuous-strip photography, and low-sun-angle photography.

For practical purposes, the best operational sensor is cloud-free, high-resolution, black-and-white photography. Black-and-white photography is still the most economical and most versatile source of remote sensing data available. Practical application of the other types of remote sensing data, therefore, must be based on the principle of "the specific sensor for the specific task"; that is, designing a particular sensor package to maximize the probability of accomplishing the specific goal of a given mission. For example, the utility of radar is most evident where cloud cover or the lack of solar illumination makes the use of conventional cameras and films impossible. In many areas, such as the tropics, coastal environments, and high latitudes during the solar night, the use of radar as a primary sensor may be justified. Thermal infrared and other imagery systems, operating in different parts of the EM spectrum than conventional aerial photography, may also provide unique data not available on photography.

This chapter will attempt to review what is happening in the broad field of geologic-geomorphic remote sensing, including (1) regional and local scale studies; (2) qualitative and quantitative studies; and (3) aerial photographs (B-W, B-WIR, color, and CIR), thermal infrared, and radar. Numerous references are cited to supplement the text.*

Qualitative and Quantitative Photogeology

Qualitative and quantitative photo interpretation of geologic-geomorphic features will be treated separately because of ease in presentation, not because they are distinct entities. "Photogeology" and "photogeomorphology" are used interchangeably throughout the text since they both deal with the same plane of reference, the earth's surface (Shaw, 1953), and utilize the same techniques. The geologist differs from the geomorphologist in that he studies landforms basically for the subsurface geologic information contained in surface morphology.

---

* Several texts and general references warrant special attention. *The Manual of Photographic Interpretation* (American Society of Photogrammetry, 1960), although published 12 years ago, provides an excellent source of references for the period before 1960 (approximately 900 entries on photogeology). The *Manual* still remains the standard reference text. Texts by Lueder (1959), Miller (1961), Ray (1960), and von Bandat (1962) are also good reference sources. The quality of photographic reproduction is best in the texts by von Bandat and Miller; however, they are also the most expensive. Richard Ray's *Aerial Photographs in Geologic Interpretation and Mapping* is inexpensive and contains photographs of good quality, adequate bibliography, and a text on basic photogeology. More detailed consideration to photogeology is given by Lueder (1959), Miller (1961), and von Bandat (1962).

An air photo index to landforms in the eastern half of the United States was compiled by Keifer (1967). The index provides several examples of landform types plus a list of photographs categorized into seven landform types. A brief description of the identifiable landforms, the location by county and state, identification number, date of photography, and corresponding USGS quadrangle map coverage are provided for each photo listed. Instructions on how and from whom the photos can be purchased are included. Two USGS publications are listed as descriptive catalogs of selected aerial photographs of geologic features within the United States (Denny et al., 1968) and outside the United States (Warren et al., 1969). A detailed description and representative photography from each set complement each other. The description includes location, photograph scale, camera focal length, date flown, map reference, geology reference, and the features illustrated. The photographs are 3 inches by 3 inches which have been reduced from the original 9 inches by 9 inches. Also included by Denny et al. (1968) and Warren et al. (1969) is an index map of the location of the photos and an order blank.

Both the geologist and geomorphologist are interested in process-related information, both past and present, which is provided by distinct landform shape, pattern, orientation, and tonal appearance.

Several journal articles and government publications dealing with photogeology-geomorphology, although published before 1960, are very informative. They are (1) "Petroleum Photogeology" by Wasem (1949); (2) "Techniques in Photogeology" by Desjardins (1950); (3) "The Aerial Photograph and Applied Geomorphology" by Tator (1958); and (4)"A Photo Analysis Key for the Determination of Ground Conditions" by Belcher (1951).

Qualitative Photogeology. The qualitative approach to photo interpretation of geomorphology can be thought of as operating as a progression of three basic steps: (1) primary reconnaissance, including all available corroborative data; (2) regional analysis; and (3) detailed analyses (Erb, 1968). In most situations, all three steps or levels of operation are utilized; and the sequence in which they are used is analogous to basic interpretation techniques, i.e., reconnaissance first, then examination from the general to the specific. Following the basic collection and assimilation of collaborative data, the landform units should be delimited on the basis of topographic texture. Topographic texture is, in essence, erosional dissection expressed as (1) drainage texture, (2) drainage and topographic patterns, (3) tone, (4) cross-sectional profile of gullies, and (5) vegetation (Figures 5-1 and 5-2). Drainage texture enables the interpreter to make some basic assumptions as to the nature of the soil of a given area. By examining a photo of an area, a knowledgeable interpreter can tell whether the soil is impervious with a large amount of runoff and low infiltration rate (dense, finely divided drainage texture) or well drained with little runoff and

Figure 5-1. Conventional black-and-white photography showing the importance of tone in delimiting the snow line (1) and the terminus of the glacier (2). Braided, glacier-fed stream (3) and the old cirque (4) are also visible.

Figure 5-2. Conventional black-and-white photography of a region in the arid southwestern United States. Several features are illustrated: (1) fault, (2) alluvial fans, (3) stream dissection, and (4) vegetation occupying gullies on an old alluvial fan. Lack of overall vegetation cover suggests an arid climate.

high infiltration (coarse or absent drainage net). Drainage density, therefore, may provide information or permeability, texture, and occasionally the identity of the surface material or lithology.

The significance of drainage patterns has for a long time received attention by geologists (Zernitz, 1932; Parvis, 1950; Howard, 1967). Aerial photographs provide a source of detailed data about drainage patterns without costly and time-consuming field mapping (Shaw, 1953). The combination of the detailed drainage patterns and geologic formations or structures is of importance to the photogeologist. Such drainage patterns as rectangular, dendritic, and annular suggest to the photogeologist joints and/or faults (rectangular), horizontally bedded sedimentaries (dendritic), and structural domes (annular), respectively. Howard (1967) describes, illustrates, and discusses the significance of what he terms the 8 basic and 17 modified drainage patterns and should be consulted for more detailed information.

Stream patterns and drainage anomalies were used as indicators of geologic and hydrologic conditions before 1940 and were mapped without aerial photography. The utility of such features has been expanded considerably with the use of aerial photography. The costs of mapping drainage nets have decreased, and accuracy and geographical coverage have increased (Figure 5-2). Rectilinear stretches suggest structural control (Howard, 1967), whereas river meandering in a sinusoidal fashion indicates the river's ability to transport the available bed load (Leopold and Wolman, 1957). Further discussion of stream patterns is provided by Johnson (1932) and Russell (1939). Local deviations in regional drainage (drainage anomalies) may provide structural or lithologic information not detectable by other means (Howard, 1967), especially in flat lowland areas such as the United States Gulf Coast and the Amazon Basin of Brazil. Russell (1939), DeBlieux (1949), DeBlieux and Shepard (1951), and Tator (1954) in their separate studies along the Gulf Coast describe various drainage anomalies and suggest the significance of such features.

Identification of local features often requires stringent flight planning, such as those expressed by Teichert and Fairbridge (1950) for interpreting coral reefs. They state that for optimum data retrieval the following conditions are mandatory: (1) photographic scale (for vertical photos) should be less than 1:5,000; (2) large-scale oblique photos are necessary for interpreting parts of the reef edge; (3) small-scale obliques for orientation; (4) 60 percent overlap for stereo viewing; and (5) photos must be taken at low tide, preferably at low sun angle to avoid glare and enhance topography with shadows (Teichert and Fairbridge, 1950). Such constraints are often prohibitive depending on additional limitations, such as time and money. Flight and photographic specifications related to the more generalized field of photogeology are given by Wasem (1949). Wasem especially deals with the relationship of acceptable scale and terrain slope and the importance of camera focal length.

Specialized keys for landform identification often make the job easier for the interpreter faced with the task of analyzing photos of an unfamiliar area or topic. A dichotomous key developed by W. E. Powers for identifying glacial landforms is a good example. Fifteen types of glacial and associated landforms are identifiable using this key (Powers, 1951). Examples of the dichotomous as well as other types of keys may be found in the *Manual of Photographic Interpretation* (American Society of Photogrammetry, 1960).

Mapping linear features, fracture traces, and lineaments* from aerial photography has been used by geologists to locate possible oil traps and zones of mineralization for several decades. The basic techniques involve the use of an air-photo mosaic viewed vertically for the prominent linears and at a low viewing angle for the more subtle linear trends (Lattman, 1958). Ronchi grating,** or other polarizing lenses or plates, can aid in the location of regional linear trends. The effect of splice lines evident on most uncontrolled or semicontrolled mosaics is reduced by incorporating small-scale photography, 1:125,000 radar imagery, or electronically dodging the mosaics. A properly prepared controlled mosaic would exhibit few, if any, splice lines that can confuse inexperienced photo interpreters or distract experienced ones.

Lineaments expressed by topographic variation or drainage alignment are easily recognized on photography. However, lineaments, suggested by tonal variations related to changing soil color or vegetation type, are often more difficult to discern.

Quantitative Photogeology. Linear, area, and volume measurements (with the aid of stereoscopy) are obtainable from aerial photos, as are azimuthal data.

---

* Lattman (1958) reviews the problem of nomenclature that has clouded the meaning of "fracture trace" and "lineament."

** A system of close equidistant and parallel lines etched or scribed on a plate to enhance and detect structural or topographic linearity.

Landform morphometry information--including slope and dip (magnitude and direction), relative relief, drainage-basin area, stream density, stream length, strike, and regional fracture orientations--are more accurately and less costly measured on air photos than in the field. Bifurcation ratios, circularity ratios, and other nondimensional parameters can also be determined from aerial photography.*

Dip-slope measurements are of extreme importance to the geologists. The accuracy of dip-slope estimates from aerial photography is dependent upon many variables, including the scale and tilt of the photos, the focal length, the skill of the interpreter, and the angle of the dip-slope. The relationship between scale and tilt of the photos and the skill of the interpreter with dip-slope accuracy should be evident. As the scale becomes larger and the interpreter's skill increases, accuracy increases. The trade-off between the photographic scale, cost, and photogeologic data is considered to balance itself at a 1:20,000 photo scale (Wasem, 1949). Although the area covered on a single photograph increases (field of view increases) as the focal length of the camera decreases, image quality is reduced and accuracy is accordingly lowered. A 12-inch or 8.25-inch lens is recommended for this reason. Vertical exaggeration introduced by stereoscopic viewing, especially when magnification is added, is an asset in estimating low dip-slopes but a hindrance in areas of high dip-slopes. The absolute accuracy of dip-slope estimates becomes lower as the magnitude of the dip-slope increases. Wasem (1949) reports dip-slope estimate accuracy of (1) 1° to 3° where dip-slopes range from 3° to 20°; (2) not more than 5° with dip-slopes between 20° and 45°; and (3) 10° or more where the dips exceed 45°.

Considerable work has been reported on drainage-basin analysis, along with lineament analysis and measurement of dip-slopes from air photos. Direct measurement of drainage-basin area, for example, is feasible on aerial photographs, if the relative relief is less than 200 feet or the drainage-basin area is small (Sternberg, 1961). A correction factor is necessary if the relief is greater than 200 feet, owing to the change in photographic scale with the distance of the photo above a datum plane. Important parameters relating to lineaments, as well as a method of collecting and manipulating lineament data from air photos, are given by Norman (1970).

The usefulness of several measurable drainage-basin parameters, such as bifurcation ratio, is limited if not nonexistent; however, this is not true of all parameters. Circularity ratios, drainage-basin area, and drainage density are all useful in predicting flood potential and discharge characteristics. The relationship of drainage density to infiltration rates has already been mentioned. In a recent study by Majtenyi and Belcher (1970), drainage density from 1:20,000-scale photos and climatic data were used to predict long-term discharge rates for small watersheds on a mature landscape.

Three other forms of quantitative photogeology are unconventional in that they require energy measurements rather than geometric measurements. Spectrophotometry, the measurement of reflected visible and near-infrared energy, is primarily a field-and-lab-oriented data-gathering technique, designed as much for

---

* Ray and Fischer (1960) list several studies that document the practical use of air-photo morphometry.

flight planning--selection of sensors and/or film and filter combinations--as it is for collection of information from aerial photographs.

Densitometry involves the quantitative measurement of tonal values, both magnitude and frequency of change from either film transparencies or paper prints. Tone is one of the major photographic keys available to the interpreter, and the quantification of such an indicator provides documentation of qualitative judgements made by the interpreter. However, this technique frequently represents only a quantitative verification of the qualitative obvious. One justification which is used for this type of analysis, however, is that in the long run it may lead to the automation of some interpretive procedures. Thus, following the densitometric determination of a diagnostic tonal value for a given feature, automatic scanning and recognition techniques can be employed for continued mapping of the feature. Tonal variations, related to changing sun angle, changing reflectance properties of the feature, film processing, and lens aberrations, limit the utility of diagnostic tonal values, unless such values are constantly updated with densitometric data from documented training sets. Frequency of tonal change, photographic texture, can be significant in describing landform features and in comparing landforms at different stages of dissection, of different lithologies, and resulting from different processes. This relationship should be expected, since photographic texture on a meso- and macroscale is primarily a function of topographic texture. Texture-oriented studies by Ray and Fischer (1960) have demonstrated that marked textural variation may exist between glacial moraines of different ages and also between morainic and alluvial topography.

Colorimetry is the measurement of chroma intensity and, as such, is similar to densitometry. Colorimetry is to quantitative data collection from air photos as stereoscopy is to photo interpretation. It adds a third dimension. Absolute chroma values have the same limitations as absolute tonal values; i.e., variability with lens aberrations, processing, etc. Before the recent development and marketing of desk model color densitometers, the color film transparency was rephotographed with B-W film using various selected filters and densitometric data taken from the resultant B-W transparencies. This was time-consuming and more expensive; also it introduced additional possibility of error. New, moderately priced color densitometers allow data collection directly from the first-generation color transparency. Various filters or filtration schemes can also be utilized for isolating or enhancing selected features, facilitating discrimination.

PHOTOGRAPHY

Film Types

The four major film types (B-W, B-WIR, color, and CIR) have been mentioned previously. Even with the introduction of color and the IR types, conventional black-and-white (panchromatic) film remains the standard format for photo interpretation.

From a mission-planning point-of-view, the major differences among the films are spatial and chromatic resolution, film speed, and cost. Poorer resolution and slower film speed have, until recent years, prohibited the use of both conventional color and color infrared photography. Recent advances in color processing and the refinement of camera lenses have helped in making color films more inviting. Today the major drawback is cost. Both types of color film are at least several times more costly than black-and-white film. Black-and-white infrared film is limited with respect to resolution and convenience (i.e., it is not as readily available from dealers). Finally, it presents a minor obstacle to the interpreter experienced with only conventional black-and-white photography, since reflected energy lying beyond the visible part of the EM spectrum is imaged.

From the interpreter's standpoint, color photography is more useful in identifying features, if chroma or color contrast is an important identifying characteristic (Fischer, 1958, 1962). It has no special advantage over black-and-white film if identification is based on geometry, texture, or topographic configuration (Fischer, 1962). Color film has been demonstrated to be useful in mapping (1) certain lithologic units; (2) residual soils; and (3) recognition of relic sink holes (Fischer, 1958, 1962). Color film was found to contain more information related to soils and surficial geology than CIR (Morrison, 1970). Color and CIR have been used successfully at a 1:6,000 scale for delimiting and differentiating erosional and mass-wasting forms of slope failure (Poole, n.d.).

CIR and black-and-white infrared photography appear to be most valuable when the geology-geomorphology is expressed by vegetation patterns, and when conventional film cannot be used to discriminate the land-water interface. Black-and-white infrared film was found to be better than black-and-white panchromatic for stream-channel detection in first- to fourth-order basins, especially basins composed of smaller channels or where the channels were nearly choked with aquatic vegetation (Parry and Turner, 1971). Black-and-white infrared was also reported to be superior to black-and-white panchromatic in (1)revealing shallow channels; (2) locating possible fording sites in river bar complexes; and (3)revealing the precise location of back swamps, surface flooding, beaver dams, etc. (Parry and Turner, 1971).

Small-Scale Photography

Small-scale photography (>1:6,000) can be obtained by using a camera with a very small focal length, mounting the camera to a very high platform (e.g., spacecraft), or some compromise of the first two, since the scale (representative fraction, or R.F.) is directly related to focal length (f.l.) and inversely related to distance from the camera to the object being imaged (altitude). Of course, the scale of the original negative or positive can be enlarged or reduced by means of optics.

The major disadvantages of short-focal-length aerial cameras (<6-inches) is that in rugged terrain the back slopes imaged around the film edges are often hidden. For example, Clark (1969) states that with a focal length of 3-1/2 inches and a field of view of 104°, slopes greater than 36° on the edge of the film and away from the nadir will be hidden. High-altitude photography also has limitations, among them, (1) increased cost of high-altitude aircraft or spacecraft, (2) resolution restrictions, (3) global cloud cover; and (4) atmospheric attenuation (Lowman, 1964).

Although small-scale photos taken from high altitudes have been available since World War II, their utility for interpretation and mapping was questionable before the photography obtained during the NASA Mercury missions flown in the 1960s (Lowman, 1964). High-altitude photography obtained before the Mercury photos was not acceptable to the geoscientist, probably because of the lower film and lens quality and the lack of experience in taking photographs through so much atmosphere.

The scale of such a photo, the altitude at which it was taken, and the platform on which the camera was mounted vary considerably. For example, scale may vary from approximately 1:60,000 to 1:5,000,000, and altitude may vary from approximately 12 miles to several hundreds of miles.* The two sensor platforms considered are aircraft and spacecraft. Studies by van der Meer Mohr (1969) indicate that the maximum altitude for useful photos is 400 miles and the smallest scale is 1:5,000,000.

The primary advantage of small-scale photographs is the large area covered on a single photography (Hemphill, 1958; Clark, 1969), resulting in a higher work efficiency and a more synoptic presentation of the terrain (van der Meer Mohr, 1969). Large-area coverage can also be secured by construction of large-scale photo mosaics. Inherent problems associated with this technique are the lack of corresponding small-scale stereo coverage and the line and tone discontinuities which are common to mosaics (Clark, 1969).

In a comparison of approximately 1:60,000 small-scale photos with approximately 1:20,000 large-scale photos from aircraft, Hemphill (1958) reported that small-scale photos are better than large-scale photos for (1) delineating and determining the geologic significance of regionally aligned features, such as fractures, faults, and streams; (2) observing subtle vegetation tone or texture irregularities that may or may not be geologically related; and (3) mapping rock units and other geologic information in certain areas. Morrison (1970), in a study using 1:60,000 to 1:240,000 color photos of Tucson, Arizona, stated that the easiest terrain information interpretable was landform type and the degree of dissection. Interpretation of soils, surficial geology, and landform age was possible, but it required secondary and even tertiary levels of inference (Morrison, 1970).

From an interpreter's standpoint, some of the best Gemini and Apollo photographs are of arid environments, such as the southwestern part of the United States, the Sahara, and the Middle East, where atmospheric attenuation is at a minimum and inaccessibility is a maximum. Gemini-4 photos of the Middle East were demonstrated to be useful for mapping drainage density, large-scale structural units (such as geofractures and fold structures), and many lithologic units (such as separating igneous from sedimentary and consolidated from unconsolidated material) (van der Meer Mohr, 1969). Pesce (1968) reports the mapping from Gemini photography of several previously unmapped, and possibly unknown, topographic features in the remote southeastern corner of Libya, as well as other areas in the Sahara, which will lead to the construction of more accurate

* These figures are for order of magnitude only. Apollo images of the earth rise photographed from the moon (approximately 240,000 miles from the earth) are a major exception.

geological maps of the area. Stratigraphic, hydrologic, and peleoclimatic determinations were also made from a study of the Gemini photography. Wobber (1969) provides many examples of space photography with detailed captions. He also sheds some light on the necessary resolution requirements and optimum solar altitude for the detection of terrain features.

Low-Sun-Angle Photography

Low-sun-angle photography has almost always been considered detrimental to photo interpretation work. Maximum sun angle, and the accompanying minimum solar shadowing, is a standard requirement for the acquisition of photographic coverage. As a result, conventional aerial photography was generally obtained during a four-hour time span, two hours before noon, sun time, and two hours past the solar noon.

Hackman (1967) was one of the first to realize the potential of flying photography other than during times of high sun angle. Hackman concluded that low-sun-angle photography increased the enhancement of topographic features; and he suggested that, if both high- and low-sun-angle photography were not feasible, a sun angle of 30° would be the most satisfactory.

The almost incidental acquisition of low-sun-angle photography during several Gemini missions illustrated the potential of enhancement of topographic features by solar shadowing. Subtle relief features that may not have been detected on high-sun orbital photography were observed by Wobber (1968). Subsequent interpretation of low-sun-angle Apollo photography by Gawarecki (1970) further substantiated the enhancement of topographic features. Gawarecki's studies also indicated that natural filtration of the shorter wavelengths by the increased atmosphere at low sun angles resulted in a degradation of the color contrast. Gawarecki (1970) agrees with Hackman (1967) that a 30° sun angle provides optimum topographic enhancement and adds that, at least in an arid environment, the 30° sun angle is also optimum for color contrast. Owing to the increase in atmospheric turbulence, dust, and thermal distortions in the afternoon, morning solar altitudes are better for low-sun-angle photography than photography taken in the afternoon at the same solar altitude (Gawarecki, 1970).

The 30° sun angle should not be construed as a hard-and-fast rule not to be broken, but rather as a guideline. Optimum solar altitudes for regions of high-terrain slope angles and large relative relief, such as the Rocky Mountains, would not provide optimum information in flat terrain, such as the Gulf Coast. The higher the terrain slope angles and relative relief, the higher the sun angle necessary for optimum topographic enhancement. Conversely, the lower the slope angles and less the relative relief, the lower is the sun angle necessary. Optimum sun angle for a given area should, therefore, be determined on the basis of an examination of the relative relief and terrain slope characteristics of the particular area.

Sequential Photography

Sequential photography is not a new technique in photo interpretation, nor can it be isolated as a separate entity. The technique crosses all types of film-sensors studies and techniques. It is truly a complementary technique that is useful in measuring net change, either qualitative or quantitative. Observation of change often leads to understanding process. The major disadvantage is that, unless sequential photography is obtained while the change is actually taking place, the exact time of the change cannot be documented, but only speculated within the time span of the sequential photography (El-Ashry and Wanless, 1967).

THERMAL INFRARED

Thermal infrared scanning sensors provide a two-dimensional output emitted of "temperature" patterns. Tone on the thermal imagery is related to the radiant temperature of the object, a function of the object's absolute temperature and emissivity. Lighter tones on an image positive are an indicator of hotter (higher) radiometric temperatures. The operation and further explanation of thermal infrared sensors is provided in Chapter 2 and in Lattman (1963), Harris et al. (1964), and Van Lopik (1968).

Thermal infrared imagery can be obtained by day or by night. The major restriction on obtaining thermal infrared imagery is cloud cover, unless the user is interested in the temperature patterns of clouds (e.g., NIMBUS and TIROS satellites). Unlike radar imagery--to be covered in the next section--thermal imagery and the type and amount of terrain information it contains vary considerably depending on the time of day and weather conditions. There is little agreement on the best time to fly infrared imagery; however, most researchers agree that the optimum daily time span is post-sunset and pre-dawn when solar energy is at a minimum. Cantrell (1964) states that the maximum geologic information from such imagery is obtained immediately following sundown; Friedman (1968) indicates the hours between 8:00 p.m. and midnight; and Gawarecki (1968) and Rowan et al. (1969) agree that pre-dawn is the best time to obtain infrared imagery. In general, it appears that lithologic and hydrologic variations are best viewed on nighttime thermal imagery (Cantrell, 1964; Friedman, 1968; Rowan et al., 1969), and topographic-relief features are best mapped from daytime thermal imagery (Cantrell, 1964; Friedman, 1968; Wolfe, 1968; Rowan et al., 1969). Northeast linear features are better enhanced on morning thermal imagery and northwest linears are better enhanced on afternoon imagery (Rowan et al., 1969). This suggests the importance of orientation.

The importance of thermal infrared data in geologic investigations is indicated by the features mapped or identified by thermal patterns. Structural features, faults, and joints, are generally areas of moisture concentration and stratigraphic offset (Sabins, 1967) and, therefore, a thermal anomaly (Cantrell, 1964; Wolfe, 1968). Lineaments are delimitable for the same reason (Van Lopik, 1968). Lithologic units (Lattman, 1963; Sabins, 1967; Gawarecki, 1968), as well as facies changes, have also been mapped (Rowan et al., 1969). Drainage patterns were delineated by Gawarecki (1968) and Cantrell (1964); geothermal features by Friedman (1968) and Matsuno et al. (1969); and volcanic features by McLerran (1967) and Garawecki (1968). McLerran (1967) also identified an eroding terrace, an old alluvial fan, and a major wash. Soil-moisture and soil-texture variations were identified on thermal infrared by Cantrell (1964).

In the past, and to a certain extent even today, two major problems for the interpreter of thermal infrared imagery are calibration and image-geometry distortions. These are basically systems design and engineering problems which are being overcome. Stingelin and Traxler (1971) reported recently on the development of a quantitative thermal scanner.

RADAR

Radar is distinguished from other remote sensors by two inherent characteristics. First, it is an active system which means it carries its own source of energy. This is in contrast to passive systems, such as a camera, which require solar illumination or some other outside source of illumination. Second, radar systems operate in the microwave portion of the EM spectrum. These two characteristics combine to give radar one of its primary advantages over other remote sensors; i.e., a nearly all-weather, 24-hour imaging capability. Being an active sensor, a radar system is independent of solar illumination and can, therefore, image day or night, producing imagery of equal quality. The longer wavelengths of EM energy used by radar systems, commonly ranging from 1 to 3 cm, have the capability of penetrating most cloud cover. The major exception is thick precipitation clouds, such as isolated thunderstorm cells.

Other advantages of radar imaging systems are their synoptic coverage and topographic enhancement. Although the scale of the image output varies considerably, the majority of the imagery is around 1:175,000 scale--easily within the range to be classified as small-scale imagery. The juxtaposition of high return (light tone) from the face slope and little or no return (dark tone) from the back slope results in a two-dimensional image that has a three-dimensional (pseudo-stereoscopic) appearance. Overlapping radar coverage can be used to obtain stereo radar imagery (Figure 5-3).

Interpretation of radar imagery, as with any type of nonphotographic imagery, is facilitated by the use of keys similar to those used in photo interpretation:

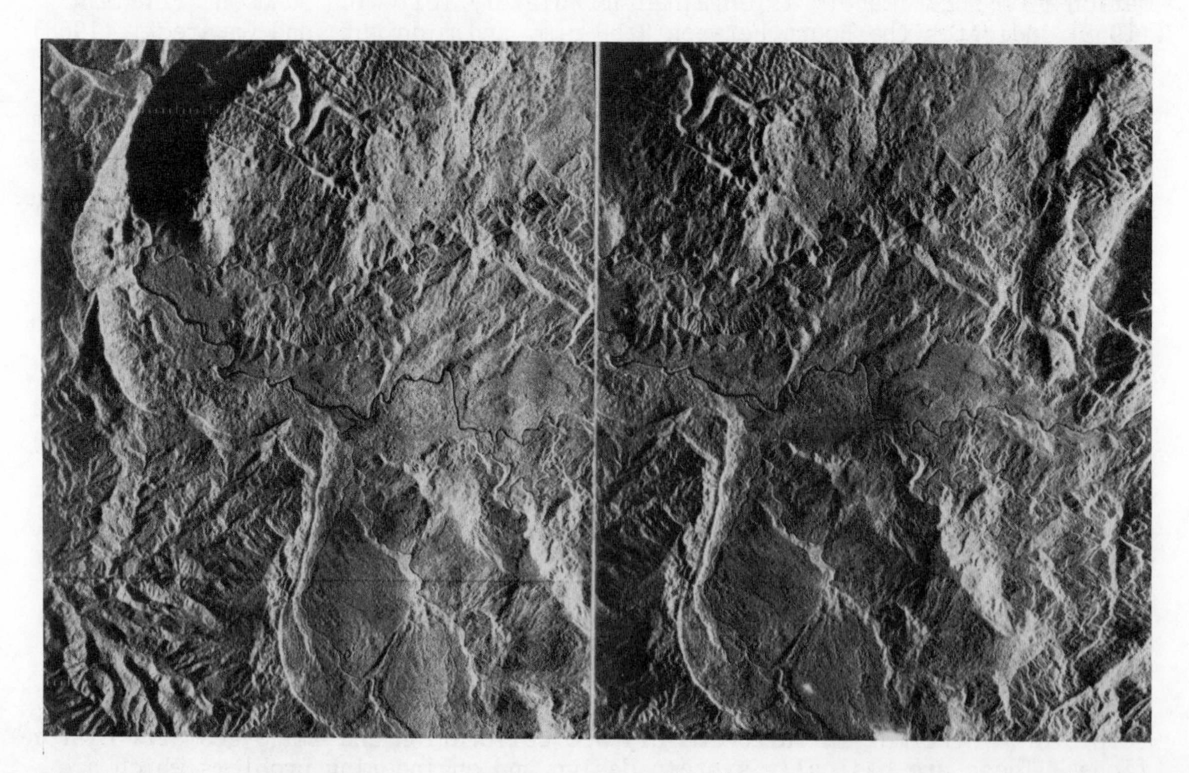

Figure 5-3. Stereoradar pair of an unknown region in New Guinea. (Courtesy of Westinghouse Corp., Baltimore, Md.)

tone; texture; size; shape; and, recently, stereo. Little difficulty is experienced when a qualified photo interpreter switches to radar imagery. The visual appearance of radar imagery is so similar to low-sun-angle, small-scale photography that this kind of photography is often dubbed "pseudoradar" (Lyon et al., 1970). However, there are important differences. The angle of illumination is essentially constant on low-sun-angle photography but may vary almost 50° on radar imagery. The angle and orientation of the illumination on the photograph is fixed by the geographic latitude, the time of day, and season of the year, whereas the angle and orientation of illumination on radar are a function of flight direction and range position, both of which can be varied to accommodate slope angle, relief, and structural grain of the topography.

Qualitative Interpretations

Regional. Regionalization is the forte of radar imagery. The synoptic presentation and the topographic enhancement by radar shadowing produces patterns on radar that are correlated with observed physical and cultural phenomena. Radar-derived regions represent an improvement over other methods of regionalization by increasing accuracy and comparability and decreasing time expenditure and cost (Nunnally, 1969).

Various types of regions have already been mapped from radar. Geomorphic regions have been delimited by Schwarz and Mower (1969) in Puerto Rico, MacDonald and Lewis (1969) along Route 17 in Panama, Nunnally (1969) in the Asheville Basin in North Carolina, Peterson (1970) in the Wasatch Range of Utah, Barr and Miles (1970) in several areas of the United States, and Lewis (1971) in the Darien Province of Panama. Tone and texture (actually frequency and length of radar shadows) were the prominent keys to regionalization, although Barr and Miles (1970) included land use, Nunnally (1969) incorporated size, shape, and arrangement, and MacDonald and Lewis (1969) added crest cross-sectional profile (rounded or sharp) for the subdivision of hills.

Surficial materials were also mapped by Peterson (1970) and Barr and Miles (1970). MacDonald (1970), using tone, texture, shape, and pattern, delimited the major lithologic units of the Darien Province, Panama. In a subsequent study, Wing (1971) delineated 30 major structural regions in eastern Panama from radar, which provided a better understanding of the global tectonics of the Isthmus of Panama.

Local or Individual Features. The resolution of unclassified radar systems (approximately 30 feet by 30 feet) is gross enough to prohibit the detection of many geomorphic-geologic features identifiable on high-resolution, large-scale photography. However, even at a scale of 1:175,000, radar imagery can be used successfully to map features found on a standard 1:62,500 USGS quadrangle map and occasionally even on a 1:24,000 topographic map.

Faults, fractures, and other geologic linears have been delimited by many authors (MacDonald, 1970; Gillerman, 1970; Jefferies, 1969; Peterson, 1970; Wing, 1971). The effect of look-direction on the detection of linears was studied by MacDonald (1970). MacDonald concluded that as the orientation of the lineament changed from parallel to perpendicular to the flight direction, detectability decreased.

Lava flows, cinder cones (Figure 5-4), collapse volcanoes, ring dikes, folds, anticlines, synclines, horsts, and grabens have been recognized on radar imagery by Schaber (1968), MacDonald (1970), and Wing (1971). Schaber (1968) was also able to distinguish between aa and pahoehoe types of lava flows, based on the tonal values on different polarizations.

The high ratio of radar return from land surfaces, compared to its return from water bodies, aids in detecting coastline changes and mapping coastal configuration and estuarine meanders (Lewis and MacDonald, 1970). Other coastal features identified on radar are tidal flats, shell reefs, direction of longshore current, beach ridges, mangrove coasts, kelp beds, vegetated foredunes, distributary channels and associated levee systems, and cheniers (MacDonald et al., 1971). Figure 5-5 illustrates some of these features.

Many erosional and depositional landforms resulting from continental and alpine glaciation are visible on radar imagery. McCauley (1972) mapped such features as moraines, U-shaped valleys, aretes, cirques, and morainic-formed lakes. Drumlins, evidence of scour by glacial meltwater, and deranged drainage can also be interpreted from radar imagery.

According to Peterson (1970), one of the greatest advantages of radar is the depiction of drainage patterns of large areas, although first-order and sometimes second-order streams are not interpretable because of the scale and resolution (Barr and Miles, 1970). Radar was also useful in determining ancestral drainage nets (Peterson, 1970), drainage anomalies (MacDonald, 1970), and stream piracy (Wing, 1971).

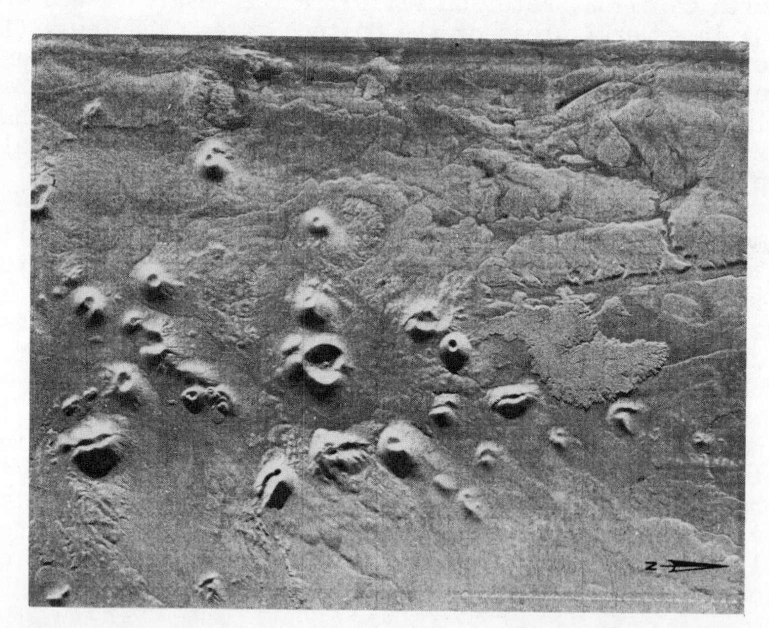

Figure 5-4. K-band radar image of the San Francisco volcanic field, north of Flagstaff, Arizona. Recent flow appears on the north (right) side of the image and originates at a symmetrical, unbreached cinder cone. Numerous breached cinder cones can also be identified. Scale of imagery is the same as Figure 5-5, i.e., original scale 1:175,000 or 16 kilometers across the image. (Courtesy of NASA; Westinghouse Corp.; and CRINC, University of Kansas).

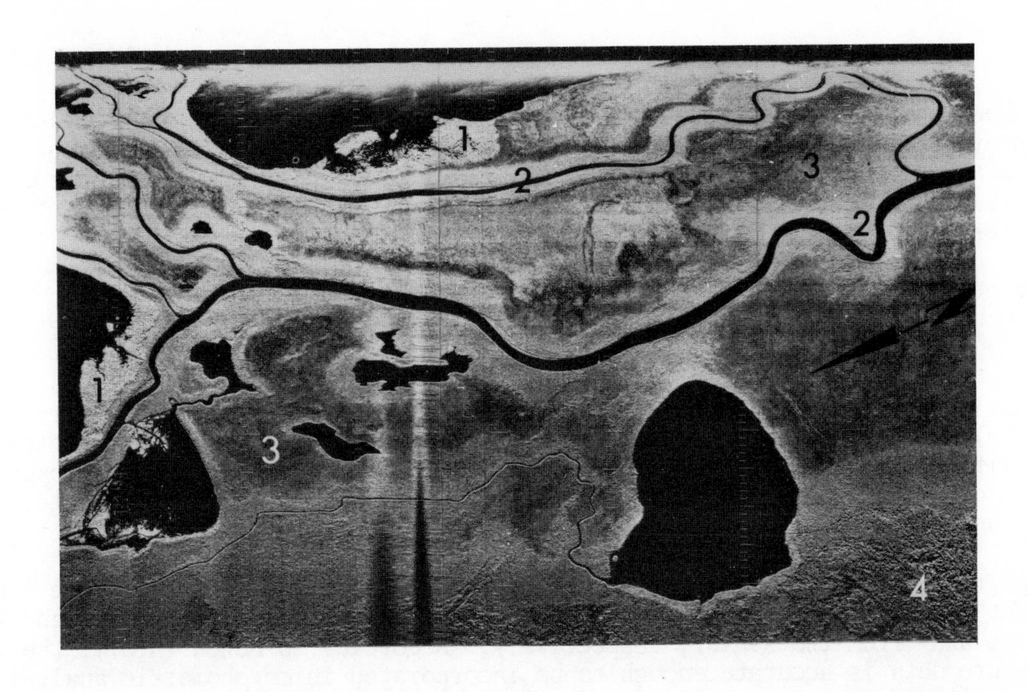

Figure 5-5. K-band radar imagery illustrating vegetation patterns in the Atrato Delta of Colombia. Patterns are related to geomorphic features. For example, (1) mangrove (tidal zone); (2) pangana community (natural levee); (3) grass and sedge community (back swamp); and (4) tropical rain forest. Approximate scale 1:175,000. (Courtesy of NASA; Westinghouse Corp.; and CRINC, University of Kansas).

Quantitative Data

The two major types of quantitative data readily available from radar imagery are morphometric (terrain slope angles and relative relief) and drainage net (such as basin order, bifurcation ratio, etc.). Morphometric data are potentially collected by way of four inherent distortions on radar imagery: radar parallax, radar layover, radar foreshortening, and radar shadows.* Of these, radar shadows are the most practical to use operationally. Foreshortening is ubiquitous, as is shadowing; however, the limited accuracy of measurements on the imagery, as compared with the sensitivity of the equations used for calculating slope and relative relief (Dalke and McCoy, 1969; Lewis, 1971), results in highly variable, inaccurate data. Radar parallax and radar layover are difficult to detect and almost impossible to measure, although equations for their use in calculating slope and relief have been derived (Levine, 1960; La Prade and Leonardo, 1969; Lewis, 1971).

The relationship of radar shadowing with terrain slope and relative relief is a simple one. The occurrence of radar shadows is a function of depression angle and terrain slope angle, and relative relief is directly related to the length of the shadow. More precisely, if a topographic feature produces a radar

* For detailed discussion of radar geometry, see MacDonald (1970), and Lewis (1971).

shadow, the terrain back slope must be greater than the depression angle; and, conversely, if no shadow occurs, the terrain back slope is less than the depression angle (Lewis and Waite, 1971a, 1971b). By sampling completely across the range (approximately 15° to 75° depression angle), a cumulative frequency curve of terrain slope can be constructed (Lewis and Waite, 1972a, 1972b).

The measurement of radar shadow lengths and subsequent correlation with map-determined relative relief data have also been demonstrated to be a successful method (Lewis and Waite, 1972).

Radar power return, a function of many parameters (one of which is terrain slope), looms as a potential source of morphometric data under certain terrain conditions (Cosgriff et al., 1960). This potential exists, if radar power return can be accurately quantified on radar imagery or radar scatterometer data are used (Lewis, 1971).

Topographic texture is reflected in radar texture, the frequency change from light to dark tone generally exhibited on the slope facing the sensor and the slope away from the sensor, respectively. According to Honea (n.d.), the radar texture data is accurate enough to be incorporated in morphometric analysis and lends itself to automatic interpretation techniques. Nunnally (1969) used radar texture, measured by micro-densitometer traces, of his "integrated landscape" regions to illustrate changing topographic texture with region.

Drainage patterns and stream anomalies can be identified on radar as stated previously. Defining drainage-basin nets from which stream numbers, drainage density, etc., are calculated, is difficult in flat marshing land and also in high-relief terrain where large areas are masked by radar shadows. Multiple look-directions should be flown, if possible, to increase the number of streams identified and aid in the determination of flow direction and position of drainage divides (Lewis, 1971).

Several drainage-basin parameters measured on radar imagery (original scale 1:175,000) compare favorably with the same parameters measured on 1:24,000-scale topographic maps (McCoy, 1969). The parameters that fare well in the comparison are drainage-basin area, bifurcation ratio, average length ratio, circularity ratio, and basin perimeter. With the sophistication of stereoradar, basin volume may be added to this list.

SUMMARY

There is little doubt that geomorphic and geologic studies have benefited by the use of remote sensing systems (primarily imaging sensors), although airborne magnetometers and other such devices have had extensive use in geologic exploration. Each sensor has its own advantages, whether it is resolution, cloud penetration, scale, or EM frequency sensitivity. These advantages may often overlap, but they can also be complementary. For a given geologic problem as for any other specific (vegetation, land use, etc.) photo-interpretation mission, the decision about which sensor or sensors are to be used is for the user to make, and should be based on specific mission objectives, geographic area, and budgetary constraints.

REFERENCES

American Society of Photogrammetry, 1960, *Manual of Photographic Interpretation*, George Banta Company, Inc., Menosha, Wis.

Barr, D. J., and R. D. Miles, 1970, "SLAR Imagery and Site Selection," *Photogrammetric Engineering*, 36:1155-1170.

Belcher, D. J., 1951, "A Photo Analysis Key for the Determination of Ground Conditions," *Landform Report Series*, vol. 1-6, Office of Naval Research, Washington, D.C.

Cantrell, J. L., 1964, "Infrared Geology," *Photogrammetric Engineering*, 30:916-922, 941.

Clark, Malcolm, 1969, "Geologic Utility of Small-Scale Airphotos," *Second Annual Earth Resources Aircraft Program Status Review*, NASA/MSC, Houston, Tex., pp.8.1-8.39.

Cosgriff, R. L., W. H. Peake, and R. C. Taylor, 1960, "Terrain Scattering Properties for Sensor System Design," *Eng. Exp. Station, Bulletin No. 181*, Ohio State University Press, Columbus, Ohio.

Dalke, G. W., and R. M. McCoy, 1969, "Regional Slopes With Non-Stereo Radar," *Photogrammetric Engineering*, 39(5):446-452.

DeBlieux, C. S., 1949, "Petroleum Geology in Gulf Coast Exploration," *American Association of Petroleum Geology Bulletin*, 33:1251-1259.

DeBlieux, C. W., and G. F. Shepard, 1951, "Photogeologic Study in Kent County, Texas," *Oil and Gas Journal*, 50(10):86, 88, 98-100.

deLoor, G. P., 1969, "Possibilities and Uses of Radar and Thermal Infrared Systems," *Photogrammetria*, 24(2):43-58.

Denny, Charles, et al., 1968, *A Descriptive Catalog of Selected Aerial Photographs of Geologic Features in the United States*, USGS Professional Paper 590, Government Printing Office, Washington, D.C.

Desjardins, L., 1950, "Techniques in Photogeology," *American Association of Petroleum Geology*, 34:2284-2317.

El-Ashry, M. R., and H. R. Wanless, 1967, "Shoreline Features and Their Changes," *Photogrammetric Engineering*, 33:184-189.

Erb, D. K., 1968, "Geomorphology of Jamaica," *Photogrammetric Engineering*, 34:1148-1160.

Fischer, W. A., 1958, "Color Aerial Photography in Photogeologic Interpretation," *Photogrammetric Engineering*, 24:545-549.

Fischer, W. A., 1962, "An Application of Radar to Geological Interpretation," *Proceedings of the First Symposium on Remote Sensing of Environment*, University of Michigan, Ann Arbor, pp. 83-84.

Friedman, Jules, 1968, "Thermal Anomalies and Geologic Features of the Mono Lake Area, California, as Revealed by Infrared Imagery," *Earth Resources Aircraft Program Status Review*, NASA/MSC, Houston, Tex., pp. 11.1 - 11.76.

Gawarecki, Stephen, 1968, "Infrared Survey of the Pisgah Crater Area, San Bernardino County, California: A Geologic Interpretation," *Earth Resources Aircraft Program Status Review*, NASA/MSC, Houston, Tex., pp. 10.1 - 10.36.

Gawarecki, Stephen, 1970, "Geologic Interpretation of Apollo 6 Stereophotography from Baja California to West Texas," *Third Annual Earth Resources Program Review*, NASA/MSC, Houston, Tex., pp. 15.1 - 15.25.

Gillerman, E., 1970, "Roselle Lineament of Southeast Missouri," *Geological Society of America Bulletin*, 81:975-982.

Hackman, R. J., 1967, *Time, Shadows, Terrain, and Photointerpretation*, USGS Professional Paper 575-B, pp. B155-B160, Government Printing Office, Washington,D.C.

Harris, D. E., C. O. Woodbridge, and L. Casper, 1964, "Terrain Mapping by Use of Infrared Radiation," *Photogrammetric Engineering*, 30:134-139.

Hemphill, W. R., 1958, "Small-Scale Photographs in Photogeologic Interpretation," *Photogrammetric Engineering*, 24:562-567.

Honea, Robert B., (n.d.), *Determination of Landform Texture from Radar Imagery*, Technical Report 16, East Tennessee State University, Remote Sensing Institute, Johnson City.

Howard, A. D., 1967, "Drainage Analysis in Geologic Interpretation: A Summation," *American Association of Petroleum Geology Bulletin*, 51:2246-2259.

Jefferies, L. H., 1969, *An Evaluation of Radar Imagery for Structural Analysis in Gently Deformed Strata: A Study in Northeast Kansas*, CRES Report 118-16, University of Kansas, Lawrence.

Johnson, D., 1932, "Streams and Their Significance," *Journal of Geology*, 40: 481-497.

Keifer, R. W., 1967, "Landform Features in the United States," *Photogrammetric Engineering*, 33:174-182.

LaPrade, G. L., and E. S. Leonardo, 1969, "Elevations from Radar Imagery," *Photogrammetric Engineering*, 35:366-371.

Lattman, L. H., 1958, "Technique of Mapping Geologic Fracture Traces and Lineaments on Aerial Photographs," *Photogrammetric Engineering*, 24:568-576.

Lattman, L. H., 1963, "Geologic Interpretation of Airborne Infrared Imagery," *Photogrammetric Engineering*, 29:83-87.

Leopold, L. B., and M. G. Wolman, 1957, *River Channel Patterns: Braided, Meandering, and Straight*, USGS Professional Paper 282, Government Printing Office, Washington, D.C.

Levine, D., 1960, *Radargrammetry*, McGraw-Hill Book Company, New York.

Lewis, A. J., 1971, *Geomorphic Evaluation of Radar Imagery of Southeastern Panama and Northwestern Colombia*, CRES Technical Report 133-18, University of Kansas, Lawrence.

Lewis, A. J., and H. C. MacDonald, 1970, "Significance of Estuarine Meanders Identified from Radar Imagery of Eastern Panama and Northwestern Colombia," *Modern Geology*, 1:187-196.

Lewis, A. J., and W. P. Waite, 1971a, "Cumulative Frequency Curves of the Darien Province, Panama," *AGARD Conference Proceedings No. 90*, 17th Symposium of Electromagnetic Wave Propogation Panel of AGARD, Colorado Springs, Colorado, June 21-25, pp. 10.1 - 10.10.

Lewis, A. J., and W. P. Waite, 1971b, "Cumulative Frequency Curves of Terrain Slopes from Radar Shadow Frequency," *American Society of Photogrammetry: Papers from Thirty-seventh Annual Meeting*, Washington, D.C., March 7-12, pp. 228-244.

Lewis, A. J., and W. P. Waite, 1972, "Relative Relief Measurements from Radar Shadows: Methods and Evaluation," *Proceedings of Association of American Geographers*, 4:65-69.

Lowman, P. D., Jr., 1964, *A Review of Photography of the Earth from Sounding Rockets and Satellites*, NASA Tech. Note, TND-1868.

Lueder, D. R., 1959, *Aerial Photographic Interpretation--Principles and Applications*, McGraw-Hill Book Company, New York.

Lyon, R. J. P., J. Mercado, and R. Campbell, Jr., 1970, "Psuedo Radar," *Photogrammetric Engineering*, 36:1257-1261.

MacDonald, H. C., 1970, "Geologic Evaluation of Radar Imagery from Darien Province, Panama," *Modern Geology*, 1:1-63.

MacDonald, H. C., and A. J. Lewis, 1969, *Terrain Analysis with Radar--A Preliminary Study*, Interim Technical Progress Report, Fourth Semi-Annual Technical Report, Project THEMIS, CRES, University of Kansas, Lawrence, pp. F.1 - F.12.

MacDonald, H. C., A. J. Lewis, and R. S. Wing, 1971, "Mapping and Landform Analysis of Coastal Regions with Radar," *Geological Society of American Bulletin*, 82:345-358.

Majtenyi, S., and D. Belcher, 1970, "Discharge Properties of Drainage Basins Observable from Aerial Photographs," paper presented at the Thirty-sixth Annual Meeting of the American Society of Photogrammetry, Washington, D.C.

Matsuno, K., H. Hase, and K. Nishimura, 1969, "On IR Imagery and Its Application to the Mapping of Geothermal Distributions," *Photogrammetria*, 25(2/3): 61-74.

MacCauley, J., 1972, "An Evaluation of Radar Imagery in Areas of Alpine Glaciation," In *Radar Remote Sensing for Geoscientists*, CRINC, University of Kansas, Lawrence, pp. 4.2-1 - 4.2-12.

McCoy, R. M., 1969, "Drainage Network and Analysis with K-band Radar Imagery," *Geographical Review*, 39:493-512.

McLerran, J. H., 1967, "Infrared Thermal Sensing," *Photogrammetric Engineering*, 33:507-512.

Melton, F. A., 1936, "An Empirical Classification of Flood-Plain Streams," *Geographical Review*, 26:39-85.

Miller, V. C., 1961, *Photogeology*, McGraw-Hill Book Company, New York.

Morrison, R. B., 1970, "Geologic Terrain Mapping from Earth Satellite and Ultra-High Aerial Photographs," *Third Annual Earth Resources Aircraft Program Status Review*, NASA/MSC, Houston, Tex., pp. 16.1 - 16.5.

Norman, J. W., 1970, "Linear Geological Features as an Aid to Photogeological Research," *Photogrammetria*, 25(5/6):177-187.

Nunnally, N. R., 1969, "Integrated Landscape Analysis with Radar Imagery," *Remote Sensing of Environment*, 1:1-6.

Parry, J. T., and H. Turner, 1971, "Infrared Photos for Drainage Analysis," *Photogrammetric Engineering*, 37:1031-1038.

Parvis, M., 1950, "Drainage Pattern Significance in Airphoto Identification of Soils and Bedrocks," *Highway Research Board Bulletin*, 28:36-42.

Pesce, Angelo, 1968, *Gemini Space Photographs of Libya and Tibesti*, Petroleum Exploration Society of Libya, Tripoli.

Peterson, R. M., 1970, *Thematic Mapping and Geographical Interpretation with Radar Imagery of the Wasatch Range, Utah*, Fifth Semi-Annual Technical Report--Project THEMIS, CRES, University of Kansas, Lawrence, pp. 183-185.

Poole, Donald H., (n.d.), *The Development of Criteria for Recognizing and Identifying Slope Failure Forms as Depicted by Remote Sensor Returns*, Technical Report 12, East Tennessee State University, Remote Sensing Institute, Johnson City.

Powers, W. E., 1951, "A Key for the Photo-Identification of Glacial Landforms," *Photogrammetric Engineering*, 17:776-779.

Ray, R. G., 1960, *Aerial Photographs in Geologic Interpretation and Mapping*, Geological Survey Professional Paper 373, Government Printing Office, Washington, D.C.

Ray, R. G., and W. A. Fischer, 1960, "Quantitative Photography--A Geologic Tool," *Photogrammetric Engineering*, 26:143-150.

Rowan, L. C., et al., 1969, "Thermal Infrared Investigations, Mill Creek Area, Oklahoma," *Second Annual Earth Resources Aircraft Program Status Review*, NASA/MSC, Houston, Tex., pp. 5.1 - 5.25.

Russell, R. J., 1939, "Louisiana Stream Patterns," *American Association of Petroleum Geology Bulletin,* 23:119-1227.

Sabins, F. F., 1967, "Infrared Imagery and Geology Aspects," *Photogrammetric Engineering,* 33:743-750.

Schaber, Gerald, 1968, "Radar and Infrared in Geological Studies of Northern Arizona," *Earth Resources Aircraft Program Status Review,* NASA/MSC, Houston, Tex., pp. 13.1 - 13.29.

Schwarz, D. E., and R. D. Mower, 1969, "The Potential for Deriving Land Form Regions from Radar Imagery: A Puerto Rican Example," in *Technical Letter NASA-140,* NASA Contract R-09-020-024, pp. 22-35.

Shaw, S. H., 1953, "The Value of Air Photos in the Analysis of Drainage Patterns," *Photogrammetric Record,* 2:4-17.

Sternberg, Irwin, 1961, "Drainage Studies from Aerial Surveys," *Photogrammetric Engineering,* 27:638-644.

Stingelin, R. W., and B. T. Traxler, 1971, "A Quantitative Airborne Infrared Imaging System," *Proceedings of the Seventh International Symposium on Remote Sensing of Environment,* University of Michigan, Ann Arbor, pp. 1483-1496.

Tator, B. A., 1954, "Drainage Anomalies in Coastal Plain Regions," *Photogrammetric Engineering,* 20:412-417.

Tator, B. A., 1958, "The Aerial Photography and Applied Geomorphology," *Photogrammetric Engineering,* 24:549-561.

Teichert, C., and R. W. Fairbridge, 1950, "Photo Interpretation of Coral Reefs," *Photogrammetric Engineering,* 16, pp. 744-755.

van der Bent, E. T., 1969, "Dip Estimate for Photogeology," *Photogrammetric Engineering,* 35:1225-1227.

van der Meer Mohr, H. E. C., 1969, "Geologic Interpretation of Hyperaltitude Photographs from Gemini Spacecraft," *Photogrammetria,* 24:167-174.

Van Lopik, J., 1968, "Infrared Mapping," *Geoscience News,* 1:3.

von Bandat, J. F., 1962, *Aerogeology,* Gulf Publishing Company, Houston, Texas.

Warren, C., et al., 1969, *A Descriptive Catalog of Selected Aerial Photographs of Geologic Features in Areas Outside the United States,* USGS Professional Paper 591, Government Printing Office, Washington, D.C.

Wasem, A. R., 1949, "Petroleum Photogeology," *Photogrammetric Engineering,* 15:579-589.

Wing, R. S., 1971, "Structural Analysis from Radar Imagery of the Eastern Panamanian Isthmus," *Modern Geology,* 2:75-127.

Wobber, F. J., 1968, "Orbital Photography--Applied Earth Survey Tool," in *Photographic Applications in Science and Technology,* IBM, pp. 21-29.

Wobber, F. J., 1969, "Environmental Studies Using Earth Orbital Photography," *Photogrammetria,* 24(3/4):107-165.

Wolfe, Edward W., 1968, "Geologic Evaluation of Thermal Infrared Imagery, Caliente and Temblor Ranges, Southern California," *Earth Resources Aircraft Program Status Review,* NASA/MSC, Houston, Tex., pp. 12.1 - 12.27.

Zernitz, Emilie R., 1932, "Drainage Patterns and Their Significance," *Journal of Geology,* 40:498-521.

Interpretation and Mapping of Natural Vegetation

Stanley A. Morain
University of Kansas

Although it may justifiably be said that few phenomena on the earth are unaffected by the actions of man, the "natural" vegetation discussed in this chapter includes primarily those plants not selectively bred by man (as distinct from agricultural crops, which have been genetically altered). Vegetation resources are important in the carbon cycle as sources of fuel, as building materials, as general indicators of ecological conditions, and for the aesthetic needs of man. Remote sensing research in this field is examined from two viewpoints: (1) the capability of various sensor systems to provide needed data and (2) the applicability of remote sensing data for generating floristic, physiognomic and structural, and ecological vegetation maps.

From crude beginnings, the art of mapping vegetation has passed from the purely symbolic form represented by Ptolemaic-type trees to complex patterns, lines, colors, and symbols, depicting not only distributions but aspects of structure, ecology, floristic composition, disease characteristics, history, and economic importance (Kuchler, 1967). Maps at all scales, from unity to those portraying the entire earth, and ranging in focus from the geographical distribution of individual plant species to more abstract phenomena (such as terrestrial and aquatic ecosystems, biomes, and life zones) are now commonplace. At present, the need for such maps is great; unfortunately, the present means of gathering and interpreting the requisite field data are grossly inefficient.

There appears, at present, to be no reasonable means for providing timely and accurate data for vegetation maps using traditional approaches. The main contribution of remote sensing will be as an aid in distinguishing seminatural and messicol* vegetation from natural communities at regional and national scales.

Much of this material is condensed from a contribution to the *Handbook of Vegetation Science*, Chapter on Vegetation Mapping, The Hague, in progress.

* "Seminatural" refers to all types of cultural vegetation not deliberately planted by man but maintained by his activities; "messicol" refers strictly to cultural vegetation, or that actually planted by man (Kuchler, 1967).

In addition, as will be shown in the following sections, a wealth of opportunities exists for mapping phenomena not easily surveyed by ground data collection alone. Nevertheless, it should be stressed that remote sensing, no matter how complete the program, will never substitute for field investigations (see Chapter 2).

SENSOR REVIEW AND ASSESSMENT FOR VEGETATION MAPPING

The following discussion of sensors is constrained in several ways. In this chapter, imagery from the region below 0.4 um (ultraviolet) will not be considered. For information on ultraviolet sensors and fuller discussion of sensors, the reader should consult Chapter 2. At the other extreme, imagery from the radar region beyond 3 cm will not be discussed because it is not widely available. Besides these restrictions, there must also be a selection of the types of sensors. Those operating in the visible region can be grouped for convenience into conventional (black-and-white photography, color, and color infrared) and nonconventional (multiband camera, multispectral scanner) systems. This discussion will not dwell upon conventional photographic sensors since they are already amply treated in the literature (Smith, 1968; Heller, 1969; Sorem, 1967; and Colwell, 1960). For the remainder, only those sensors capable of producing images will be discussed, in the belief that these constitute the best mapping base. Specifically, these sensors are multispectral scanners, thermal infrared imagers, multiband cameras, and radar imagers. For comprehensive bibliographies of these sensors (including photography) and their applications to natural vegetation, see Krumpe (1972) and Sapp et al. (1971).

Multispectral Scanners

The strategy behind multispectral scanning is that, by separating the spectrum into a number of bands, a unique signature may be obtained for a given object or phenomenon. Implicit in this approach is acceptance of the spectral-signature concept; that is, each entity in nature has an identifiable spectral "fingerprint." Multispectral scanning thus aims to divide the spectrum into narrow parts, which may be utilized to isolate the entities under study. Data are not collected necessarily in an image format, and the consequent number of "bits" of data for any scene may be staggering. The sorting and recombination may be handled best by a computer.

In general, three kinds of vegetational information can be obtained by spectral signature analysis in the spectral region between 0.4 um and 2.6 um. This is the region most finely partitioned by present scanning systems. Variations in pigmentation are detectable in the visible bands (0.4 to 0.7 um); structural differences in spongy mesophyll are indirectly observable in the near-infrared region (0.8 to 1.0 um); and moisture stress is best detected in the far infrared region (between 1.6 um and 2.6 um) (Rohde, 1971; Rohde and Olson, 1971). Variations in pigmentation may be useful for certain mapping problems if they are used in concert with image texture and collateral ecological information. Indeed, a significant advantage of multispectral scanning over conventional color aerial photography lies in its capability for detecting subtle tonal variations. It also implies that optimum information will be obtained from low-altitude aircraft surveys rather than from space altitudes because the desire to delineate subtle differences suggests that the major vegetation pattern is already known and that minor internal differences are being sought. At higher altitudes and coarser resolution (both spectrally and spatially), one might anticipate that only gross variations in pigmentation would be mappable; and, for these variations, photography will probably remain the most efficient tool.

Recording subtle tonal variations and converting them to mappable categories is extremely difficult if performed over large areas, because species and community reflectivities vary directionally and temporally. The angular dependencies of bluegrass (Poa pratensis) and sycamore (Platanus occidentalis) leaves illustrate the point. Mary (1964) found that bluegrass having randomly oriented blades 2 inches long had a narrow range of reflectivities, irrespective of viewing angle, in the spectral band between 0.067 um and 1.03 um. Sycamore leaves, however, showed a reflectance peak of 0.545 volts at 20° and a null of 0.2 at 84°. Egbert and Ulaby (1972) went a step further by measuring changes in grass reflectivity as a function of solar altitude, incidence angle (camera angle), and azimuth angle (e.g., pointing into or away from the sun) for various spectral bands. An example of their results is given in Figure 6-1. Consequently, the prospect of measuring and comparing these relationships for each species and community, for each angle scanned by the system, and for each spectral channel employed staggers the imagination. Intuitively, the spectral-signature concept is valid. However, difficulties arise in matching theory with practice; that is, to match ground and canopy measurements with aircraft and spacecraft measurements. In the absence of such matching, there is no convenient way to interpret differences enhanced by spectral partitioning. In short, until a data bank of consistently repeatable signatures for different vegetation types (based on directional and temporal reflectance variability) is obtained, the interpretation accuracy using multispectral techniques will continue to be less than optimal.

Beyond conventional vegetation typing on the basis of what are assumed to be "normal" color (spectral) differences, agronomists, foresters, and ecologists are also concerned about mapping moisture stress, pollution damage, and disease infestations; that is, "abnormal" color differences. Mapping moisture stress is theoretically possible because of the interrelationship between stomatal aperture and transpiration. Under stress conditions, leaf stomata close to conserve water. The consequent reduction in transpiration rate diminishes the effectiveness of the plant's cooling mechanism; and, thus, its temperature, and often its reflectance, are altered. Reportedly, in stressed vegetation the visible reflectance increases but the direction and degree of infrared reflectance varies (Knipling, 1969). The largest differences of all, both within and between species, are believed to occur in the infrared portion of the spectrum at wavelengths between 1.4 um and 2.6 um (Rohde and Olson, 1971).

In practice, tonal abnormalities are detectable on large-scale imagery. Rohde (1971), for example, observed that false color images produced from scanner data permitted easier detection of needle cast disease on Scotch pine (P. sylvestris) and Fomes annosus damage on Red pine (P. resinosa) than did either conventional color or color infrared films. Weber and Polcyn (1971) reported similar success in detecting stress in forests. The most obvious limitation in extrapolating the technique to large areas, however, is that the causes of color change in vegetation are legion and directly related to the recent history of each habitat. While it may be possible to detect differences, the need for field observations, at least on a sampling basis, is still essential for classification.

Processing and displaying data from multispectral scanners is a complicated and

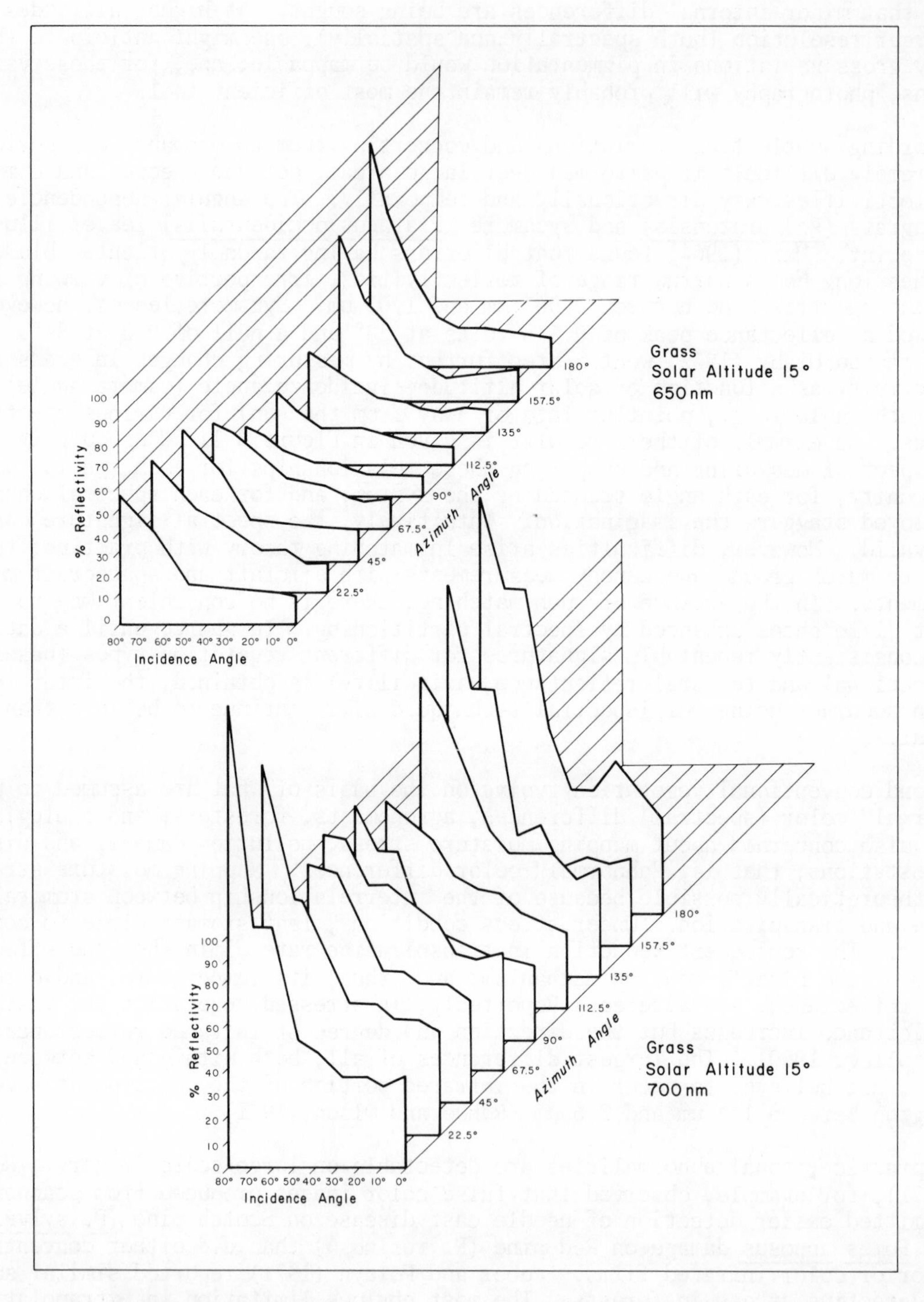

Figure 6-1. Reflectance from grass as a function of incidence angles (viewing angle), azimuth angle (camera looking into or away from sun), solar altitude, and spectral wavelength. The amount of reflectivity from grass at 0.65 um and 0.7 um, when the sun is 15° above the horizon, varies considerably depending upon camera and solar geometry. By knowing these relationships for each of the major growthform categories in a vegetated scene, one can more effectively design remote sensing experiments to capitalize on spectral differences. From Egbert and Ulaby (1972).

costly endeavor and would become even more so if international mapping standards were met. The data are stored on magnetic tape and later converted to an image format. Individual bands or combinations of bands can be displayed with color added to aid the delineation of categories. The most pressing difficulties remain those of geometric infidelity. Nevertheless, for rapid, special-purpose surveys of small areas, where the results are not intended for long-term use, these problems are surmountable. The object in these kinds of applications is to gain as near a real-time picture as possible of short-term vegetational phenomena. Usually, as in the case of disease attack or moisture stress, the potential savings more than offset the expense of collecting and processing the data. "Maps," in the usual sense of the word, are not the object of the program.

Thermal Infrared Scanners

In the thermal infrared region of the electromagnetic spectrum, we record that part of the absorbed solar energy that is reemitted. This thermal sensing is made possible by the fact that an object's total radiation is temperature dependent according to the Stefan-Boltzmann law.* Tone values recorded by this type of sensing device represent the total radiation incident upon a highly sensitive detector. When viewed in a positive (as opposed to photographic negative) form warm objects in the landscape appear in relatively light tones; cooler ones in darker tones. More sophisticated interpretation may be constrained by intervening variables, the most important of which relate to the atmosphere and the spectral characteristics of specific objects.

In Figure 6-2, a thermal scan image is shown of Kalgin Island in Cook Inlet, Alaska. The imagery was obtained during spring daylight hours so that the water appears relatively cooler (darker) than the land. Intuitively, the observable tones are related to vegetational cover. Boundaries are easily traced between types but interpretation beyond this level of generalization is difficult. The renditions in Figure 6-2 represent independent attempts by knowledgeable phytocenologists of differing backgrounds in remote sensing and in their knowledge of Alaskan vegetation. It is clear from these examples that there is a strong tendency to interpret this kind of imagery as though it were photography.

Thermal infrared "signatures" are a constantly changing function of the diurnal cycle; hence relative tonal differences between objects are of little inherent value except insofar as they facilitate boundary detection between communities. The obvious exception, of course, relates to extreme temperature anomalies (e.g., forest fires), and it is precisely here that thermal imaging has found a unique application in vegetation science.

In spite of the above difficulties, one should not despair for future applications of infrared line scanners. With continued research into the thermal properties of species and species groups, into methods for calibrating the imagery,

* The Stefan- Boltzmann law states that the total radiation from an object is equal to the product of the fourth power of its absolute temperature and the Stefan-Boltzmann constant.

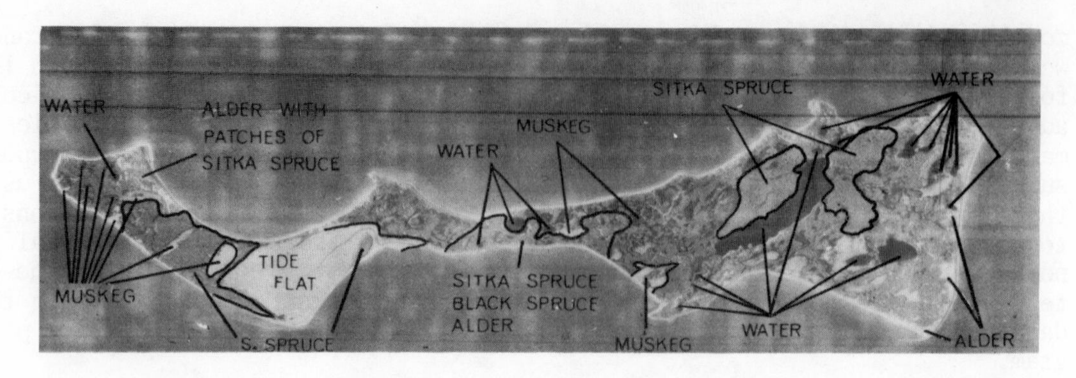

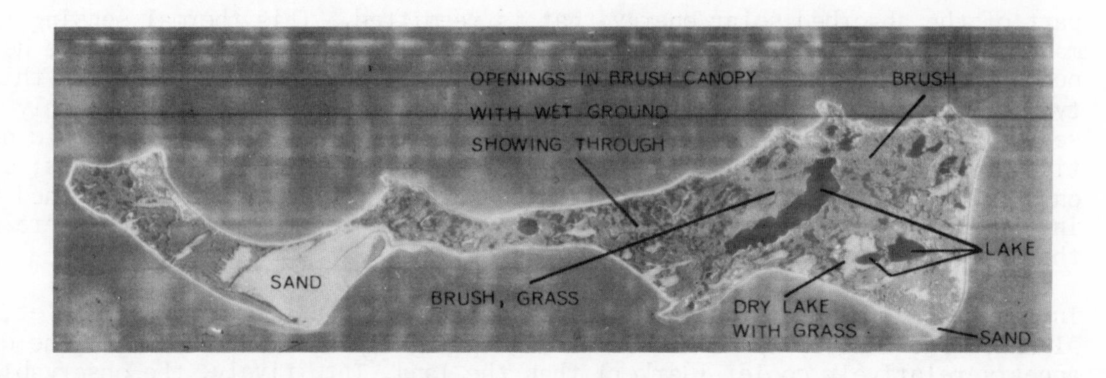

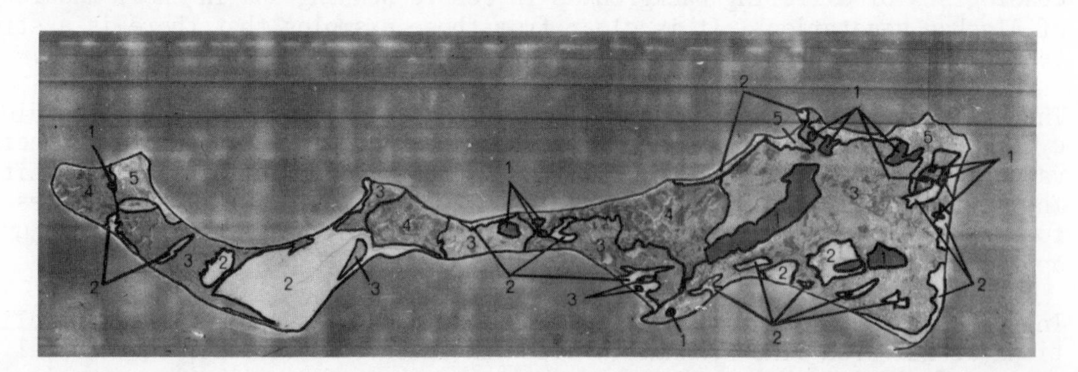

Figure 6-2. Thermal infrared image of Kalgin Island, Cook Inlet, Alaska. (Top) An interpretation by foresters familiar with the area but not with thermal imagery; (Middle) An interpretation by foresters moderately familiar with both the imagery and the study area; (Bottom) An interpretation by the author, with the following categories: 1 = open water, 2 = unvegetated (probably sand), 3 = moderate to well drained (probably spruce forest), 4 = poorly drained (probably alder and willow with "islands" of category 3), and 5 = transition between 2 and 3 (proportions of elements vary). Each interpretation was done independently. The results indicate the need for ground observations to aid interpretation of observable patterns as well as a need for understanding the sensor system.

and into rectification techniques, we may someday be able to map and interpret extremely subtle ecological differences and apply these data to energy-budget studies of ecosystems. It is even conceivable that such measures as community productivity, as registered by CO_2 turnover, may be qualitatively estimated by comparing image intensities through an atmospheric window (perhaps at 3.5 to 4 um), with those obtained in a CO_2 absorption band (say at 2.8 um or 4.3 um) (Cooper, 1964). While ideas such as these present problems, their solution is theoretically practical and they are not beyond the scope of technical feasibility.

Multiband Photography

Multiband photography, like multispectral scanning, utilizes the signature concept. It differs from scanning in its use of film-filter combinations instead of detectors for spectral partitioning. Since the medium is film rather than magnetic tape, the range of sensitivity is confined by film-emulsion technology to the visible and near-infrared regions (.4 to 1.0 u). However, the number of film types and filters is constantly increasing; and, since each gives a somewhat different range of spectral signatures under different exposure and development situations, it is clear that this approach to vegetation mapping has considerable versatility.

From the standpoint of mapping, multiband photography should be preferable to scanner data, though probably not in all instances. Slices of the visible spectrum, as narrow as those obtainable using detectors, can be achieved while retaining a metric mapping base. Moreover, camera systems are capable of fine resolution so that image texture and scene content are in large part preserved to aid interpretation.

The selection of proper film-filter combinations that exploit tonal differences between the phenomena being mapped is important. This can be done only after careful consideration of the reflectance properties of those phenomena (Colwell and Lent, 1967). Reflectances for most species and communities have not been measured, and for those cases where they have (e.g., Gates et al., 1965; Olson and Good, 1962), we are quite uncertain about the relationships linking ground or laboratory measurements with tonal renditions on aerial and space photographs.* In short, the capability for quantitative measurements of tone is no greater or less than it is in multispectral scanning; but the potential for mapping moderately subtle tonal differences is increased by the multiband approach.

If spectral curves for every species, group of species, and ecological situation (as well as for their growth stages, etc.) were available we could predict which entities should be distinguishable along any given slice of the spectrum and choose our film-filter combinations accordingly. In the absence of these data, we must accept the notion that some desired categories will be lost (and some

---

* Kondrat'yev et al. (1970) have recently reported on the results of joint aircraft and spacecraft spectrophotometry experiments involving natural terrain surfaces. Their results are among the first attempts of this kind and are encouraging.

undesirable ones included) in the "noise" in any selection of films and filters. This raises an interesting question regarding how many categories or classes of phenomena can be meaningfully extracted from a given set of images. The utilization of images from six different bands of a heterogeneous landscape may be sufficient to distinguish upper-canopy growthforms and some ecological situations, but be insufficient for species identifications. Images from six additional bands may permit some floristic identifications but lead to ambiguities related to differences in their growth stages or vigor. The same 12 bands, when employed over a relatively homogeneous landscape (e.g., a broad expanse of Great Basin sage, A. tridentata), may provide no more discrimination than a single well-chosen band. If these two environments are now compared for the same 12 bands, or any combination thereof, the interpretation and categorization are extremely complex. The excessive number of images may overload the interpreter with too much information.

The scale of multiband photography is also an important consideration. For many routine forest and range mapping requirements, where the final objectives may be local timber typing, volume estimates, or animal-carrying capacities, large-scale photographs (1:3,000 to 1:20,000), especially those maximizing tonal and spatial distinctions, are considered best by most interpreters. As a rule, large-scale photographs are also most useful in terms of special-purpose mapping for the identification of plant stress (moisture, disease, pollution damage). At present, however, our knowledge of how to isolate and interpret stress conditions on imagery is incomplete and, as long as the area to be mapped remains relatively small, multispectral scanning probably has an advantage over multispectral photography insofar as it may provide data over a wider bandwidth. The area should be small, however, in order for the scanner to be flown low enough to maintain maximum spatial and spectral resolution.

At the opposite extreme, over very large areas or at high aircraft altitudes, only reconnaissance or semidetailed interpretations are usually required. In these situations, broad-band color and color infrared films have been shown to be best. If need be, such photographs can be color separated in the laboratory to partition the data into essentially the same bands which may be obtained utilizing a multiband camera.

Active Microwave (Radar)

Imaging radar has become a focus of interest for vegetation mapping only within the past decade. Only since the late 1950s have such systems been employed for any purposes outside the military establishment; hence, interpretive arts and techniques are just now developing. The part of the spectrum usually regarded as the microwave region ranges from just under 1 cm to about 100 cm. For all practical purposes, however, we need consider only the bandwidth between 0.8 cm and 3 cm (the so-called K- and X-bands).

Radar systems are unique among the sensors discussed here for several reasons. First, because they operate by transmitting a signal and receiving that portion reflected by the surface, they are described as active sensors. Second, because they do not rely on solar illumination, they can acquire imagery at times when photographic sensors may be inoperable. Third, as a consequence of their long wavelength, they can obtain imagery through thick cloud layers and, depending upon their precise wavelength, through many kinds of precipitating clouds.

Finally, they are capable of producing intermediate and small-scale reconnaissance-type imagery which is geometrically correct for mapping purposes. The sum of these attributes suggests that metric quality imagery of regions hitherto inaccessible either because of remoteness or because of persistent cloud cover could be obtained using radar as the primary sensor.

Side-looking airborne radar (SLAR) sensors do possess some undesirable features, most of them imposed by their peculiar design and problems of geometry. Among these, and perhaps most important for vegetation mapping, is their design based on a single frequency. Others include (1) their moderate-to-coarse resolution and (2) the fact that, at present, all SLARs are uncalibrated. These problems and their possible solutions are detailed by Moore (1970), but deserve brief comment here.

Use of single-frequency (monspectral) imaging systems is extremely limiting for vegetation identification. A pseudomultispectral capability is presently achieved by altering the polarization of transmitted and received signals from horizontal to vertical. Thus, a scene imaged at any given frequency may be displayed in four polarizations: horizontal transmit and receive (HH), horizontal transmit, vertical receive (HV), VV, or VH. Unfortunately, there exists only scant theoretical information regarding the reflectance properties of species and natural communities as a function of polarization; and, as a result, most of the current ability to interpret imagery is derived from empirical observations supported by incomplete or (sometimes) inappropriate ground data. For similar reasons (and more) there are difficulties surrounding the interpretation of multifrequency imagery. Nevertheless, there is some evidence to indicate that the broad-band microwave response to vegetation is at least as variable as its visible response; and, since sensors operating in the visible portion of the electromagnetic spectrum will always be time-of-day dependent, it would seem highly desirable to develop a true multispectral radar capability for use in vegetation science.

Most imagery flown for civilian use in the United States is described as having a ground resolvable distance of 12-to-15-meters. This means that objects spaced more closely than this in the landscape cannot be separately resolved. The question of resolution, however, is considerably more complex than this because the factors governing resolution along the flight path are different from those across the path.* Moreover, various signal-averaging techniques which affect resolution are used in producing imagery, and the film emulsion itself has resolution limits. Usually the resolution of film emulsions is far higher than that of the sensor systems, but it is conceivable that a high-resolution synthetic-aperture radar, operated at hyper or space altitudes and employing a wide swath width and narrow film format, could approach the resolution limits of the film.

Aside from frequency and resolution limitations, problems of calibration are perhaps most serious. Even if we knew, quantitatively, the microwave reflectance characteristics of different vegetation types, we could not interpret them quantitatively from radar imagery. There are so many uncalibrated data transformations from point reflectance to processed imagery that only qualitative statements can be made relative to the contents of a single image. Oftentimes,

---

* For more on resolution, see Chapter 2.

even these are questionable unless the sensing aircraft is equipped with roll, pitch, and yaw recorders. In other words, part of the unique advantage of radar as an "active" sensor is lost because systems have not been designed to accurately measure differences in received signal strength.

Radar imagery for an area east of Klamath Falls is shown in Figure 6-3 to illustrate the use of radar in vegetation mapping. Three general regions can be readily identified. The mottled pattern of high and low return on the left is typical of swamp or marsh vegetation where areas of standing water (black) intersperse with dense grass (white) having high water content. The broad region of medium grey tones in the center of the image can be segregated on the basis of subtle textural changes into two types. The coarse (spongelike) texture represents mature ponderosa pine forest (Pinus ponderosa) with trees of uneven heights and ages. The more subdued (blurred) texture represents chaparral shrubland dominated by manzanita (Arctostaphylos). Finally, the dark region on the

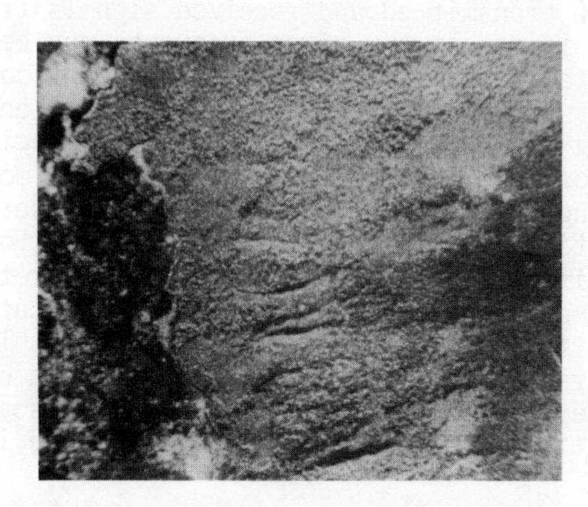

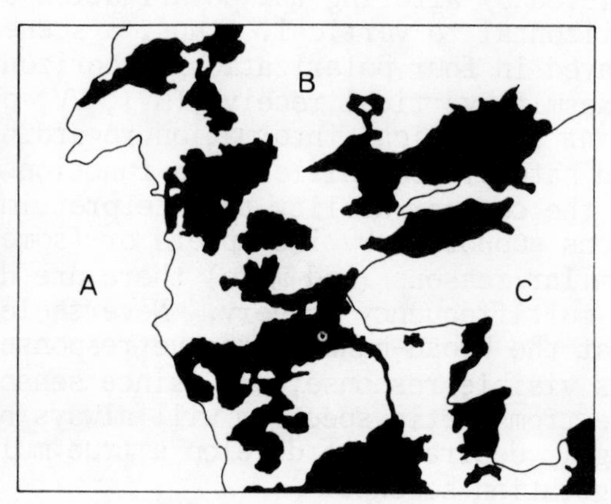

Figure 6-3. Ka-band radar image illustrating the HH tone and texture renditions of major physiognomic vegetation types. Area A, which appears on the image in mottled black-and-white, is a swampy meadow wherein the lighter tones are wet spots and the darker tones are dry. The extensive area of B is pine forest dominated by Pinus ponderosa. It has a medium grey tone, but is distinguishable by its relatively coarse texture. Area C is a fir forest (Pseudotsuga menziesii), distinguished by both its dark tone and more or less prominant texture. Chaparral communities, dominated by Arctostaphylos, are portrayed in solid black on the map. They are not immediately apparent on the imagery but are detectable by their finer texture in comparison with surrounding pine forest. Imagery courtesy of NASA.

right of the image is a fir forest (Abies concolor). It differs from ponderosa pine in tone, more than in texture, for reasons that are not yet clear but which are probably related to needle orientation and density, moisture content, and associated vegetation.

Examples of HH and HV images for various natural environments are shown in Figure 6-4a to c. Figure 6-4a is an excellent portrayal of plant community patterns near Horsefly Mountain, Oregon, and it is clear that boundary delineation is easier on the HV than on the HH presentation. We seldom see such contrasts in dry-land vegetation; and, when we do, there are attendant uncertainties regarding their interpretation. In this specific example, there is little visual HH-HV difference in the tonal or textural appearances of the forest ("spongy" areas), but the nonforest category (smoother texture) has a darker tone on the HV image. One may conclude from these relations that pine forest is a moderately good signal scatterer in both the horizontal and vertical modes (perhaps slightly

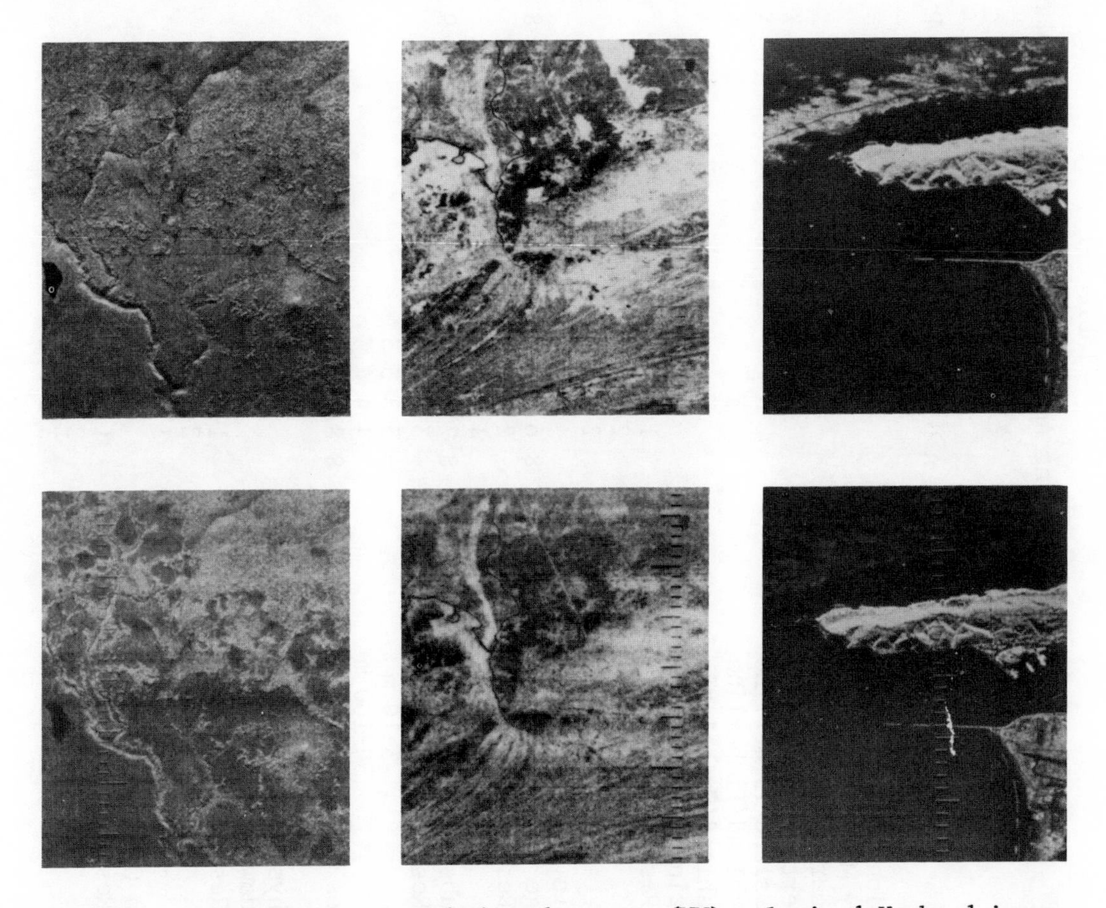

Figure 6-4. Examples of like- (HH) and cross- (HV) polarized Ka-band imagery from three vegetational environments: (a) Oregon pine forest; (b) Texas coast; (c) California giant kelp. Grey tones can be compared only within a single image due to uncalibrated changes in receiver gain, but relative tone shifts can be compared between like and cross images. The greatest range of tones usually is associated with scenes having complex patterns of vegetation moisture as in (a) and (b). Height and cover are equally important in forested areas, especially at small incidence angles. Kelp is visible in (c) because the small pear-shaped "floats" increase surface roughness and hence the backscatter coefficient against surrounding water which is a near-specular reflector (black) at small incidence angles. Imagery courtesy of NASA.

Table 6-1

Remote Sensing Applications to Vegetation Mapping

	SENSORS[a]																				
	A	B	C	D	E	F	G	H	I	J	K	L	M	N	O	P	Q	R	S	T	
I. Identification																					
A. Boundary Mapping																					
1. Timberline			X				X				X			X		X	X	X	X		Badgley, 1966[b]
2. Desertline			X				X				X			X		X			X		
3. Grassland/Timberline			X				X				X			X		X			X		
4. Brushland/Timberline			X				X				X			X		X			X		
5. Brushland/Grassland			X				X				X			X		X			X		
6. Grazing/Nongrazing																					
Resolution <1 m		1	1	1	1													2			Carneggie
3-10 m		2	1	2	1													2			
30-100 m		2	2	3	1													3			
B. Taxonomic (Species, Genera, Family)																					
1. Range Grasses and Forbs	8	6	5	8	8	8	8	8	8	(6	5	8	8)	7	9	8	8	8	9	9	Vogel et al., 1971[d]
Resolution <1 m		2	1	2	1													3			Carneggie, 1968
3-10 m		4	4	4	4													4			
2. Shrubs	8	7	5	8	8	8	8	8	8	(7	5	8	8)	6	9	9	9	9	9	9	Vogel et al., 1971
Resolution <1 m		3	2	3	2													3			Carneggie, 1968
3-10 m		3	3	3	3													4			
30-100 m		4	4	4	3													4			
3. Trees	8	8	5	7	8	8	8	8	8	(8	5	7	8)	6	9	8	8	8	9	8	Vogel et al., 1971
II. Structure/Physiognomy																					
1. Meadow																					
Resolution <1 m		1	1	1	1													2			Carneggie, 1968
3-10 m		2	2	2	1													2			
30-100 m		3	2	2	1													2			
2. Open Grassland																					
Resolution <1 m		1	1	1	1													2			
3-10 m		2	1	2	1													2			
30-100 m		3	2	3	2													3			

	A	B	C	D	E	F	G	H	I	J	K	L	M	N	O	P	Q	R	S	T	
3. Brushland																					
Resolution <1 m		1	1	1	1													2			
3-10 m		2	2	3	1													2			
30-100 m		3	2	3	2													3			
4. Forest (Coniferous vs. Deciduous)		1	4	3	2												1*	2*	3*	5	Wilson, 1969[e]
5. Forest Structure	8	6	5	8	7	8	8	8	8	(6	5	8	7)	8	8	8	9	9	9	9	Vogel et al., 1971
6. Shrub Structure	8	6	5	8	8	8	8	4	8	(6	5	8	8)	7	9	9	9	9	9	9	
7. Tree Height	4	1	2	4	3	4	4	4	4	(1	2	4	3)	4	10	10	10	10	10	10	
8. Tree Crown Diameter	4	3	1	4	2	4	4	4	4	(3	1	4	2)	4	9	9	8	8	10	9	
9. Tree Counts			X				X					X		X		X	X	X	X		Badgley, 1966
10. Canopy Density	8	1	3	4	4	4	4	4	4	(1	3	4	4)	2	8	8	8	8	9	9	Vogel et al., 1971
11. Forest Understory	8	5	6	8	7	8	8	8	8	(5	6	8	7)	8	9	9	8	8	10	9	
12. Shrub Density	8	1	2	4	3	4	4	4	4	(1	2	4	3)	8	9	9	9	9	9	9	
13. Grass Density	8	1	2	4	4	4	4	4	4	(1	2	4	4)	3	9	9	9	9	9	8	
Resolution <1 m		3	2	3	1													3			Carneggie, 1968
3-10 m		3	3	3	1													4			
30-100 m		4	3	3	2													4			
III. Distribution	3	2	2	2	1	2	2	2	1	2	2	2	1		2		3	2	2	2	Bowden, 1970[f]
1. Area of Forest Tracts	4	1	3	2	4	4	4	4	4	(1	3	2	4)	4	4	4	4	4	4	4	Vogel et al., 1971
2. Area of Clearings	4	1	2	4	3	4	4	4	4	(1	2	4	3)	4	4	4	4	4	4	4	
IV. Condition																					
1. Stress	3	3	3	2	2	3	3	2	2	3	3	2	2		3		3	2	3	4	Bowden, 1970
2. Forest Fire Detection	9	6	7	8	8	8	8	8	8	(6	7	8	8)	8	8	8	1	1	10	10	Vogel et al., 1971
3. Forest Fire Prediction	3	3	2	3	1	3	2	3	1	3	2	3	1		3		3	2	3	3	Bowden, 1970
4. Range Condition																					
Resolution <1 m		3	2	3	1													3			Carneggie, 1968
3-10 m		3	3	3	1													4			
30-100 m		4	3	3	2													4			
5. Phenology	9	8	6	7	5	8	8	8	8	(8	6	7	5)	5	8	8	9	9	9	9	Morain[g]

Footnotes (Table 6-1):

a. Sensors:

A. Ultraviolet Scanner (0.029-0.05 um)
B. Panchromatic B & W Film
C. Color Film
D. B & W Infrared
E. Color Infrared

Metric Mapping Camera

F. Panchromatic B & W Film
G. Color Film
H. B & W Infrared
I. Color Infrared

Panoramic Camera

J. Panchromatic Film
K. Color Film
L. B & W Infrared
M. Color Infrared

Ultra-High-Resolution

N. Multiband Camera (0.0355-X um)
O. Television Camera
P. Multispectral Scanner (0.02-0.15 um)
Q. Thermal Infrared Scanner (0.35-0.55 um)
R. Thermal Infrared Scanner (0.8-1.4 um)
S. Active Microwave (X- and K-band Radar)
T. Passive Microwave (K-band)

b. The information reported by Badgley (1966) was compiled by the United States Department of Agriculture. In the visible region, emphasis was placed on camera systems rather than film-filter combinations. No distinction is made between low- and high-range thermal infrared scanners.

c. The data from Carneggie (1968) are all in the context of range management. In his scale, ranging from 1 to 4:

(1) The feature can be consistently detected, identified, and measured.
(2) The feature is usually interpretable by range managers trained in remote sensing.
(3) The feature is not consistently interpretable, though it may be detectable.
(4) The feature is almost never detectable or interpretable by experts.

The compilation assumes the use of a metric mapping camera. Other camera systems listed should give comparable results.

d. Vogel et al. (1971) have a complex scheme for evaluating sensors based on interpreter experience and state-of-the-art techniques. For purposes of this tabulation, their symbolization has been converted to a numerical format ranging from 1 (best) to 10 (worst). Sensor priorities as listed below are based on the information content of the imagery plus ease of acquisition and interpretation.

(1) Interpreter success probable even at low experience levels, 1st priority
(2) , 2nd priority
(3) , 3rd priority
(4) , suitable

(5) Interpreter success probable at high experience level only, 1st priority
(6) , 2nd priority
(7) , 3rd priority
(8) , not recommended
(9) Probable interpreter failure at current state of the art without supporting field observations
(10) Sensor cannot be applied to this problem

e. Wilson (1969) ranks "target identification requirements" on a scale of 1 (best) to 10 (worst) for each of the sensors listed. Those values listed with an asterisk (*) represent nighttime sensors.

f. Bowden's data (1970) are extremely general and are all in the context of remote sensing in Southern California. For data in the visible region, he lists neither the camera system not the resolution requirements for the films listed. All his data assumes the use of a mid-altitude platform.

g. Using a numbering scheme identical to that given in footnote (d) above.

better in the vertical) and that the nonforest zone (dominated by basalt) is a reasonably good signal "swallower" (perhaps better in the vertical). The net result is for clearer boundaries on the HV image.

In terms of recorded information, the most important parameters affecting radar reflectivity are scene geometry (roughness) and moisture content (including surface films such as dew). This means that measurable changes in signal backscatter can occur instantaneously with the passage of a single storm or gradually as growth cycles are played out. For any given "look" at the terrain, therefore, one has to distinguish between phenological stages and ephemeral attributes. This is true, not only for radar, but also for all other sensors. For radar, none of the problems listed is insurmountable. Fully calibrated, multifrequency, fine-resolution systems are within the present technological state of the art.

VEGETATION MAPPING APPLICATIONS

No aspect of remote sensing is more controversial than that referring to "applications." We speak glibly of research and applications as if the two are separable, although in a seminar titled Operational Remote Sensing (American Society of Photogrammetry, 1972) it became obvious that an application in one context might well represent research in another. While engineers and system designers consider many sensors to be operational, user groups continue to regard them as untested tools for data collection. Failure to recognize the difference between operational sensors and operational sensing has been one of the major oversights of those who attempt to "sell" remote sensing.

Most operational or routine applications in remote sensing are those performed under contract to government agencies or large commercial organizations. Moreover, the majority of all such programs are based on low-altitude aerial black-and-white photography. In vegetation science, almost no remote sensing is conducted in which the production of maps is the sole objective. Vegetation patterns are usually mapped as an intermediate step and because of this we may begin to compile a list of vegetational phenomena known to be mappable using available sensors. Table 6-1 is a representative selection of these applications as recorded by Badgley (1966), Carneggie (1968), Wilson (1969), Bowden (1970), and Vogel et al. (1971). In the remainder of this section, I will comment on particular aspects of Table 6-1 and, where possible, add to it.

Delineation of Boundaries

Since knowledge of the nature of transitions between types is basic to any vegetation map, detectability of gradients is crucial in remote sensing. Sensor resolution and image scale are two of the most important parameters in boundary mapping. In addition, one must consider that different phenomena will be recorded depending upon (1) the sensor used, (2) season of the year or time of day, and (3) scene characteristics such as radiance and contrast with surroundings. Detection is defined by Waddell and Waddell (1969) as the ability to see that something has been imaged. This is a joint function of the spectral and spatial resolution of the imagery and of the sensor that produced it. Identification, on the other hand, is the ability to classify that phenomenon at some hierarchical level and is determined in large part by the scale and resolution of the original image. On first consideration, the mapper may feel that identification is the more important. Accurate classification, however, requires that matters of resolution also be considered, especially when map legends are being devised. If these are ignored, the legend may contain phraseology that implies more or less sophistication than is actually possible.

A boundary map produced from space photography of Alice Springs, Australia (Figure 6-5), will serve to illustrate the boundary detection-identification problem. On this map, boundaries are shown in line styles similar to those used by Hueck (1960) but with an added dimension of complexity. Hueck's boundaries referred only to vegetation types. The boundaries in Figure 6-5, however, can be classified as phytocenotic, biotopic, biogeocenotic,* etc. Moreover, each can be

---

* A biogeocenose is a mappable unit consisting of the totality of plant and animal lifeforms and the communities they define within a given abiotic environment (synonymous with "ecosystem"). A biotype is an area having relatively uniform physical features and occupied by one particular plant community (phytocenose). For further definition of vegetational terms, see Kuchler (1967).

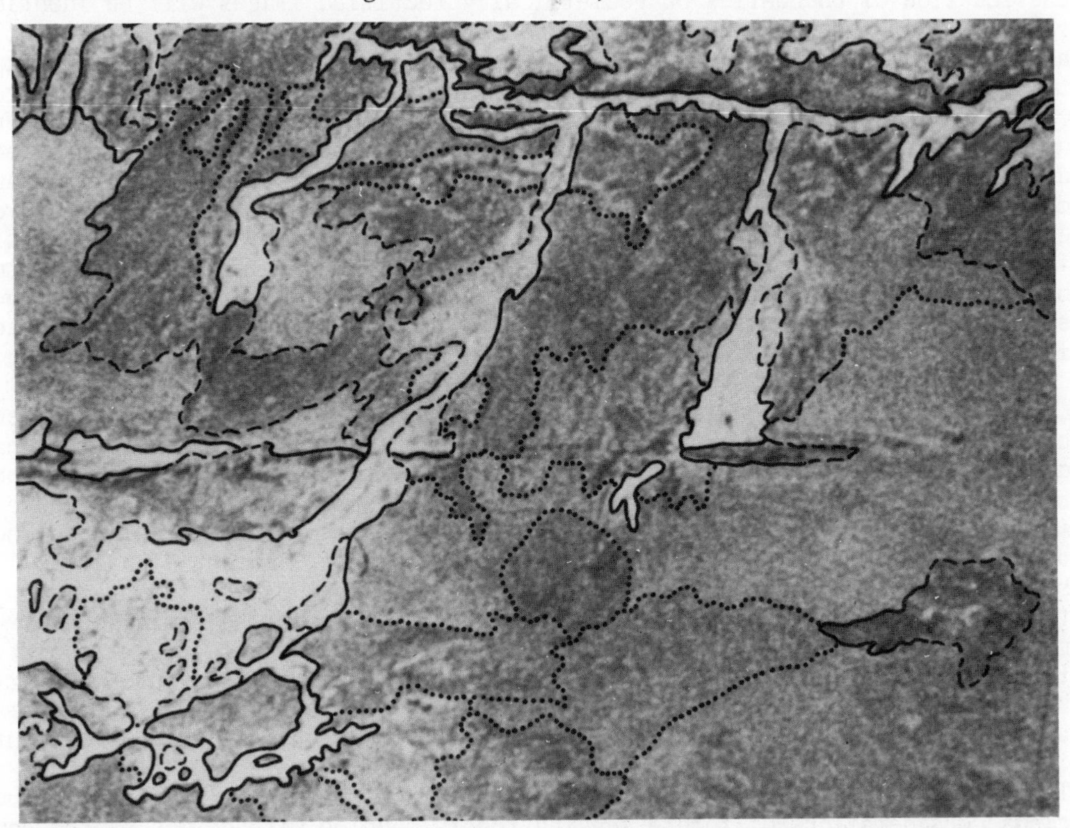

Figure 6-5. Portion of the Gemini-5 space photograph of the Alice Springs Area in Australia. The original photograph was recorded on ektachrome MS 70-mm aerographic film in August 1965 at a scale of about 1:3,000,000. The image shown here was taken from a 6X red separation plate. Boundaries are superimposed in solid, dashed, and dotted lines representing sharp, intermediate, and diffuse environmental gradients respectively. Detectability varies as a function of interpreter experience and photo quality. For a more complete discussion of the boundary detection problem see Simonett et al., 1969. Photo courtesy of NASA.

represented by any of the three line styles. Several different kinds of vegetation maps could therefore be produced using these same boundaries, but the most realistic map will be the one that best takes cognizance of the resolution and scale limitations. Thus, a vegetation map produced from this photograph that claimed to show vegetation communities would be as unrealistic as one claiming to show species boundaries. Without considerable field checking, the mapper does not know which of the boundaries are phytocenotic and which are biotopic; consequently, for the image interpretation phase of the project, he would be better off mapping boundaries of broad landscape units in roughly the same manner as those shown by Perry (1960) for this area. Goodier and Grimes (1970) phrased it very well when they stated that "the areas that we delineate on the photographs as distinguishable plant communities cannot be completely defined on the basis of the species and physiognomy of the plants they contain, but are often the result of a complex interaction between the visual effects of geomorphology, soil type, moisture content and the vegetation."

A further dimension to the boundary problem focuses on the choice of sensors. The fact that each spectral region provides unique information to the vegetation mapper influences classification more than detectibility. In most instances, the location of boundaries on geometrically rectified images will be identical regardless of whether they were obtained by photographic, thermal infrared, or active microwave (radar) sensors. The net result is that one should not expect to see unique or vastly different phytocenotic patterns on "exotic" imagery, but rather to see the same boundaries more or less prominently displayed. The boundary-classification problem thus reduces to the fact that various sensors record different attributes of the same boundary, e.g., radar records structural and moisture changes, while thermal infrared sensors record relative temperature gradients. To be completely logical in terms of information actually contained in the image, therefore, the primary classificatory units of map legends should be consistent with what the sensor actually records. These map legends, however, should also be translated into appropriate structural, physiological, or ecological terms.

Certain major vegetational boundaries are listed in Table 6-1 as being detectable by various sensors. Some, like the altitudinal timberline, may have regional or continental importance while others, e.g., the latitudinal tree line, may be global phenomena. Although the mapping of some of these boundaries might have only minor economic significance, the location and nature of their occurrence could be useful information in assessing natural resources. Aldrich et al. (1971) have already shown that it is possible to map portions of the forest-tundra ecotone in Canada from weather-satellite imagery. By comparing their boundary segments with those from other published studies, they were able to extrapolate a trans-Canadian boundary. The authors admit that their tone-texture boundary can be interpreted in several ways, but they believe it represents a line separating areas with at least 30 percent woodland from those with less than 30 percent.

The delineation of vegetational boundaries can be substantially aided by judicious considerations of remote sensing theory coupled with common sense. Boundaries, including zones too wide to perceive visually or those having spectral differences too narrow to trace, should in many cases be mappable if the right sensor and platform are used (Morain, 1973). The advance of the so-called green wave (and its seasonal opposite--yellow wave) represents a seasonal boundary of considerable importance. Since it advances as a zone and is detectable by a spectral shift and increase in near-infrared reflectivity, it should best be viewed from space with sensors operating in the 0.6-to-1.0 um range. Spatial resolution and scales are less important than spectral sensitivity, as is shown by Aldrich et al. (1971).

In general, the problem of boundary detection can be summarized as follows. If the gradient is sharp between two phytocenoses of different structure and growth form, the boundary may remain visible even as scale diminishes. This can occur as long as the spectral contrast between communities is greater than the spectral resolution. Of the two elements (boundary width and spectral contrast), contrast is perhaps the more important in that high contrast will produce a detectable boundary even when the transition is sharper than the spatial resolution would otherwise allow for detection. At diminishing scales and higher levels of generalization, these persistent boundaries can be come "noise" if they add unwanted complexity.

As traditional interpretation aids are eliminated by decreasing scale (e.g., crown shape, tree height, cover), the ability to classify the boundary is also diminished. Thus, at space altitudes, it is impossible on color photography to differentiate forest/grassland boundaries from wet-grass/dry-grass boundaries (except by inference) because in both cases the interpretation of these boundaries are made largely on the basis of observable tonal differences. The ERTS-1 photo of Monterey Bay, California (front cover) amply illustrates the difficulty involved in boundary analysis from these types of data.

Floristic Vegetation Maps

Once boundaries have been detected and identified, the task remains to classify the units. It is most often true in remote sensing applications that categories are derived by inference from the mapper's knowledge of the area, known ecological relationships, or existing maps and reports for the region. Images in remote regions, for which there is little available supporting information, may therefore be of limited utility until field observations can be supplied. Nevertheless, such images are valuable for future studies tracing a region's short-term vegetational history.

Without question, one of the most difficult tasks in vegetation sensing is the production of floristic maps.* This is in part reflected in section 1B of Table 6-1, where it is revealed that even high-resolution photography is generally inadequate for species identification. Several general factors contribute to the problem. First, at the species and generic levels, classification is often a problem requiring the microscope. Second, in almost all cases, sensors record only the top layer of the canopy. This means that at large scale and fine resolution, only conspicuous attributes of individuals in the canopy can be used to classify taxa. At intermediate and small scales the canopy itself must be unique.

---

* In the broadest sense, floristic maps include those showing insect damage, fungus diseases, pollution damage, etc., insofar as these effects may be confined to an individual taxon. Mapping of healthy versus stressed stands is, <u>sensu strictu</u>, a form of subspecific or population mapping.

For natural and seminatural vegetation, remote sensors can supply data for floristic maps, provided the mapper knows the characteristic signatures of the taxa shown on the image. Multicategory maps are possible using supporting field data depending upon one's classification scheme and mapping purpose (Kuchler, 1956). Perhaps the best example of such a map is presented by Krumpe et al. (1971) in their study of phytocenoses in part of the southern Appalachian region (Figure 6-6). Using color and color infrared 70 mm imagery flown at two scales (1:3,900 and 1:10,000) during the autumn and winter seasons (a total of eight corresponding images), the authors learned to identify 24 tree species on the basis of 33 crown characteristics and a set of Munsell color classes. These attributes were combined into a dichotomous elimination key. In each of the areas delineated on the photo interpretations, the most important taxa in terms of canopy density were then used to classify the entities. By this procedure, they were able to combine species into 28 floristic categories and one growthform category. Many of the oaks and pines could be identified as to individual species, but the hickories could not. Consequently, the categories vary in hierarchical level from specific to generic association. In general, their classification agreed nicely with type names derived independently by Martin (1966) from sample-plot data, the major difference being the elimination of an understory tree not usually visible in the upper canopy.

The Appalachian study is remarkable for its achievement, but not all endeavors of this kind are fortunate enough to cover small areas and utilize large-scale photography. Whenever small scales are involved, inference becomes a more important part of the floristic interpretation. Studies by Minnich et al. (1969) and Orme et al. (1971) of the infrared responses of vegetation in the San Bernardino Mountains and on Santa Cruz Island, respectively, are excellent examples of the role inference may play in floristic mapping. The photography in both cases was on the order of 1:20,000. For Santa Cruz Island the authors state:

Although many (Chaparral) subdivisions are suggested by the imagery, it seems reasonable to distinguish simply between an open chaparral scrub on south-facing slopes and an arborescent scrub-oak chaparral on north-facing slopes. The open chaparral scrub is dominated by species that provide a bright red tone, namely *Quercus dumosa*, *Rhus integrifolia* and *Rhus ovata*. *Cercocarpus betuloides* var. *Blancheae*, *Ceanothus arboreus*, *Ceanothus insularis*, *Prunus lyonii*, and *Lyonothamnus floribundus* var. *asplenifolious* provide a red tone and are either co-dominant with *Quercus dumosa* and *Rhus* spp., or locally dominant. At the western end of the island, this community reveals an exceptionally bright red record where wind-pruned and prostrate vegetation forms an extensive ground cover composed of *Quercus dumosa*, *Rhus integrifolia*, *Comdrostaphylis diversifolia*, and occasional *Pinus*. The Island Manzanita (*Archtostaphylos insularis*) provides a distinctive pink tone (Orme et al., 1971).

Note in the above remarks that two genera have bright red tones, that four are "red," and that one is "pink." In this environment, therefore, tone appears to be inadequate at 1:20,000 for mapping at the generic level, except in the case of island manzanita. Moreover, since tone brightness (radiance value) for the chaparral community apparently varies from one island to another, it is evident that the only consistent attribute upon which floristic inference can be drawn is ecologic position. For this to work, one must assume that wherever south-facing slopes occur, each of the genera also occurs.

Floristic mapping of herbaceous and shrubby species is possible using very large

Table 6-2

Eliminative key prepared from 1:920 scale color infrared photography by Driscoll and Reppert (1968) for the identification of herbaceous and shrubby species found in selected Colorado environments.

1. Plants with detectable flowers.
   2. Flower stalks appear tall to medium in height; basal foliage may be visible or may blend into an inconspicuous mass with the associated vegetation.
      3. Flower stalks tall in bright, white, prominent heads that look like cottonballs; basal foliage, when visible, appears as a dark, dull greenish color (*Achillea lanulosa*).
      3. Flower stalks medium height with flowers as white or yellowish specks; basal foliage appears reddish-green when distinguishable (*Erigeron macranthus*).
   2. Individual flower stalks indistinct; flowers appear as tiny white specks; individual plants not visible, but appear as granular, small to medium sized, irregular shaped clusters; foliage medium green color tinged with lavender (*Chrysopsis villosa*).
1. Plants with no detectable flowers.
   4. Plants with regular to irregular rosette or whorled shapes.
      5. Foliage distinctly whorled; leaves large and distinct, good shadow; bright lavender color (*Swertia radiata*).
      5. Foliage rosette in form, leaves small and somewhat indistinct, no shadow; dull lavender to light purple color or white with a greenish tinge.
      6. Leaves dull lavender to light purple with whitish tips (*Helenium hoopesii*).
      6. Leaves whitish and indistinct (appears as plant litter) but greenish tinge on the edges (*Taraxicum officinale*).
   4. Plants not with irregular or whorled shapes.
   7. Plants medium to large in size, casting a fair to good shadow.
      8. Foliage very fine and compact; bluish grey to grey tinged with pink (*Artemisia tridentata*).
      8. Foliage clumpy or granular.
         9. Foliage in small to large loose clumps; irregular shape; maroon, purplish red, greenish red, or reddish-charcoal color apparently depending on size and age of plants (*Chrysothamnus parryi*).
         9. Foliage in small clumps to granular; entire; pinkish-red, greenish-red, or orange-green (*Potentilla fruticosa*).
   7. Plants smaller and with little or no shadow.
      10. Foliage granular.
         11. Foliage loosely granular; gold color; may occur in large groupings (*Geranium fremontii*).
         11. Foliage tight granular; usually appears as individual plants; dull to reddish lavender (*Lupinus* sp.).
      10. Foliage fuzzy.
         12. Individual plants indistinct; appears as a mottled greyish-green unit (*Poa pratensis*).
         12. Individual plants appear as a tuft.
      13. Plants distinct, medium size, with entire shape; indistinct shadow; light pink, reddish green or dull orange, frequently with a whitish to light grown tinge. Caused by standing old growth (*Festuca thurberi*).
      13. Plants indistinct, small with no apparent shadow; light to medium green with faint pinkish tinge (*Festuca idahoensis*).

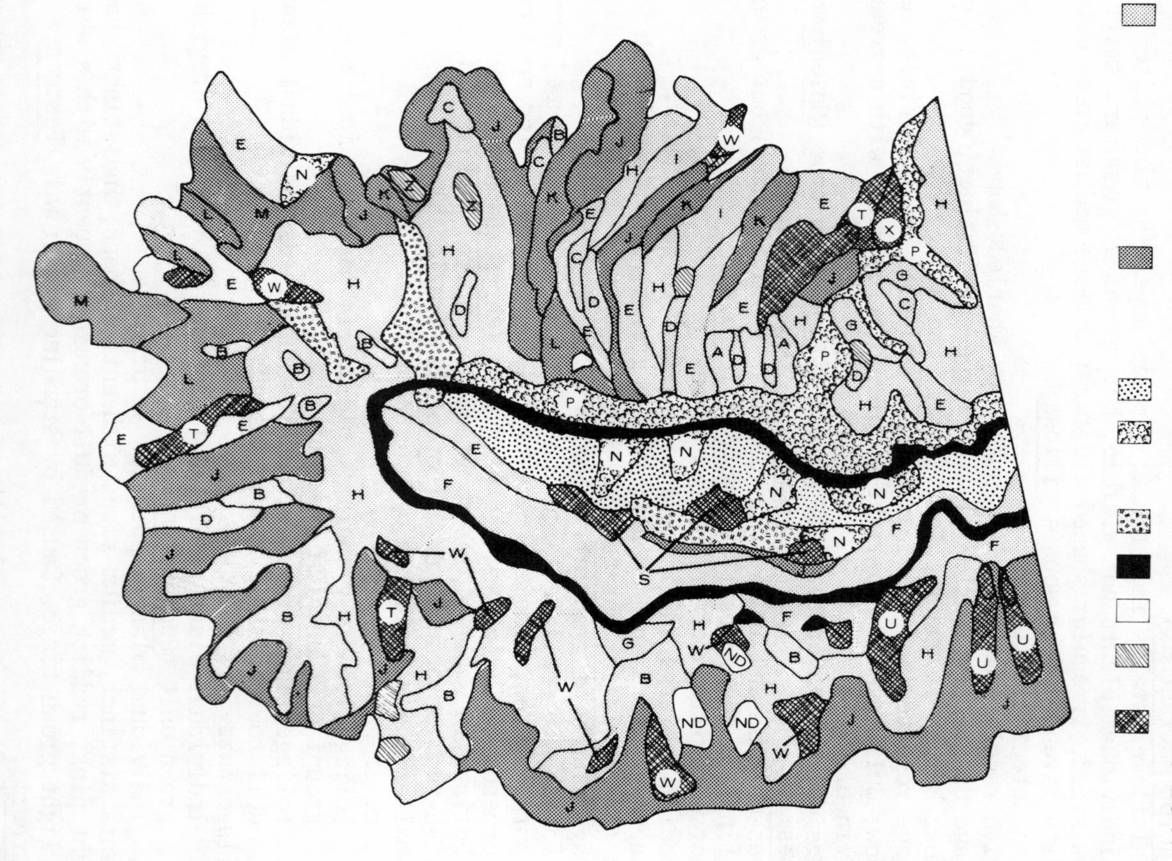

Figure 6-6. Floristic map of portion of the southern Appalachian region (approximately 4 square miles) (Redrafted from Krumpe et al., 1971). Multicategory maps at the generic and specific levels can be produced using data obtained from large-scale color and color infrared photography. For this map a combination of Munsell color classes and crown characteristics was used to aid the interpretation.

scale imagery but is nevertheless a tedious proposition. The report by Driscoll and Reppert (1968) gives many insights into the nature of the problems involved. Driscoll and Reppert used color and color infrared photographs combined with data from intensive field work to devise an elimination key (Table 6-2) for species occurring in several environments in Colorado. Photographs ranged in scale from 1:600 to 1:2,400, the key being produced from color infrared photos at 1:920 scale.

The key in Table 6-2 had not been tested at time of reporting, nor had floristic maps been compiled using it as an identification aid. The fact that a key was produced, however, is proof that herbaceous species can be detected using traditional aids like pattern and texture, relative size, shapes, shadow, and color. What is even more remarkable is the suggestion that such difficult distinctions as those between *Festuca thurberi* and *F. idahoensis* may be possible.

The essential points involved in the production of floristic maps from remote sensor imagery can be summarized as a series of sensor/terrain interactions. To produce large-scale, single-category maps at the species or generic level requires that the taxon have a recognizable form and spectral signature. At intermediate and small scales, the taxon must be not only spectrally detectable but also areally extensive and must dominate the canopy. "Spectrally detectable" in this case includes discovering the relationship between changes in the image tone for a given stand as a function of changes in the taxon's proportional representation in the canopy. The desire for multicategory maps, on the other hand, implies the presence of many taxa; and these may exist either as a continuum or set of distinct phytocenoses. For these situations, maps of species or genera are extremely difficult to produce even at very large scales. At higher levels of generalization (e.g., Family, through Class), however, the number of categories is systematically reduced such that even the production of small-scale maps are possible.

The use of remote sensors for tracing phenological change represents a further refinement in taxonomic mapping and necessitates using both the temporal and spectral concepts. Sequential imaging alone will be inadequate for most purposes, unless the interpreter knows a priori how each taxon or group of taxa should appear at each point in time. Gross seasonal contrasts may be an exception to this in certain regions, but even these will be troublesome if recorded on coarse-resolution, small-scale imagery of poorly known areas.

In terms of current remote sensing needs for studying growth stages, it is becoming increasingly clear that sequential spectral data of both specular and total hemispherical kinds, collected from directly overhead, are crucial in deciphering data from more distantly placed sensors. Furthermore, to be quantitative, such data will have to be calibrated against a standard; otherwise subtle variations in reflectivity may be extremely difficult, if not impossible, to interpret. Finally, depending upon the research goals, it will be necessary to distinguish between physiologic stress and normal changes in growth stage. For all these data needs, of course, the question still to be resolved regards the relationship between the first date of budding, flowering, etc., and the date of the first spectral detectability, where the latter varies according to sensor, resolution, and scale. Here is a rich area for research.

Applications that employ phenologic change in their experimental design currently use it as a surrogate for nonphenological ends; namely, for monitoring forestry, rangeland, and agricultural phenomena. Among the better known and more recent contributions to an evaluation of the time dimension are articles by Brunnschweiler (1957), Boesch and Brunnschweiler (1960), Olson and Good (1962), Haralick et al. (1969), Steiner (1969), and Driscoll and Francis (1970). Only those treating agricultural topics fall into the category of applied remote sensing. By virtue of earth-orbiting satellites (e.g., ERTS-1), however, man may be able, for essentially the first time, to "view" and record a significant part of the earth sequentially. For vegetation science, this means that phenology will begin to play a more central role in the routine analysis of phytocenoses, and it also suggest that future vegetation maps will need to include these data as part of their classification schemes. Whereas modern vegetation maps employ mostly physiognomic, floristic, or ecological criteria, or combinations of these, future maps will likely include phenologic criteria.

Physiognomic and Structural* Vegetation Maps

Physiognomy and structure are the most prominent attributes an interpreter consciously recognizes on most forms of imagery. It is not surprising, therefore, that the earliest attempts to use aerial photography in vegetation focused on these features, and over the years there has grown a lengthy list of structural and physiognomic attributes that can be accurately measured (see Table 6-1, section 11). Examination of any scale photography obtained from conventional, hyper, and space altitudes proves that observed tonal patterns often arise from differences in the gross outward appearance of phytocenoses. Closer scrutiny of the units comprising the pattern may subsequently yield more detail about stand structure. A few examples may aid the reader in this realization as well as illustrate changes in hierarchical levels as scale decreases.

Paijmans (1966), using photographs at a scale of 1:50,000, writes that for northern Papua "structural and tonal photo differences enable the distinction and delineation of vegetation types within each habitat. The tree canopies, closure, height, degree of regularity, and sizes and shapes of crown are valuable indicators (P.I.)." For this environment, Paijmans' interpretation focused initially on habitat and secondarily on physiognomy and structure as revealed by image tone and texture.

Proceeding to smaller scale, Nielsen and Wightman (1971) have shown that forest regions in Canada can be delineated on 1:160,000-scale color infrared photography. The boundaries coincide closely with those given by Rowe (1959). Although Rowe based his classification on four criteria (namely, the distribution and range of conspicuous species, their growthforms, the physiognomy and relative areal extent of communities, and the pattern of the total vegetation), only the latter two were useful on small-scale photographs. Similarly, Aldrich and Greentree (1971), in tests conducted in the pine-hardwood region of Alabama and Georgia with 1:420,000 infrared photography, discovered that the most consistent distinction was between forested and nonforested areas. These results illustrate

---

*"Physiognomy" refers to the appearance of the vegetation regardless of its floristic composition. "Structure" describes the height and cover of the individual layers defining a plant community (see Kuchler, 1967).

that, as scale diminishes, there is a corresponding shift in the level of classification such that subdivision within stands becomes extremely difficult. In lieu of internal differences associated with tone and texture, the mapper learns to rely increasingly on ecological relationships.

At space altitudes and/or scales approaching 1:1,000,000 only very broad physiognomic distinctions are meaningful if imagery is used without supporting information. Poulton et al. (1971) have suggested a scheme intended for the annotation of space photos of North America. The key words really represent the major continental biochores: desert, steppe, savanna, forest, and tundra. In the hands of local experts, however, classification refinements would certainly be possible based on knowledge of the regional ecology, library resources, and personal field experience.

Reduced to their basic elements, structural and physiognomic maps describe aspects of the spatial relations and geometries of a phytocenose. Consequently, any film record, whether produced from photographic, thermal infrared, or radar imaging systems, is potentially useful for this kind of map production. This "usefulness," of course, depends upon image scale and resolution, as these will influence the amount of detail visible to the interpreter.

The compilation of physiognomic and structural vegetation maps from "exotic" forms of imagery has not been vigorously pursued beyond the experimental stage. A search of available literature shows that most of the effort so far has been directed at the use of color and color infrared photography and radar. Less effort has focused on structural mapping from multiband and multispectral scanning, and none has employed thermal infrared imagery for this purpose. Preliminary experimental results involving multiband photography can be obtained in Peterson et al. (1969) and for multispectral scanning in Haralick (1969), especially Chapter 8. Although Bowden (1970) indicates that both thermal infrared and passive microwave sensors have some capability for physiognomic mapping in southern California (Table 6-1), there are no experimental results available for confirmation.

One of the most thorough studies, in terms of describing an interpretive methodology and presenting actual results, is the one by Minnich et al. (1969). An example of their work is presented in Figure 6-7, which shows one of the map products. Using color infrared photography as a base, these authors delineated and identified the major physiognomic types of the San Bernardino Mountains in southern California, an area of about 1,500 square miles. The scale of the imagery on which most of the mapping was carried out ranged from 1:60,000 to 1:24,000. Later flights were conducted to update and revise the classification; for these the scale ranged from 1:16,000 to 1:120,000. After completing the photo-mapping phase, the boundaries and legend symbols were overprinted onto 1:62,500 Geological Survey quadrangles. In all, seven ecophysiognomic divisions were recognized (Table 6-3). These were then split into 9 subtypes and 18 tertiary types on the basis of ecological, structural, and floristic variations.

Single-frequency radar has been evaluated in several studies for its contribution to physiognomic mapping (compare Morain and Simonett, 1967; Howard and Sapp, 1970; Hardy et al., 1971; and Daus and Lauer, 1971). As with imagery from other sensors, a wealth of information may be gleaned from radar imagery, especially if the interpreter is personally familiar with the region or has access to supporting maps and data. Howard and Sapp, for example, were able to map nine

Table 6-3

Map legend from Minnich et al., 1969, for vegetation types of the San Bernardino Mountains, California

I. CS COASTAL SAGE SCRUB (*Artemesia californica*, *Salvia* spp., *Erioganum fasciculatum*, *Encelia farinosa*, herbaceous undergrowth)

II. C CHAPARRAL

- A. C True Chaparral (Brush)
  - 1. C_S "Soft" Chaparral Chamise dominant with some *Ceanothus crassifolius*, scattered individuals in *Arctostaphylos* spp., *Rhus* spp. and *Cercocarpus betuloides*.
    - a. C_{af} Pure Chamise Chaparral (*Adenostema fasciculatum*). Possibility for widely scattered bushes of *Erioganum fasciculatum* or *Rhus ovata*.
  - 2. C_H Hard Chaparral *Deanothus leucodermis* dominant with *C. crassifolius*, *Arctostaphylos glauca*, *A. glandulosa*, *Cercocarpus* spp. and scattered chamise.
  - 3. C_{SO} Scrub Oak Chaparral *Quercus dumosa* likely dominant with *Q. chrysolepus* increasingly evident above approximately 3,500 feet.
  - 4. C_{WD} Emergent Oak Woodland in Hard Chaparral scattered or clustered individuals of *Quercus wislizenii* and/or *Q. chrysolepus* in C_H.
  - 5. C_{WD} Interior Oak Woodland *Quercus wislinaii* with no C_H, but with possible mixing of PJ, PF, species.
  - 6. C_D Desert Chaparral Noncontiguous cover, *Ceanothus gregii*, *C. crassifolius*, *Arctostaphylos* spp., *Cercocarpus* spp., *Fremontia californicus*, some *Quercus wislizenii*. Many small scrubs and herbaceous plants between the principle shrubs.
- B. CF Forest Enclaves in Chaparral
  - 1. CF_{bs} Big Cone Douglas Fir dominant (*Pseudotsuga macrocarpa*)
  - 2. CF_{CO} Canyon Oaks dominant (*Quercus chrysolepus*)

    In both cases, chaparral undergrowth absent.
- C. CE Conifer Emergents in Chaparral
  - 1. CE_{cp} Coulter Pine dominant (*Pinus coulteri*)
  - 2. CE_{kb} Knolcone Pine dominant (*Pinus attenuata*)

    In both cases, scattered individuals with Chaparral undergrowth.

III. DF DRY FOREST Coulter Pine and Black Oak (*Quercus kelloggii*) of about equal incidence; occasionally there are nearly pure strands of Black Oak.

IV. PF MONTANE CONIFEROUS FOREST

- A. TF Marginal Conifer Forest basically an ecotone. A mixture between PF species with CF, and occasionally CE tree species.

B. PF Yellow Pine-White Fir Forest
  1. PF "Pure Yellow Pine-White Fir Forest *Pinus ponderosa*, *P. jeffreyi*, *P. lambertiana*, *Lebocedrus decurrens*, *Abies concolor*,--*Juniperus occidentalis* in drier margins.
  2. PF_M Mixed Yellow Pine - White Fir Forest with Black Oak. All the species in PF and *Quercus kellogii*.
  3. CT Timberland Chaparral *Arctostaphylos patula*,*Ceanothus integerrimus*, *Castanopsis sempervirens* with scattered trees of the PF and occasionally LP groups.

V. LP Subalpine Forest *Pinus murrayana*, *P. flexilus*

VI. DW DESERT WOODLAND
  A. PJ Pinyon-Juniper Woodland (*Pinus monophylla* dominant)
    1. PJ_D "Dense" Western Juniper and Mountain Mahogany prominent, *Juniperus occidentalus*, *Cercocarpus ledifolius* and scattered Great Basin sage species (*Artemesia tridentata*, *Chrysothamnus nauseosus*).
    2. PJ "Pure" Mostly Pinyon Pine with scattered *Juniperus californica* or *J. occidentalis*.
    3. PJ_O "Open" with desert undergrowth, a few chaparral species in *Arctostaphylos*, *Quercus*; Pinions and Junipers widely scattered.
  B. GB Great Basin Sage *Artemesia tridentata*, *A.* spp. *Chrysothamnus nauseosus*. Sediment flats.

VII. D_H HIGH DESERT VEGETATION
  A. JS Joshua Tree Woodland *Yucca brevifolia* with GB or D undergrowth.
    1. JJ Juniper-Joshua Woodland *Yucca brevifolia* and *Juniperus californica* with GB or D undergrowth.
  B. D Open desert vegetation

MISCELLANEOUS

S SUBCLIMAX VEGETATION
G GRASSLANDS OR MEADOWS
B BARREN
R RIVERINE VEGETATION - in the absence of trees species of the prevailing plant grouping, i.e., this vegetation type includes tree or brush species ecologically adapted to stream environments only.
  A. Below 4,000 feet, either Sycamore (*Plantanus racemosa*) or Cottonwood (*Populus trichocarpa*).
  B. 4,000 feet to 7,000 feet, White Alder (*Alnus rhombifolia*).
  C. Above 7,000 feet, Willow (*Salix*).
  D. Fish Creek, Quaking Aspen (*Populus tremuloides*).

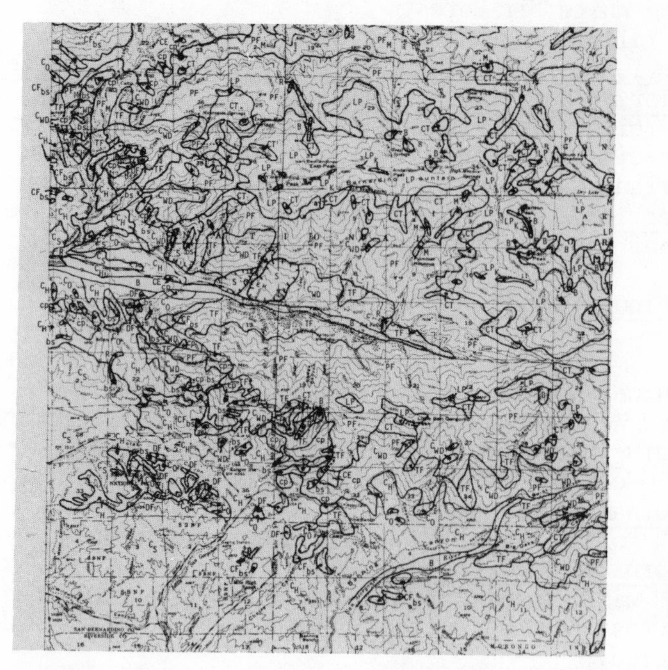

Legend

Forest and Woodland

- C_{WD} Oak Woodland
- $C_{F_{bs}}$ Big Cone Spruce Groves
- CE_{cp} Coulter Pine Groves
- PF Montane Coniferous F.
- LP Subalpine Forest
- DF Dry Forest
- R Riparian Forest
- TF Transition Forest

Chaparral

- C_H Hard Chaparral
- C_S Soft Chaparral
- C_O Oak Chaparral
- CT Timberline Chaparral

Grassland

- M Meadow
- G Dry Grassland

Unvegetated

- B Bare

Figure 6-7. Portion of the San Gorgonio Quadrangle, San Bernardino Mountains, southern California, showing overprint of phytocenoses. Boundary delineation was accomplished using infrared photography ranging in scale from 1:16,000 to 1:120,000. Communities were classified on the basis of ecological position plus their image tone and texture. The primary division is physiognomic but subdivisions include physiognomic, ecological, and floristic terms. Map and interpretation courtesy of Richard Minnich, Department of Geography, UCLA.

ecophysiognomic vegetation types on Ka-band imagery of the Atrato Delta, Columbia. Morain and Simonett and Hardy et al. did likewise for coniferous regions in south-central Oregon and northwestern Wyoming, respectively. In all instances, the authors delineated communities on the basis of image tone and texture, then classified them according to published descriptions. Used in this fashion, SLAR imagery is no different from other image forms discussed.

The study by Morain and Simonett (1965) exemplifies the present state of the art for physiognomic and structural mapping by radar. In Figure 6-8a, b, two Ka-band radar images (HH and HV polarizations) are presented for the area surrounding Horsefly Mountain, Oregon. From the combination of these images, two maps have been compiled (Figure 6-8c,d). The more general map shows five physiognomic categories. In Figure 6-8d, an increase in image scale to approximately 1:50,000 permitted structural variants to be delineated. In general, three basic forest structures were recorded: sapling stands, even-aged pole timber, and residual (mature) stands. The latter of these was further divided according to the nature of the coniferous understory. Boundaries for the structural map were not easily detectable on the enlarged imagery, but a careful interpretation did reveal subtle differences in tone and texture qualities. When

Figure 6-8. Dual polarized Ka-band imagery of Horsefly Mountain, Oregon. By combining the interpretation of boundaries from these images (a = HH, b = HV), ecophysiognomic and structural vegetation maps have been produced. Classification schemes for both maps were based partly on published records and partly on field observations. The original image scale was about 1:500,000. Mapping scale was about 1:125,000 for the physiognomic map (c) and 1:50,000 for the structural subtypes (d). Imagery courtesy of NASA, Mission 59.

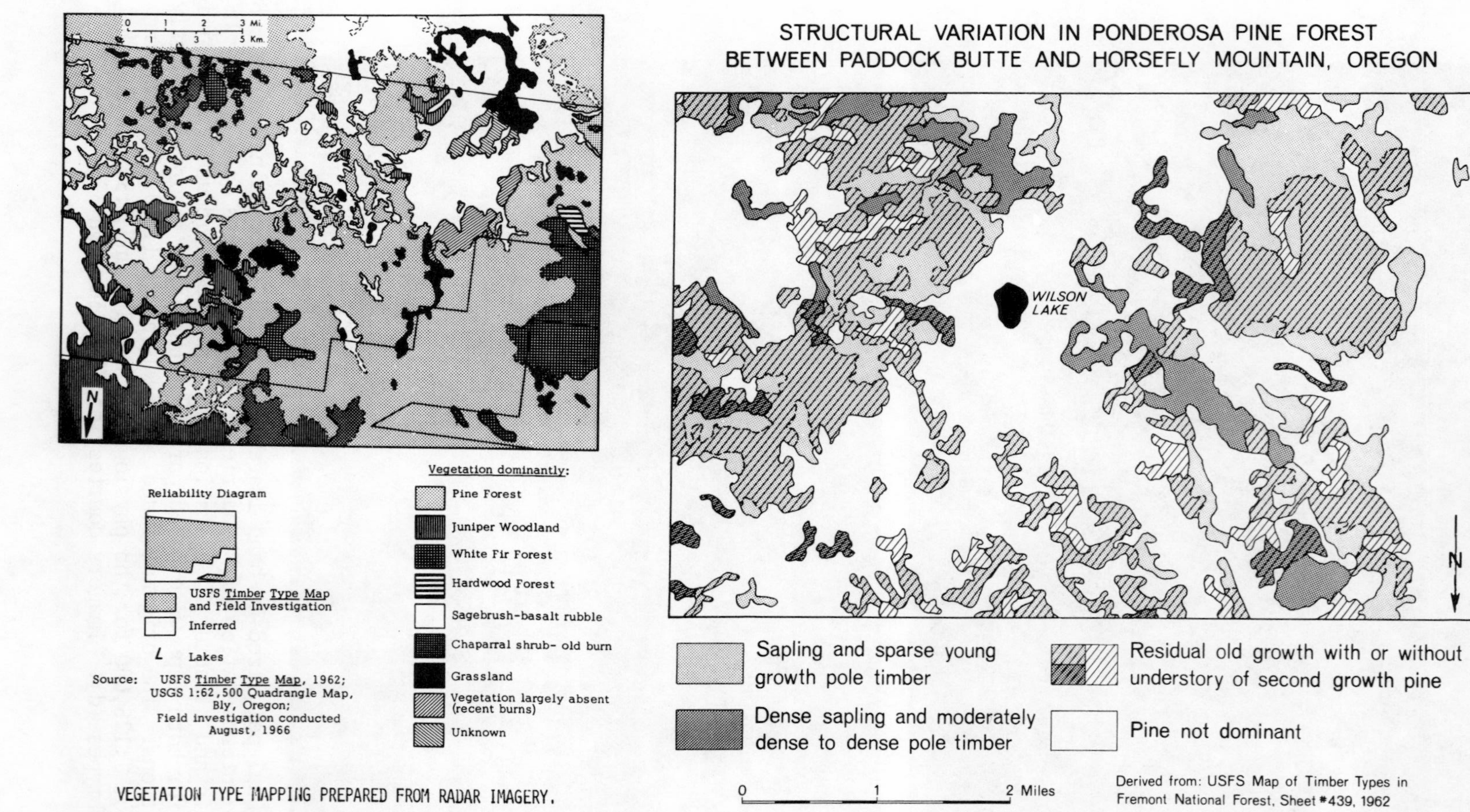
0 1 2 3 Mi.
1 3 5 Km.
N
Reliability Diagram
USFS Timber Type Map and Field Investigation
Inferred
L Lakes
Source: USFS Timber Type Map, 1962; USGS 1:62,500 Quadrangle Map, Bly, Oregon; Field investigation conducted August, 1966
Vegetation dominantly:
Pine Forest
Juniper Woodland
White Fir Forest
Hardwood Forest
Sagebrush-basalt rubble
Chaparral shrub- old burn
Grassland
Vegetation largely absent (recent burns)
Unknown
VEGETATION TYPE MAPPING PREPARED FROM RADAR IMAGERY.
STRUCTURAL VARIATION IN PONDEROSA PINE FOREST
BETWEEN PADDOCK BUTTE AND HORSEFLY MOUNTAIN, OREGON
WILSON LAKE
N
Sapling and sparse young growth pole timber
Dense sapling and moderately dense to dense pole timber
Residual old growth with or without understory of second growth pine
Pine not dominant
0 1 2 Miles
Derived from: USFS Map of Timber Types in Fremont National Forest, Sheet #439, 1962

Figure 6-8 (cont.).

these differences were delineated and compared with a preexisting timber-type map, there was sufficient correspondence in patterns that meaningful categories could be assigned to each of the areas delimited. Furthermore, the tones and textures within each category were generally similar.

In the future, there may be added scope for radar in structural and physiognomic mapping, but this will depend on improving the spatial resolution of the various sensor types, developing interpreter experience regarding the meaning of tone and texture, and exploiting the fact that radar signals can penetrate canopies to varying depths depending upon the frequency and moisture relations. Research has only begun to explore the contents of radar imagery and the best ways to interpret it.

Ecological Vegetation Maps

One of the basic strengths of remote sensing in vegetation science lies in the holism of ecological analysis. Storage and retrieval of selected information from time-sequential, multisensor imagery and the use of that information for appropriate ecological ends has in the past been the main argument for justifying expensive remote sensing programs. Vegetation mappers will be among those most benefited by this new data source because their products are an essential part of these analyses.

Remote sensor imagery can be used in two ways for interpreting ecological and vegetational data. The first focuses on the extraction of vegetation patterns by using ecological surrogates, i.e., vegetational phenomena are inferred from known habitat relations. The second part addresses the converse; namely; ecological inference from known vegetation patterns. This latter approach is becoming widely used in environment quality studies and by regional planners.

The mapping of vegetation patterns by their correlation with topographic, hydrologic, edaphic, and other factors may take several forms. The use of this technique by Minnich et al. (1969) for floristic mapping has already been discussed. These authors used relatively large scale infrared photography to interpret tone, texture, slope orientation, and elevation. From these it was possible to map several phytocenoses and to deduce their dominant floristic composition.

A different approach was used by Hardy et al.(1971) for Yellowstone National Park, Wyoming. The legend for his map is reproduced in Table 6-4. This investigation was based on the interpretation of single-frequency small-scale radar imagery having comparatively poor spatial resolution (about 50 feet). As a consequence, the chain of inference and the use of supporting materials differed from those employed by Minnich et al. Boundary delineation was accomplished by first interpreting the HH polarized image and then adding boundaries from the HV that were not easily seen on the HH. At this point, image tone and texture were the only interpretation aids. For classification purposes an elimination key based on tone and texture was devised. By comparing these properties with observed topographic position, also obtained from the imagery, nine ecological types could be listed. Further reference to published materials and topographic maps then permitted eight of these to be categorized physiognomically and, in part, floristically. Only the thermal areas in the park could not be categorized in this way.

Table 6-4

Legend for Hardy et al. (1971) vegetation map from radar imagery.

Lodgepole Pine - Mixed Coniferous Forest
Douglas Fir Forest
Marsh (Sedges, Wetland Grasses)
Moist Sedgegrass-Shrub Complex (2,200-2,700 meters; Willows, Wetland Sage, Grasses)
Dry Lowland Grass-Sagebrush Complex (2,200-2,700 meters; Dryland Sage, Drought Tolerant Grasses)
Dry Subalpine Sagebrush Meadow (2,700-3,000 meters)
Dry Alpine Grassland (Above 3,000 meters; Short Grasses, Some Sedges, Flowering Plants)
Dry Subalpine Grassland/Conifer Complex (Lodgepole Pine, Drought Tolerant Grasses)
Thermal Areas (Varying Vegetation Types)

The converse role of ecologic mapping (i.e., using vegetation patterns to infer other biophysical attributes) is widely documented in the literature. The examples are far too numerous to review considering the myriad types, resolutions, and scales of imagery and methods used for their interpretation. Therefore, examples from the literature on fire and dry-land ecology are presented.

In the case of fire and fire-related phenomena, there have been a few studies from each part of the EM spectrum. Detection of actively burning fires by thermal infrared scanners is well known and will not be discussed in detail here. These images are normally obtained for the sole purpose of delimiting the perimeter of a burn in order to better fight its progress. They are seldom, if ever, used for the production of a map. For other parts of the spectrum, Mealor and Prunty (1968) and Sullivan and Brooner (1971) have investigated color and color infrared photography, and Simonett and Morain (1967) have looked briefly at radar.

The rationale for Mealor and Prunty (1968) was to sequentially map burn patterns and interpret successional recovery stages. Their study involved the Florida Flatwoods, which is an area characterized by surface fires rather than crown fires. They studied the information contained on color, color infrared, and thermal infrared imagery at various scales. In general, they found that temperature anomalies revealed on thermal imagery could be used to determine the relative age of burns less than three months old. Color photography was useful for dating burns less than one year old but showed insufficient contrast to distinguish between burns older than that. Finally, the color infared photography provided a means for separating burn scars as old as three years on the basis of community successional stages.

Sullivan and Brooner (1971) utilized vegetation patterns on color infrared photography to estimate fire potential in chaparral. Interpretation focused on mapping the distribution of as many communities as possible according to the experience gained by Minnich et al. (1969). Since their entire study area had been periodically and variably burned, it was not possible using 1:24,000 imagery alone to infer chaparral subcommunities or their floristic composition. Rather, it appeared more feasible to separate "sparse" and "dense" chaparral owing to differences in their physiognomy and then to estimate relative fuel volumes according to data in published Forest Service reports. To the vegetational information were added data on location of houses, their roofing materials, natural and man-made firebreaks, and other features that had a bearing on either the starting or suppression of a fire. Once these were compiled in map form, the study area could be regionalized into four zones of greater or lesser fire potential.

The last topic for discussion addresses arid-zone ecology. Considering the areal extent of dry lands, the general lack of vegetational and ecological information, and the difficulties usually associated with equipping and sustaining field crews for extended periods, it is logical that a major effort should be placed on extracting information from remote sensor data. The fact that species and entire phytocenoses in these environments have evolved narrow tolerance limits to moisture, salinity, and other ecological factors has long been recognized as an aid in deciphering habitat relations from photography (Vinogradov, 1961).

Vegetation is best used as an indicator of edaphic, hydrologic, and geologic conditions and for estimating agricultural potential. The best known effort for systematically extracting such information from photography is the Australian program for Land Research and Regional Surveys (LRRS). In this series of reports, data from reconnaissance field studies by multidisciplinary teams are added to information derived from photo interpreters to produce "land system" maps. Each system is comprised of a set of "land units," which are in turn defined by their combination of landform and biological characteristics (Christian, 1959). Using the combination of field studies to learn the basic relations among soil, vegetation, and drainage for each land unit, it is possible to then map their aerial extent on large- to medium-scale photography (about 1:50,000). On small-scale and space photography, the delineation of land systems makes it possible to estimate land-unit composition and to infer much about the details of their phytocenoses.

In savanna landscapes, Zonneveld et al. (1971) state that vegetation patterns on 1:40,000-scale black-and-white photographs can be valuable in delineating land units and aiding in the explanation of their genesis. Although the authors did not include a vegetation map of their study area, they described in detail the criteria used to interpret a pseudo dune pattern* and a black-and-white dot pattern related to termite mounds. In both instances, they combined field work with photo analysis to generate hypotheses relating soil genesis and vegetation. It is an excellent example of the extent to which photo interpretation can facilitate ecological studies.

Extraction of ecological information from small-scale and space photographs is

---

* A very similar photo pattern is presented by Wickens (1966) for a savanna region in Sudan and one wonders whether the interpretation is also similar.

far more difficult than from imagery of scales greater than 1:50,000. It happens that on space photographs tones are highly related to the vegetation density and textures to landform. The joint interpretation of these data provides the basis for vegetation mapping and subsequent extension to ecological inference. By the same token, landscape context is an aid to vegetational inference on space photography, so in this instance at least the dichotomy erected at the beginning of this section is artificial.

The use of multispectral scanners, multiband photography, and thermal infrared scanners for ecological vegetation mapping is not documented in the literature. Radar imagery has been interpreted for its contribution, but only in a casual way (Morain and Simonett, 1965). Recent unpublished research by the author suggests that for dry environments, dominated by sclerophyllous or thorny microphyll species, vegetation height and density, more than moisture, are the pertinent attributes affecting radar return. The greatest advantage for radar in dry-land environments is that its coarse resolution and small scale eliminate much of the confusing detail of conventional photography.

SUMMARY AND CONCLUSIONS

Three points of this chapter should be emphasized. The first is an implicit realization that, with respect to vegetation analysis, our knowledge about the strategies for interpretation and uses to which various sensors may be put is in its infancy. Vinogradov and Kondrat'yev (1970) pinpointed the problem when they stated, "Despite the undoubted advantages of the sensing techniques in the biosphere, this particular aspect has been making slow progress. This is due largely to inadequate work on optical and geometric generalization since elementary biogeographic units tend to be rather small." In the biological world, spectral properties for each entity are high frequency variables in time, space, and geometry. We have not learned to interpret differences within and between entities for even panchromatic black-and-white images at 1:20,000. Every new image type and format with their inherent resolution/scale properties thus represent quantum increases in complexity.

The second major point I wish to make regards the production of vegetation maps. Few if any of the authors cited in the preceding discussion have paid adequate attention to the mechanics of vegetation mapping. Researchers, teachers, and students all need training in the creation and design of map legends so as to maximize their information content and at the same time remain credible in terms of distinguishing that part of the information derived from the imagery and that part derived by other means. As we become more sophisticated in our ability to interpret "exotic" imagery, it will become increasingly important for the sake of map reliability to state explicitly what part of the information has been derived by remote sensing techniques. By this I do not mean to imply that remotely sensed information is less reliable than other kinds; indeed it may be more reliable. The production of vegetation maps, like any other science, is exacting. The efforts of Gaussen, Kuchler, Braun Blanquet, and other phytocenologists, who have devoted their careers to furthering our knowledge and skills of vegetation mapping, should be central to our own efforts. We are, after all, not trying to reinvent the wheel, but to progress with the aid of a new tool.

Finally, as stated elsewhere in this text, it can never be stressed too strongly that remote sensing is not a substitute for detailed field surveys. An entire section on sampling strategies has been deferred from this chapter (see Chapter 2), although it is clearly an area in which geographers can make a significant contribution. Some readers may have gained the impression that I sought to sidestep the need for supporting field data. Any such impression arises from the fact that I stressed the kinds of information obtainable from the imagery itself, plus that available from supporting materials. I am confident that any one of the studies cited could have had substantially better results, if they had been done in the context of a routine agency operation.

REFERENCES

Aldrich, R. C., and W. J. Greentree, 1971, "Microscale Photo Interpretation of Forest and Non-Forest Land Classes," in *Monitoring Forest Land from High Altitude and from Space*, Annual Report to the NASA Earth Resources Survey Program from the Forestry Remote Sensing Laboratory, University of California, Berkeley.

Aldrich, S. A., F. T. Aldrich, and R. D. Rudd, 1971, "An Effort to Identify the Canadian Forest-Tundra Ecotone on Weather Satellite Imagery," *Remote Sensing of Environment*, 2:9-20.

American Society of Photogrammetry, 1972, *Operational Remote Sensing*, Proceedings of a seminar held in Houston, Tex.

Badgley, P. C., 1966, "Orbital Remote Sensing and Natural Resources," *Photogrammetric Engineering*, 35(2):780-799.

Boesch, H., and D. Brunnschweiler, 1960, "Seasonal Changes of the Agricultural Landscape Interpreted from Aerial Photographs," *Geographica Helvetica*, 15(4): 257-261.

Bowden, L., 1970, "Sensor Evaluation in Southern California," *Proceedings Association of American Geographers*, San Francisco.

Brunnschweiler, D. H., 1957, "Seasonal Changes of the Agricultural Pattern: A Study in Comparative Airphoto Interpretation," *Photogrammetric Engineering*, 23 (1):131-139.

Carneggie, D. M., 1968, "Analysis of Remote Sensing Data for Range Resources Management," Annual Progress Report to the NASA Earth Resources Survey Program from the Forestry Remote Sensing Laboratory, University of California, Berkeley.

Christian, C. S., 1959, "The Eco-Complex in its Importance for Agricultural Assessment," in *Biogeography and Ecology in Australia*, Monographiae Biologieae, 8:587-605.

Colwell, R. N., Ed., 1960, *Manual of Photographic Interpretation*, American Society of Photogrammetry.

Colwell, R. N., and J. D. Lent, 1967, "A Test of the Concept and Practical Application of Multiband Reconnaissance," Annual Report from the Forestry Remote Sensing Laboratory, University of California, Berkeley to the NASA Office of Space Sciences and Application.

Cooper, C. F., 1964, "Potential Applications of Remote Sensing to Ecological Research," *Proceedings of the Third Symposium on Remote Sensing of Environment*, University of Michigan, Ann Arbor, pp. 601-606.

Daus, S. J., and D. T. Lauer, 1971, "SLAR Imagery for Evaluating Wildland Vegetation Resources," American Society of Photogrammetry Fall Convention, San Francisco, pp. 71-333.

Driscoll, R. S., and R. E. Francis, 1970, "Multistage, Multiseasonal and Multiband Imagery to Identify and Qualify Non-Forest Vegetation Resources," Annual Progress Report from the Forestry Remote Sensing Laboratory, University of California, Berkeley, to NASA Earth Resources Survey Program.

Driscoll, R. S., and J. N. Reppert, 1968, "The Identification and Quantification of Plant Species, Communities and Other Resource Features in Herbland and Shrubland Environments from Large Scale Aerial Photography," Annual Report to the NASA Earth Observations Survey Program from the Forestry Remote Sensing Laboratory, University of California, Berkeley.

Egbert, D. D., and F. T. Ulaby, 1972, "Effect of Angles on Reflectivity," *Photogrammetric Engineering*, 38(6):556-564.

Gates, D. M., H. J. Keegan, J. C. Schleter, and V. R. Weidner, 1965, "Spectral Properties of Plants," *Applied Optics*, 4(1):11-20.

Goodier, R., and B. H. Grimes, 1970, "The Interpretation and Mapping of Vegetation and Other Ground Surface Features from Air Photographs of Mountainous Areas in North Wales," *Photogrammetric Record*, 6(36):553-566.

Haralick, R. M., 1969, "Multi-Image Pattern Recognition: Ideas and Results," Ph.D. Dissertation, Kansas University School of Engineering. Published as CRES Technical Report 133-11, Kansas University, Lawrence.

Haralick, R. M., F. Caspall, and D. S. Simonett, 1969, "Using Radar Imagery for Crop Discrimination: A Statistical and Conditional Probability Study," *Remote Sensing of Environment*, 1:131-142.

Hardy, N. E., J. C. Coiner, and W. O. Lockman, 1971, "Vegetation Mapping with Side-Looking Airborne Radar: Yellowstone National Park," *Proceedings of NATO AGARD XCVII EPP Technical Meeting*, Colorado Springs.

Heller, R. C., 1969, "Imaging with Photographic Sensors," Ch. 2 in R. Shay, Ed., *Remote Sensing with Special Reference to Agriculture and Forestry*, National Academy of Sciences, Washington, D.C.

Holter, M. P., 1971, "Infrared and Multispectral Remote Sensing," *Proceedings of NATO AGARD XCVII EPP Technical Meeting*, Colorado Springs.

Howard, G. E., and C. D. Sapp, 1970, "Evaluation of SLAR Imagery for Interpretation of Tropical Lowland Vegetation," American Society of Photogrammetry, Thirty-sixth Annual Meeting.

Hueck, K., 1960, "Mapa de Vegetacion de la Republica de Venezuela," Merida Instituto Forestal Latino Americano de Investigacion y Capacitacion.

Knipling, E. B., 1969, "Leaf Reflectance and Image Formation on Color Infrared Film," in Johnson, P. L., Ed., *Remote Sensing in Ecology*, University of Georgia Press, Athens.

Kondrat'yev, K. Y., A. A. Buznikov, et al., 1970, "Some Results of Spectrophotometry of the Earth from the Soyuz-7 Spacecraft," Doklady Akademii Nank SSR, 195(5), pp. 1084-1087. Also available as U.S. Department of Commerce JPRS Document 54047.

Krumpe, P. F., 1972, "Remote Sensing of Terrestrial Vegetation: A Comprehensive Bibliography," University of Tennessee, Knoxville.

Krumpe, P. F., H. R. DeSelm, and C. C. Amundsen, 1971, "An Ecological Analysis of Forest Landscape Parameters by Multiband Remote Sensing," *Proceedings of the Seventh International Symposium on Remote Sensing of Environment*, University of Michigan, Ann Arbor, 1:715-730.

Kuchler, A. W., 1956, "Classification and Purpose in Vegetation Maps," *Geographical Review*, 46(2):155-167.

Kuchler, A. W., 1967, *Vegetation Mapping*, Ronald Press, New York.

Martin, W. H., 1966, "Some Relationships of Vegetation to Soil and Site Factors on Wilson Mountain, Morgan County, Tennessee," Unpublished Master of Science thesis, University of Tennessee, Knoxville.

Mary, D. J., 1964, *Directional Reflectance of Certain Materials in the Near Infrared*, Technical Manual 64-29, U.S. Army Material Command.

Mealor, W. T., and M. C. Prunty, 1968, *Vegetation Changes caused by Fire in the Florida Flatwoods as Observed by Remote Sensing*, U.S. Geological Survey Technical Letter, NASA-148.

Minnich, R. A., L. W. Bowden, and R. W. Pease, 1969, "Mapping Montane Vegetation in Southern California from Color Infrared Imagery," in *Remote Sensing of Southern California and Related Environments*, Technical Report III, University of California at Riverside, Department of Geography.

Moore, R. K., 1970, "Ground Echo," in M. I. Skolnik, Ed., *Radar Handbook*, McGraw-Hill Book Company, New York.

Morain, S. A., 1973, "Phenology and Remote Sensing," in H. Lieth, Ed., *Phenology and Seasonality Modeling*, Proceedings of a Symposium held at Twenty-fifth AIBS Meeting, Minneapolis. To be published by Springer.

Morain, S. A., and D. S. Simonett, 1965, "Vegetation Analysis with Radar Imagery," *Proceedings Fourth Symposium on Remote Sensing of Environment*, University of Michigan, Ann Arbor, pp. 605-622.

Morain, S. A., and D. S. Simonett, 1967, "K-Band Radar in Vegetation Mapping," *Photogrammetric Engineering*, 33(7):730-740.

Nielsen, U., and J. M. Wightman, 1971, *A New Approach to the Description of the Forest Regions of Canada Using 1:160,000 Color Infrared Photography*, Information Report FMR-X-35, Canadian Forestry Service, Forest Management Institute.

Olson, C. E., and R. E. Good, 1962, "Seasonal Changes in Light Reflectance from Forest Vegetation," *Photogrammetric Engineering*, 28(1):107-114.

Orme, A. R., L. W. Bowden, and R. A. Minnich, 1971, "Remote Sensing of Disturbed Insular Vegetation from Color Infrared Imagery," *Seventh International Symposium on Remote Sensing of Environment*, University of Michigan, Ann Arbor, pp. 1235-1243.

Paijmans, K., 1966, "Typing of Tropical Vegetation by Aerial Photographs and Field Sampling in Northern Papua," *Photogrammetria*, 21:1-25.

Perry, R. A., 1960, *Pasture Lands of the Northern Territory, Australia*, CSIRO Land Research Series, No. 5.

Peterson, R. M., G. R. Cochrane, S. A. Morain, and D. S. Simonett, 1969, "A Multi-Sensor Study of Plant Community Densities and Boundaries at Horsefly Mountain, Oregon," in P. L. Johnson, Ed., *Remote Sensing in Ecology*, University of Georgia Press, Athens.

Poulton, C. E., B. J. Schrumpf, and E. Garcia-Moya, 1971, "A Preliminary Vegetational Resource Inventory and Symbolic Legend System for the Tucson-Wilcox-Fort Huachuca Triangle of Arizona," in R. N. Colwell, Ed., *Monitoring Earth Resources from Aircraft and Spacecraft*, NASA Document SP0275, Government Printing Office, Washington, D.C.

Rohde, W. G., 1971, "Multispectral Enhancement of Disease in Forest Stands," in *Color Aerial Photography in the Plant Sciences*, Third Biennial Workshop, American Society of Photogrammetry, pp. 131-143.

Rohde, W. B., and C. E. Olson, Jr., 1971, "Estimating Foliar Moisture Content from Infrared Reflectance Data," in *Color Aerial Photography in the Plant Sciences*, Third Biennial Workshop, American Society of Photogrammetry, pp. 114-164.

Rowe, J. S., 1959, "Forest Regions of Canada," *Forestry Branch Bulletin*, Canadian Department of Northern Affairs, National Resources No. 123, 71 pp.

Sapp, C. D., et al., 1971, "Selected Bibliography of the Terrain Sciences," Raytheon Company, Wayland, Mass.

Simonett, D. S., and S. A. Morain, 1967, "Remote Sensing from Spacecraft as a Tool for Investigating Arctic Environments," in H. E. Wright, Ed., *Arctic and Alpine Environments*, Indiana University Press, Bloomington.

Simonett, D. S., G. R. Cochrane, S. A. Morain, and D. D. Egbert, 1969, "Environment Mapping with Spacecraft Photography: A Central Australian Example," Annual Report to U.S. Geological Survey on Contract #14-08-001-10848, from the Center for Research, Inc., University of Kansas, Lawrence.

Smith, J. T., Ed., 1968, *Manual of Color Aerial Photography*, American Society of Photogrammetry.

Sorem, A. L., 1967, "Principles of Aerial Color Photography," *Photogrammetric Engineering*, 33:1008-1018.

Steiner, D., 1969, "Time Dimension for Crop Surveys from Space," *Photogrammetric Engineering*, 35(2):187-194.

Sullivan, A. E., and W. G. Brooner, 1971, *Remote Sensing of Chaparral Fire Potential: Case Study in Topanga Canyon, California*, Technical Report T-71-1, U.S. Department of the Navy, Office of Naval Research (ONR), Project Themis.

Vinogradov, B. V., 1961, "Vegetation as an Indicator in the Interpretation of Aerial Photographs of Desert Landscapes in Western Turkmenia," from *Izvestiya Veseoyuznogo Geograficheskogo Obshchestva*, also available as IPST Technical Translation 65-50064.

Vinogradov, B. V., and K. Y. Kondrat'yev, 1970, "Geographical Applications of Remote Sensing," Materialy Vsyezda Geograficheskogo Obshchestva SSR, reprinted in *Soviet Geography*, June 1971, pp. 383-392.

Vogel, T. C., M. J. Lynch, A. O. Lind, and R. W. Birnie, 1971, "A Matrix Evaluation of Remote Sensor Capabilities for Military Geographic Information," Geography Sciences Division, U.S. Army Engineer Topographic Laboratories, Fort Belvoir, Va.

Weber, F. P., and F. C. Polcyn, 1971, "Remote Sensing with Optical Mechanical Scanners to Detect Stress in Forests," American Society of Photogrammetry, Thirty-seventh Annual Meeting.

Wickens, J. E., 1966, "Practical Application of Aerial Photography for Geological Surveys in the Savannah Regions of Africa," *Photogrammetria*, 21:31-41.

Wilson, J. E., 1969, "Sensor Detection Capability Study," USGS Circular 616.

Zonneveld, I. S., P. N. de Leeuw, and W. G. Sombroek, 1971, *An Ecological Interpretation of Aerial Photographs in a Savanna Region of Northern Nigeria*, Series B, No. 63, International Institute for Aerial Survey and Earth Sciences (ITC), Enschede, The Netherlands.

7

Interpreting Land Use From Remote Sensor Imagery

Nelson R. Nunnally
University of Oklahoma

Land use is a primary indicator of the extent and degree to which man has made an impression on the earth's landscape. It reflects political, social, and economic aspects of human cultures, and provides an index of the intensity of human lifestyles. Since particular land uses generally have "unnatural" expressions in the landscape, land use is especially susceptible to study by remote sensing techniques. This chapter provides an overview of remote sensing research on land use, emphasizing problems and approaches in conducting such investigations. Fuller treatment is accorded agricultural and urban land use in subsequent chapters, since these are major research areas in their own right.

There is little doubt that remote sensing technology can make one of its biggest and most significant contributions in the area of land-use data collection. The statement is particularly true for agricultural land-use data because of the importance of agriculture in the economies of developing and undeveloped countries and because of the costs and problems involved in collecting agricultural data on a repetitive basis in developed countries. Although in recent years, planners and urban geographers have looked increasingly to imagery as a source of urban land-use data, they have not placed as much emphasis on imagery as a primary data source nor have they been as active in researching the problems and developing interpretation techniques as have those groups interested in nonurban environments or those researchers whose interests in land use are more comprehensive. Undoubtedly this situation is attributable partly to the fact that the urban landscape is both more complicated and more detailed, thus rendering it more difficult to extract urban land-use data from imagery. Much of the material discussed in this chapter reflects the general interest in agricultural land use. Although the discussion relates to general problems of land use and interpretation, many of the examples reflect the specific agricultural interests of the investigators. Readers with other interests should be able to apply directly or adapt with minor changes many of the ideas and methodologies discussed.

The format chosen for presentation is centered around three themes: (1) problems encountered in extracting land-use data from imagery, (2) current applications, and (3) the future of land-use studies. Some of these topics overlap somewhat with other sections of the book, but the specific orientation toward land use seemed to provide justification enough for their inclusion in this chapter. No attempt has been made to provide an exhaustive review of the published literature on land-use applications of remote sensing. Nor is the objective to instruct the reader in fundamentals of interpreting land use from imagery. Either task would be too formidable to undertake in the limited space available, and the latter would require a laboratory or tutorial approach, since interpretation is best learned through personal experience.

PROBLEMS ENCOUNTERED IN EXTRACTING LAND-USE DATA FROM IMAGERY

Anyone desiring to interpret land-use data from remote sensor imagery should be fully aware of the factors which will affect his ability to extract and use these data. They may appropriately be considered as problems: problems of land use classification, interpretation problems, and sampling and statistical problems. Each is considered separately in the following sections. The first two are discussed in this section, and sampling and statistical problems are discussed in the section on thematic land-use mapping.

Classification Problems

Three general problems have been recognized by those who collect and use land-use data: the problems of (1) defining terms and describing categories, (2) compatibility of systems used by different investigators, and (3) the establishment of hierarchical classification systems. Clawson and Stewart (1965) have discussed all three types of problems and their resolution within a general context, and Nunnally and Witmer (1968, 1970a, 1970b) have discussed them with particular reference to remote sensing. Both studies agree that no single classification system can be developed which would serve the purposes of all users of land-use data or would be applicable in all geographical areas. Nunnally and Witmer also concluded that no single classification system could be used with all scales and types of imagery. They believe that it would be impossible to develop a hierarchical system in which the more generalized hierarchical levels could be equated with land uses identifiable on small-scale or low-resolution photography. For example, a 40-acre wheat field might be easily identifiable from space photography whereas more generalized categories of urban use might not. Like Clawson and Stewart, they recommend an inductive approach to land-use classification in which the interpreter would interpret use in as much detail as possible, given the scale and resolution limitations of the imagery provided, and then group the uses into the categories most appropriate to his own investigation (hierarchical if desired). If basic classes were properly defined and adequately described, the original data could then be used effectively by others since all detail would have been preserved. An approach such as the one they propose could use as input automatically interpreted land-use data. The use of automatic interpretation with fixed a priori classifications, while not impossible, would certainly be more difficult.

Anderson (1971, 1972) believes that a general-purpose classification scheme can be developed for use with space and high-altitude aircraft imagery--a scheme which would (1) be usable or adaptable over a large area; (2) be usable on imagery acquired at different times of the year; (3) be compatible with orbital imagery, conventional data sources, and existing classifications, and (4) have subcategories which could be obtained from ground surveys or from larger-scale imagery. He proposed two tentative classifications, one for use with orbital imagery alone and one for use with orbital imagery with some supplemental information (Anderson, 1971, pp. 386-387). A more complete classification with explanations was presented by Anderson at the Conference on Land Use Information and Classification in June 1971. The first two levels of classification are contained in USGS Circular 671 (Anderson et al., 1972). The classification has been used successfully by the Geological Survey Geographic Applications Program (GEOGAP) in their land-use studies which are discussed in the section on land-use change.

Interpretation Problems

Of particular interest to those who work with imagery are the problems encountered in actually interpreting land use. These can be grouped generally into the categories of scale and resolution, type of sensor system, time of acquisition, cultural background, and interpreter training. Each of these is discussed briefly.

Scale and Resolution. Anyone with photo-interpretation experience is aware that, all other things being equal, much more detail is apparent on large-scale photos than small-scale, and land-use data are no exception. There are also differences in resolution that may produce the same effect. As seen in Chapter 2, resolution refers to the ability of a system to record two distinct and separate objects on the ground as separate phenomena. Frequently the term "ground resolution" is used in order to provide a basis for comparison that is more or less independent of scale. The contrast in spectral irradiance between a target and its background is a factor in evaluating resolution, and this concept is discussed more fully in Chapter 2.

Few studies have been undertaken which have attempted to evaluate the effects of scale and resolution on an interpreter's ability to identify different types of land use. Virtually nothing is known as to the effects on accuracy of land-use data caused by variations in scale and resolution, although analysis of variance experiments could be designed to systematically evaluate the effects. Instead, all we have available are a few independent studies which have attempted to evaluate the effectiveness of specific scales and resolution of imagery for land use mapping.

Stone (1956) proposed a system for extracting data from photos for geographic studies and set forth guidelines which specify the kinds of features that should be interpreted at small, medium, and large scales, respectively. He made no attempt, however, to assess the limitations of the different scales on interpretation.

Recent studies by Rudd (1971), MacPhail and Campbell (1970), Thrower and Senger (1970), Schwarz et al. (1969), Simonett (1969a), Simonett et al. (1970), and Thrower (1972) are among those that have attempted to make some evaluation of the land-use mapping capabilities of small-scale space imagery. Rudd used simulated space photography at a scale of 1:400,000, and the other studies used Gemini and Apollo photography. In all instances, results were inconclusive as to the general applicability. There was considerable variation in accuracy of interpretation by land-use category, with some types being correctly identified only 50 to 60 percent of the time while others were more than 90 percent correct.

One of the obvious complicating factors which affected accuracy was the complexity of the landscape. In areas where the landscape was more complex, accuracy was generally lower while relatively simple landscapes produced higher levels of accuracy. This might be considered as another type of target background contrast.

Board (1965), Munn et al. (1966), Sridas (1966), and Steiner (1965) authored a series of articles appearing in *Photogrammetria* which were written for the Rural Land Use Working Party of the Commission on Interpretation of Aerial Photographs. Each of the authors reviewed the application of aerial photography to land-use studies in the country of concern. There is little doubt as to the ability of photography to supply the land-use data sought or as to the heavy dependence placed upon photography as a data source. In most instances, interest was focused on broad categories of use, and no assessment was made of the level of accuracy sought or that achieved.

Sensor Types. Sensor evaluation studies are similar to the scale studies cited. They are a series of independent studies done by authors interested in specific systems. There has been no attempt by anyone to systematically evaluate the relative effectiveness of all of the different sensors capable of recording land use data.

Anson (1965), Colwell (1965), Samol (1968), Hannag (1969), and Neumann and Simonett (1970) have analyzed color, color infrared, and black-and-white photography in land-use studies. All are in agreement that both color and color infrared are superior to black-and-white. There is some disagreement, however, as to whether color or color infrared photography is a better general-purpose land-use sensor.

Using multispectral scanner imagery, investigators from the Laboratory for Agricultural Remote Sensing (LARS) at Purdue University (1967, 1968) have successfully discriminated among selected crop types. Wellar (1971) used multispectral photography to estimate residential units in the Chicago area.

Simonett (1968) has reviewed the literature dealing with land evaluation studies in the infrared and radar regions. In addition, a number of studies originating from the Center for Research in the Engineering Sciences at the University of Kansas (Simonett, 1969b; Coiner and Morain, 1970) have explored the utility of radar as a means of discriminating land use, especially agricultural and vegetative uses.

Olson (1967) evaluated the accuracy of land-use interpretations from thermal imagery. He found that while some crops such as alfalfa could be correctly identified most of the time, other crops (corn and soybeans) could be identified only 65 to 70 percent of the time, and separation of pasture and brushland could not be achieved 50 percent of the time. Colwell et al. (1966) also have analyzed the usefulness of thermal and related imagery in evaluating agricultural resources.

Time of Imagery Acquisition. Time of photography is especially important when studying land uses which vary seasonally or are undergoing relatively rapid change. The seasonal effect is most obvious with crops. In fact, the accuracy with which crops and vegetation can be identified is highly dependent upon season of photography. Boesch and Brunnschweiler (1960), Brunnschweiler (1957),

Bomberger and Dill (1960), investigators at the Laboratory for Agricultural Remote Sensing at Purdue (1967), and Steiner (1966, 1969) have all investigated the seasonal effect on crop identification.

All land use (urban or rural) is dynamic, and the mixture of uses existing at any one time might be thought of as a finite sample of a hypothetical infinite universe (Kelly, 1970). If viewed in this manner, sampling procedures can be planned that will ensure representative sampling and maximize the ability to accurately interpret cyclic uses. The nearly all-weather capability of radar and thermal imagery makes this a more feasible proposition.

Cultural Background. One of the problems which is frequently encountered but seldom discussed is the limitation on the transference value of land-use interpretation from one cultural situation to another. This can be a problem even within the continental United States, where interpreters have gained their experience largely within one area and are subsequently exposed to imagery acquired elsewhere that may contain unfamiliar uses or familiar uses in an unfamiliar context. The concept that the environment modulates the quality of information transfer has been called the environmental modulation transfer function (Schwarz et al., 1969). The problem is self-evident when comparing different parts of the world.

Interpreter Training. Little has been done to evaluate the training and ability of persons involved in interpreting land use. On the basis of evidence collected during several interpretation experiments and discussions with other scientists engaged in training interpreters, I am convinced that the level of training and ability of many interpreters is a matter of serious concern. In one study conducted with another investigator (Nunnally and Witmer, 1970a), we found variations in accuracy of land-use interpretation by different subjects, all trained interpreters, ranging from approximately 50 percent to more than 90 percent. At least two conclusions might be drawn from such data: (1) Interpreters have not had sufficient firsthand experience in interpreting land use. This is indeed a problem since one must have imagery of familiar areas or areas which are sufficiently accessible so that results can be evaluated. This is generally not the case with many newer types of imagery. (2) Those of us who train interpreters do not emphasize interpretation skills as much as we should. Certainly the increased emphasis on theory is justified as long as interpretive skills are not deemphasized. The teaching of interpretation has probably changed very little since the first course was taught, and no real research has been done into determining the most effective way to teach interpretation. No one would seriously deny that a high correlation exists between experience and interpretive ability, but we need to establish more effective means of passing that experience on to students.

One way of minimizing the effects of experience is to establish interpretation keys. Two kinds of keys have been used most frequently in land-use studies--elimination keys and selective keys (Rabben, 1960, pp. 112-113). Most elimination keys are dichotomous and are designed to sequentially eliminate all but one object from all of those possible. At each step an either/or-type question is asked, and the interpreter is instructed for the next step to proceed to different places in the key based on the answer.

Selective keys consist of single images or stereogram sets, plus an explanation or description of each of the objects. There must be an image of each object under consideration, and the interpreter must select the one which most closely matches the unknown object.

Knight and Harnapp (1971) have discussed the construction and use of keys in identifying broad land-use elements in tropical areas. Morain et al. (1970) have developed a key for identifying crop types from radar imagery at Garden City, Kansas. Keys for identifying industrial uses can be found in Chapter 12 of the *Manual of Photographic Interpretation* (Wray, 1960, pp. 701-703) and in Chisnell and Cole (1958).

For general discussion of keys and their problems, see Bigelow (1963, 1966), Black (1955), Delancie et al. (1957), Frost (1952), and Lewis (1957).

Some of the problems in using keys relate to their limited flexibility. Not only are they specific to the range of uses expected, but they are image-specific and, frequently, area-specific. The same key might not be applicable for identifying irrigated and dry land wheat, although the land use is the same. Also, keys developed for use in a given area, for example southern California (Colwell, 1970), might not necessarily be useful in an analogous area, such as southern Italy.

LAND-USE APPLICATIONS OF REMOTE SENSING

Two basic approaches appear to dominate land-use applications of remote sensing --the comprehensive land-use inventory and thematic land-use mapping. Since the two techniques have different purposes, they utilize different techniques and present different sets of problems; they will be discussed separately. Separate sections are devoted to the "integrated-landscape" method of analysis which relies heavily on both land use and physical elements and land-use change detection.

Inventories

The objective of an inventory is to systematically determine the detailed use of all land in the area under consideration. Detailed data such as these are frequently required by city and county planners or others whose ultimate objective is decision making at the local level. Data are usually stored on maps in raw or slightly aggregated form. Once the data have been inventoried, they may be aggregated by artificial data units or otherwise generalized in producing thematic maps. The New York land-use and natural resources inventory was carried out in this manner (Shelton, 1968).

A good example of the inventory approach, as applied to urban land use, is that of Hannah (1969). He found that urban use data of the type normally required by Asheville metropolitan planners (single-family residential, multifamily residential, retail commercial, light industry, etc.) could be acquired more accurately from large-scale color photography than by the field mapping techniques local planners currently were employing.

Investigators at the University of California at Riverside have also carried out partial inventories of urban areas in San Diego County, California, and rural land use in the Imperial Valley (Imperial County, California) using medium and large-scale color and color infrared photography (Bowden, 1968a; Johnson, C. W., 1969; Johnson, C. W. et al., 1969). They found that of the use categories needed by the planning commission, 24 percent were identifiable 100 percent of the time, 50 percent were identifiable more than 50 percent of the time, and 26 percent were identifiable less than 50 percent of the time from the imagery they were using.

Problems encountered in inventorying land use are of two types--classification problems and interpretation problems (see first section of this chapter). Since by nature an inventory must be detailed and must be carried out using relatively large-scale imagery, one would imagine that hierarchical problems would be minimal. This is not entirely true. It is far easier to interpret crop types than it is to identify types of retail establishments or types of chemical processing plants, even though most investigators assign them similar hierarchical classes (Bowden, 1968a).

Thematic Land-Use Mapping

Thematic land-use mapping differs from the inventory approach in that generalized land-use data are collected rather than complete enumeration. There is some loss of detail due to grouping error (caused by data aggregation within enumeration cells) by sampling error, or both. The use of uniformly sized data units does facilitate computer storage and computer mapping procedures, however.

Different investigators have attempted to resolve the statistical and sampling problems inherent in thematic mapping in different ways. In urban areas Wray (1960, pp. 680-684) advocates mapping gross land use and then subdividing the study area into "analytical areas" about 2 million square feet in size and possessing apparent homogeneity in type and intensity of use. In other studies, the area is first completely subdivided into data units, usually with a grid or quadrat of some size, and land use within each unit is determined. Then the unit is assigned to that category which is most prevalent (a disastrous consequence for those uses occupying small areas), or all uses are recorded by the percent of the grid area they occupy. The Minnesota Land Management Information System is of this type.

If interest lies in estimating the percentage of uses by categories rather than mapping the entire study area, then statistical sampling can be used effectively. Kelly (1970) believes that, at least as far as agricultural land use is concerned, "utilization of the full potential of sensor data will probably require a restructuring of sample survey designs now used by the agricultural statistician." Berry (1962) has proposed the use of a stratified systematic, unaligned sample for such studies. Land use can be interpreted at each sample point rather than having to make decisions about the size of data units. When point sampling procedures are used, no unbiased estimates can be made concerning average size of parcel or range of sizes for different land-use categories, unless special efforts are undertaken to stratify the sample for this purpose.

The main problems in thematic mapping involve (1) the number and size of sample cells and the sampling technique, if a sample is used; (2) the size of the quadrat and the map projection, if a quadrat approach is used (certainly quadrat sizes should be no smaller than the ground resolution of the system used); and (3) the policy decisions regarding the type of classification system to be used and the specific interpretation approach selected (recording the dominant use only or all uses by percentage of cell area occupied, etc.). Simonett (1969) and Rudd (1971) have discussed these problems from slightly different perspectives.

Rudd (1971), Schwarz et al. (1969), Simonett et al. (1970), Simonett (1969b), and Thrower and Senger (1970) have either made thematic land-use maps or assessed the reliability of interpretative techniques from simulated space imagery, Gemini and Apollo photography, and radar. Results were variable.

Simonett concluded that few, if any, existing land-use maps could be duplicated from space photography, owing largely to the inability to interpret specific categories (Simonett, 1969).

Land-Use System and Landscape Approaches

Frequently the focus of an investigation is to identify and map agricultural or other land-use systems or to identify and map associations of the elements making up the landscape (land use is the most generally dominant element in most landscapes occupied by man). The central theme in both system studies and landscape methods is to regionalize the landscape and to characterize the mapped areas with generalized descriptions rather than to focus on specific uses.

Knight and Harnapp (1971) used a systems approach to study tropical agriculture in Puerto Rico, South Vietnam, and Tanzania. The Australians have been ardent advocates of the integrated-landscape approach (Christian and Stewart, 1968; Francis, 1968; Schneider, 1967). MacPhail (1971) has applied the approach in Chile, but called it photomorphic mapping, and Nunnally (1969) mapped integrated-landscape regions in the Asheville basin using radar.

Landscape methods have their drawbacks, too. Probably the biggest one is the highly subjective nature of the technique. Knight and Harnapp (1971) have tried to establish an approach for interpreting tropical agriculture systems that could be automated, thereby removing the subjective aspect. Implicit in this interpretation system is the deterministic assumption that all possible systems can be cataloged unambiguously enough to identify the unknown system correctly. Investigations are under way currently at East Tennessee State University to automate MacPhail's photomorphic-region concept.

Detecting Land-Use Changes

The dynamic nature of land use and its effect upon interpretation has been discussed earlier in this paper. Since changes are constantly occurring, a number of investigators have focused their attention on the detection of land-use changes (Avery, 1965; Falkner, 1968; Richter, 1969; Wellar, 1971). Some have advocated the development of special systems solely for the purpose of detecting and recording land-use changes so that maps and data banks can be updated quickly. High-quality, high-resolution synoptic satellite imagery could remove many of the problems inherent in automatic change detection.

The Geological Survey Geographic Applications Program (GAP) is currently involved in several research projects concerned with developing procedures for monitoring current land-use changes using satellite and high-altitude aerial photography as the primary source of information (Alexander, 1972; Ellefsen and Peruzzi, 1972; Place, 1972; Wray, 1972a, 1972b). In all experiments, the intent has been to relate land use to other environmental and socioeconomic data recorded in a computerized data bank. Of the four principal projects currently being undertaken, three are regional: southern Arizona, the Ozarks region, and the Central Atlantic Regional Ecological Test Site, described by Place (1972) and Alexander (1972). The Anderson land-use classification system has been tested in each of these three regions and has been found to work satisfactorily, even when used with satellite imagery. The fourth project is the Census Cities, described by Wray (1972a), which relates land-use changes detected in various American metropolitan areas to data from the 1970 census.

THE FUTURE OF LAND-USE STUDIES

Few would deny the applicability of remote sensor imagery to land-use studies. Yet, imagery is not fully utilized in collecting land-use data, despite the fact that, with current technology, accurate land-use data could be obtained from imagery more efficiently and economically than by traditional methods. Should H.R. 7211 (National Land Policy, Planning, and Management Act of 1972) be passed in its present amended form or in some modified version, one of the major requirements under Title II, Section 201, for any comprehensive land-use planning process is an "adequate data base." Although the data base would utilize existing data whenever feasible, an unbelievable amount of ecological, environmental, hydrological, natural resource, and land-use data would need to be collected, both for state and federal lands. It seems fair to assume that this task could not be accomplished without remote sensing. ERTS-A (now designated ERTS-1) and future satellites, such as ERTS-2, Skylab, and EOS (Earth Observation Satellite) will produce worldwide coverage of imagery at a common scale and on a repetitive basis. How will we make full use of all these images? Obviously the future of land use interpretation will rest largely on automated techniques. Holter (1970) summarizes the consequences of reliance on manual inputs in data collection succinctly. He says that manual methods cannot produce high enough precision owing to the low density of sample points that can be manually interpreted, that there are many classes of information needed that cannot be generated, and that manual methods cannot produce results that are timely enough.

Automatic interpretation studies generally follow one of the four basic discriminating or identification techniques: (1) spectral, (2) spatial (shape and/or texture), (3) polarization, or (4) temporal (either rapid temporal changes such as doppler shifts used in migratory-bird studies or slower changes like those associated with land use) (Holter, 1970, pp. 358-359).

Spectral approaches have dominated the literature on automatic identification of specific land uses, especially crops. Studies at Kansas, Purdue, Michigan, and Berkeley have focused on spectral discrimination and have used, for the most part, linear or polynomial discriminant functions to assign unknown samples to the most similar group. A representative sampling of this literature can be found in the following: Brooner (1969), Caspall et al. (1968), Coiner and Morain (1970), Colwell (1965), Doverspike et al. (1965), Haralick (1968, 1969), Haralick and Kelly (1969), Haralick et al. (1970), Hoffer (1967), Johnson, G.E. (1972), Knight and Harnapp (1971), Laboratory for Agricultural Remote Sensing (1967, 1968), Malila (1968), Neuman and Simonett (1970), and Schwarz and Caspall

(1968). As readers will note, in virtually all of the references cited, the interest has been on identifying crop and cover types.

Though some of the studies have been able to classify certain crop types accurately, it must be realized that spectral input data in each case come from very limited geographical areas (in some instances only one field), involve a restricted number of types, and are sampled from a narrow range of crop maturity stages. Because of this, the systems developed frequently will not work or will work poorly with the same crops in other areas, with different mixes of crop types or with imagery acquired at a different time. Much of the spectral discrimination work done to date, then, is sensor-specific, area-specific, time-specific, and use-specific, thereby nullifying its general application and necessitating complete recalibration with each new application.

Steiner (1969) and Steiner and Maurer (1969) have added height data and temporal density data to improve the discrimination of crops. Their system also uses a discriminant function approach.

Investigators at Kansas University have worked with polarization as a discriminating variable with radar, but little else has been done elsewhere. Polarized photography as a means of differentiating among land uses has received little attention.

A few studies of land use have attempted to use spatial information as a discriminant. Some of them have used Fourier and other filtering techniques to identify regular patterns associated with cultural features (Brody and Ermlich, 1966). These studies have generally not focused upon identifying specific uses but upon combination of uses which compose urban and agricultural landscapes.

Haralick and Kelly (1969) have developed a classification system using spectral and spatial characteristics of data points. Not much progress has been made in applying automatic shape analysis to the classification of land-use data on imagery, even though shape techniques have been successfully applied to optical scanning problems (Holter, 1970, pp. 398-399). The IDECS (Image Discrimination Enhancement Combination and Sampling) system developed at Kansas and some of the commercial data analysis systems currently on the market contain automatic edge-enhancing capability made possible by differentiating the signal voltage from the image scanner to pick out the rapid rate of change in film density associated with boundaries. Ideson (1970) has developed an automatic terrain-recognition system which combines edge enhancement, Fourier analysis, and spectral-density data into a single system. It has performed well in identifying tropical terrains dominated by rice paddy, water, jungle, brush, etc.

It would appear that any reliable automatic interpretation system will have to incorporate spectral, spatial, and temporal discriminants in order to work well for all types of uses and under all conditions. Spectral approaches work fine for crops but fail utterly for most urban uses. Though the basic input will be spectral data, spatial and temporal information must be incorporated. Until we can develop a capability to extract land use data from imagery on a completely automatic basis, we will not be able to make full use of imagery. In the meantime, although we can use imagery effectively as a source for land use data, we must be aware of the problems encountered and take action to nullify or control those which affect the quality of the data acquired.

REFERENCES

Aldrich, R. C., 1953, "Accuracy of Land-Use Classification and Area Estimates Using Aerial Photographs," *Journal of Forestry,* 51:12-15.

Aldrich, R. C., 1971, "Space Photos for Land Use and Forestry," *Photogrammetric Engineering,* 37:389-401.

Alexander, Robert H., 1972, "Central Atlantic Regional Ecologic Test Site," *Fourth Annual Earth Resources Program Review,* vol. III, NASA/MSC, Houston, Tex., pp. 72-1 to 72-9.

Anderson, J. R., 1971, "Land-Use Classification Schemes," *Photogrammetric Engineering,* 37:379-388.

Anderson, J. R., E. Hardy, and J. T. Roach, 1972, *A Land-Use Classification System for Use with Remote Sensor Data,* Geological Survey Circular 671, Washington, D.C., 16 pp.

Anson, A., 1965, "Comparative Interpretation from Panchromatic, Color, and Ecktachrome I.R. Photography," report of Working Group I, Committee on Color Photography, American Society of Photogrammetry.

Avery, Gene, 1965, "Measuring Land-Use Changes on United States Department of Agriculture Photographs," *Photogrammetric Engineering,* 31:620-624.

Avery, T. E., 1968, "Agriculture and Land-Use Patterns," in *Interpretation of Aerial Photographs,* Burgess Publishing Company, Minneapolis, pp. 160-178.

Belcher, D. J., E. E. Hardy, R. L. Shelton, and E. L. Schepis, 1967, *Potential Benefit to Be Derived from Applications of Remote Sensing of Agriculture, Forest and Range Resources,* Center for Aerial Photographic Studies, Cornell University, Ithaca, N.Y.

Berry, B. J. L., 1962, *Sampling, Coding, and Storing Flood Plain Data,* USDA Handbook 237, Government Printing Office, Washington, D.C.

Bigelow, G. F., 1963, "Photographic Interpretation Keys--A Reappraisal," *Photogrammetric Engineering,* 29:1042-1051.

Bigelow, G. F., 1966, *Human Factors Problems in the Development and Use of Image Interpretation Keys,* Army Project No. 2J620901A721, U.S. Army Personnel Research Office.

Binsell, R., 1967, *Dwelling Unit Estimation from Aerial Photographs,* Northwestern University, Geographic Applications Program, Evanston, Ill.

Black, L. W., 1955, "Regional Keys Are Valid Geographical Generalizations," *Photogrammetric Engineering,* 21:706-708.

Board, C., 1965, "Use of Air Photographs in Land Use Studies in South Africa and Adjacent Territories," *Photogrammetria,* 20:163-171.

Boesch, H., and D. Brunnschweiler, 1960, "Seasonal Changes of the Agricultural Landscape Interpreted from Aerial Photographs," *Geographica Helvetica,* 15:257-261.

Boesch, Hans, and Dieter Steiner, 1959, *Interpretation of Land Utilization from Aerial Photographs,* Geographisches Institute der Universitat, Zurich.

Bomberger, E. H., and H. W. Dill, Jr., 1960, "Photo Interpretation in Agriculture," Chapter 11 in *Manual of Photographic Interpretation,* R. N. Colwell, ed., American Society of Photogrammetry, Washington, D.C., pp. 561-666.

Bowden, L. W., 1968a, *Multi-Sensor Signatures of Urban Morphology, Function and Evolution,* Status Report II, University of California, Riverside.

Bowden, L. W., 1968b, "Southern California Regional Resources Studies," *Earth Resources Aircraft Program Status Review,* NASA/MSC, Houston, Tex., vol. 1, pp. 4-1 to 4-13.

Bowden, L. W., N. J. W. Thrower, and C. Tiedeman, 1968, *Status Report on Remote Sensing of Southern California and Related Environments,* University of California, Riverside.

Branch, Melville C., Jr., 1948, *Aerial Photography in Urban Planning and Research,* Harvard City Planning Series 14, Harvard University Press, Cambridge, Mass.

Brody, R. H., and J. R. Ermlich, 1966, "Fourier Analysis of Aerial Photographs," *Proceedings of the Fourth Symposium on Remote Sensing of Environment,* University of Michigan, Ann Arbor, pp. 372-392.

Brooner, William, 1969, "Agricultural Crop Discrimination with Color Infrared Photography: A Study of Douglas County, Kansas," Unpublished M.A. Thesis, University of Kansas, Lawrence.

Brunnschweiler, D. H., 1957, "Seasonal Changes of the Agricultural Pattern: A Study in Comparative Airphoto Interpretation," *Photogrammetric Engineering,* 23:131-139.

Carneggie, D. M., and J. N. Reppert, 1969, "Large-Scale 70mm Aerial Color Photos," *Photogrammetric Engineering,* 25:249-257.

Caspall, F., R. M. Haralick, R. K. Moore, and D. S. Simonett, 1968, "A Conditional Probability and Statistical Study of Crop Discrimination Using Radar Images," Unpublished paper presented at the IEEE Annual Convention, New York, March, 1968.

Chapman, T. G., Ed., 1968, *C.S.I.R.O. Symposium on Land Evaluation,* Macmillan of Australia, Canberra.

Chisnell, T. C., and G. E. Cole, 1958, "Industrial Components--A Photo Interpretation Key on Industry," *Photogrammetric Engineering,* 24:590-602.

Christian, C. S., and G. A. Stewart, 1968, "Methodology of Integrated Surveys," in *Aerial Surveys and Integrated Studies,* UNESCO, Paris, pp. 233-280.

Churchill, E. D., and R. L. Stitt, 1955, "Association Analysis Applied to the Interpretation of Aerial Photographs," *Photogrammetric Engineering*, 21:598-602.

Clawson, M., and C. S. Stewart, 1965, *Land Use Information*, Resources for the Future, Inc., The Johns Hopkins Press, Baltimore.

Coiner, J. C., and S. A. Morain, 1970, *An Evaluation of Fine Resolution Radar Imagery for Making Agricultural Determinations*, Technical Report 177-7, University of Kansas, Center for Research, Inc., Lawrence.

Colwell, R. N., 1965, "Spectrometric Considerations Involved in Making Rural Land Use Studies with Aerial Photography," *Photogrammetria*, 20:15-30.

Colwell, R. N., 1968a, "Determining the Usefulness of Space Photography for Natural Resource Inventory," *Proceedings of Fifth Symposium on Remote Sensing*, University of Michigan, Ann Arbor.

Colwell, R. N., 1968b, "Aerial and Space Photography as Aids to Land Evaluation," in G. A. Stewart, Ed., *Papers of a CSIRO Symposium Organized in Cooperation with UNESCO*, Macmillan of Australia, Canberra, pp. 324-341.

Colwell, R. N., Ed., 1969, *An Evaluation of Earth Resources Using Apollo IX Photography*, Forestry Remote Sensing Laboratory, University of California, Berkeley, California.

Colwell, R. N., Ed., 1970, "Application of Remote Sensing in Agriculture and Forestry," in *Remote Sensing with Special Reference to Agriculture and Forestry*, National Academy of Sciences, Washington, D.C.

Colwell, R. N., J. E. Estes, C. E. Tiedeman, and J. E. Fleming, 1966, *The Usefulness of Thermal Infrared and Related Imagery in the Evaluation of Agricultural Resources*, NASA Contract No. 12-14-100-8316 (20), Forestry Remote Sensing Lab, University of California, Berkeley.

Colwell, R. N., E. H. Roberts, and R. T. Lauer, 1966, *The Inventory of Livestock and Crops by Means of Aerial Photography*, School of Forestry, University of California, Berkeley.

Delancie, R., W. W. Steen, R. E. Pippin, and A. Shapiro, 1957, "Quantitative Evaluation of Photo Interpretation Keys," *Photogrammetric Engineering*, 23:858-864.

Dill, H. W., Jr., 1959, "Use of the Comparison Method in Agricultural Air Photo Interpretation," *Photogrammetric Engineering*, 25:44-49.

Dill, H. W., Jr., 1968, "The Role of Air Photo Interpretation in Land Resource Inventory in the Developing Countries," *Papers from the Thirty-Fourth Annual Meeting of the American Society of Photogrammetry*, Washington, D.C., pp. 110-113.

Doverspike, G. E., F. M. Flynn, and R. C. Heller, 1965, "Microdensitometer Applied to Land Use Classification," *Photogrammetric Engineering*, 31:294-306.

Draeger, William C., and L. R. Pettinger, 1970, "A Regional Resource Survey Using Small Scale Aerial and Space Photography," *Papers from the 1970 American Society of Photogrammetry American Congress of Mapping Fall Convention,* Washington, D.C., pp. 128-145.

Dutton, J. A., 1967, "Comparative Photo Interpretation from Panchromatic, Color, and Color IR Photography," Unpublished Master's thesis, Department of Geography, Ohio State University, Columbus.

Ellefson, R. H., and Duilio Peruzzi, 1972, "An Application of Remote Sensing in Land Use Mapping and Urban Change Detection in the San Francisco Bay Area," *International Geography, 1972: Papers Submitted to the Twenty-second International Geographical Congress, Canada,* Montreal, pp. 967-968.

Estes, John E., 1966, "Some Applications of Aerial Infrared Imagery," *Annals of the Association of American Geographers,* 56:673-682.

Falkner, Edgar, 1968, "Land Use Changes in Parkway School District," *Photogrammetric Engineering,* 34:52-57.

Francis, D. A., 1968, "Examples of Integrated Land-Use Surveys Being Carried out by the Food and Agriculture Organization of the United Nations Using Aerial Techniques," in *Aerial Surveys and Integrated Studies,* UNESCO, Paris, pp. 289-299.

Frost, R. E., 1952, "Discussion of Photo Recognition, Analysis, and Interpretation and Photo Keys," *Photogrammetric Engineering,* 18:502-505.

Gimbarzevsky, P., 1966, "Land Inventory Interpretation," *Photogrammetric Engineering,* 32:967-976.

Goodman, M., 1959, "A Technique for the Identification of Farm Crops on Aerial Photographs," *Photogrammetric Engineering,* 25:131-137.

Goodman, M., 1964, "Criteria for the Identification of Types of Farming on Aerial Photographs," *Photogrammetric Engineering,* 30:984-990.

Green, N. E., 1956a, "Scale Analysis of Urban Structures: A Study of Birmingham, Alabama," *American Sociological Review,* 21:8-13.

Green, N. E., 1956b, "Aerial Photographic Analysis of Residential Neighborhoods: An Evaluation of Data Accuracy," *Social Forces,* 35:142-147.

Green, N. E., 1957, "Aerial Photographic Interpretation and the Social Structure of the City," *Photogrammetric Engineering,* 23:89-99.

Green, N. E., Chairman, and Robert B. Monier, 1959, "Report of Working Group 5, Interpretation of Urban, Rural, and Indistrial Structures: Interim Progress Report for Commission VII," *Photogrammetric Engineering,* 25:128-130.

Haefner, H., 1967, "Air Photo Interpretation of Rural Land Use in Western Europe," *Photogrammetria,* 22:143-152.

Hannah, J. W., 1969, *A Feasibility Study for the Application of Remote Sensors to Selected Urban and Regional Land Use Planning Studies,* Technical Report 11, East Tennessee State University, Johnson City.

Haralick, R. M., 1968, "Adaptive Pattern Recognition of Agriculture in Western Kansas by Using a Predictive Model in Construction of Similarity Sets," *Proceedings of the Fifth Symposium on Remote Sensing of Environment,* University of Michigan, Ann Arbor, pp. 343-356.

Haralick, R. M., 1969, *The Bayesian Approach to Identification of Remotely Sensored Environment,* Technical Report 133-9, University of Kansas, Center for Research, Inc., Lawrence.

Haralick, R. M., F. Caspall, and D. S. Simonett, 1970, "Using Radar Imagery for Crop Discrimination: A Statistical and Conditional Probability Study," *Remote Sensing of Environment,* 1:131-142.

Haralick, R. M., and G. L. Kelly, 1969, "Pattern Recognition with Measurement Space and Spatial Clustering for Multiple Images," *Proceedings of the IEEE,* 57: 654-665.

Heath, G. R., 1955, "An Associative Method of Regional Photo Interpretation," *Photogrammetric Engineering,* 21:589-598.

Heath, G. R., 1956, "A Comparison of Two Basic Theories of Land Classification and their Adaptability to Regional Photo Interpretation Key Techniques," *Photogrammetric Engineering,* 22:144-168.

Henderson, Floyd M., 1971, *Local Level Agricultural Practices and Individual Farmer Needs as Influences on SLAR Imagery Data Collection,* Technical Report 177-15, University of Kansas, Center for Research, Inc., Lawrence.

Herriques, D. E., 1949, "Practical Application of Photogrammetry in Land Classification as Used by the Bureau of Land Management," *Photogrammetric Engineering,* 15:540-548.

Hoffer, Roger M., 1967, *Interpretation of Remote Multispectral Imagery of Agricultural Crops,* Research Bulletin 831, Laboratory for Agricultural Remote Sensing, Purdue University, Lafayette, Ind.

Holter, Marvin W., 1970, "Research Needs: The Influence of Discrimination, Data Processing, and System Design," in *Remote Sensing with Special References to Agriculture and Forestry,* National Academy of Sciences, Washington, D.C., pp. 354-421.

Howard, J. A., 1965, "Small-scale Photographs and Land Resources in Nyamueziland, East Africa," *Photogrammetric Engineering,* 31:287-293.

Howard, W. A., and J. B. Kracht, 1972, "Developing Remote Sensing Display Modes to Satisfy Urban Planning Data Input Needs," *International Geography, 1972: Papers Submitted to the Twenty-Second International Geographical Congress, Canada,* Montreal, pp. 968-970.

Idelson, J. M., 1970, "A Learning System for Terrain Recognition," paper presented at the 1970 Symposium on Computational Photogrammetry, Alexandria, Va., Jan. 7-9.

Johnson, C. W., 1969, "Imperial Valley Land Use Studies: A Continuum from Mission 73 to Apollo IX," *Second Annual Earth Resources Aircraft Program Status Review,* NASA/MSC, Houston, Tex., Section 14.

Johnson, C. W., L. W. Bowden, and R. W. Pease, 1969, *Studies in Remote Sensing of Southern California and Related Environments, a System of Regional Agriculture Land Use Mapping,* Status Report III, Technical Report II, U.S. Department of Interior, Contract 14-08-111-1-10674, Washington, D.C.

Johnson, G. E., 1972, "Cover Type Identification Capabilities of Remote Multispectral Sensing Techniques," *International Geography, 1972: Papers Submitted to the Twenty-Second International Geographical Congress, Canada,* Montreal, pp. 973-975.

Jones, R. G. B., 1959, "Air Photo-Interpretation in Soil and Land Classification Surveys," *South African Journal of Science,* 55:129-132.

Kelly, Bruce W., 1970, "Sampling and Statistical Problems," in *Remote Sensing with Special Reference to Agriculture and Forestry,* National Academy of Sciences, Washington, D.C., pp. 329-353.

Knight, C. Gregory, and Vern R. Harnapp, 1971, *Remote Sensing of Tropical Agricultural Systems,* University of Kansas, Center for Research, Inc., Lawrence.

Kohn, C. F., 1951, "The Use of Aerial Photographs in the Geographical Analysis of Rural Settlements," *Photogrammetric Engineering,* 17:759-771.

Komarsov, V. B., 1968, "Aerial Photography in the Investigation of National Resources in the U.S.S.R." in *Aerial Surveys and Integrated Studies,* UNESCO, Paris, pp. 143-185.

Laboratory for Agricultural Remote Sensing (LARS), 1967, *Remote Multispectral Sensing in Agriculture,* Research Bulletin 832, Purdue University, Lafayette, Ind.

Laboratory for Agricultural Remote Sensing (LARS), 1968, *Remote Multispectral Sensing in Agriculture,* Research Bulletin 844, Purdue University, Lafayette, Ind.

Lewis, G. K., 1957, "The Concept of Analogous Area Photo Interpretation Keys," *Photogrammetric Engineering,* 23:874-878.

Lindgren, D. T., 1971, "Dwelling Unit Estimation with Color-IR Photos," *Photogrammetric Engineering,* 37:373-378.

MacPhail, D. D., 1971, "Photomorphic Mapping in Chile," *Photogrammetric Engineering,* 37:1139-1148.

MacPhail, D., and L. F. Campbell, Jr., 1970, *The El Paso, Texas-New Mexico Study Area: A Comparative Analysis of Gemini V and Apollo VI and IX Space Photography,* Technical Report 69-8, Commission on Geographic Applications of Remote Sensing, East Tennessee State University, Johnson City.

Malila, W. A., 1968, "Multispectral Techniques for Image Enhancement and Discrimination," *Photogrammetric Engineering,* 34:556-576.

Marschner, F. J., 1959, *Land Use and Its Patterns in the United States,* USDA Handbook 153, Government Printing Office, Washington, D.C.

Miller, R. G., 1960, "The Interpretation of Tropical Vegetation and Crops on Aerial Photographs," *Photogrammetria,* 16:232-240.

Moore, E. G., and B. Wellar, 1968, *Remote Sensor Imagery in Urban Research: Some Potentialities and Problems,* USGS Interagency Report NASA-118, Northwestern University, Evanston, Ill.

Morain, S., J. Holtzman, and F. Henderson, 1970, *Radar Sensing in Agriculture: A Socio-Economic Viewpoint,* Technical Report 177-14, University of Kansas, Center for Research, Inc., Lawrence.

Munn, L. C., J. B. McClellan, and L. E. Philpotts, 1966, "Air Photo Interpretation and Rural Land Use Mapping in Canada," *Photogrammetria,* 21:65-77.

Neumann, A. M., and D. S. Simonett, 1970, "Crop Discrimination in Lawrence, Kansas, by Means of Color, Color Infrared and Multiband Photography," in *The Utility of Photography and Other Remote Sensor Imagery in Thematic Land Use Mapping from Spacecraft and Aircraft,* final report, USGS Contract 14-08-0001-12077, University of Kansas, Center for Research, Inc., Lawrence.

Nunnally, N. R., 1969, "Integrated Landscape Analysis with Radar Imagery," *Remote Sensing of Environment,* 1:1-6.

Nunnally, N. R., and Richard E. Witmer, 1968, "A Strategy for Developing Classifications of Land Use as Interpreted from Remote Sensor Imagery," *Papers from the Thirty-Fourth Annual Meeting of the American Society of Photogrammetry,* Washington, D.C., pp. 179-186.

Nunnally, N. R., and Richard E. Witmer, 1970a, "A Land Use Interpretation Experiment," Commission on Geographic Applications of Remote Sensing, *Annals of the Association of American Geographers,* East Tennessee State University, Johnson City.

Nunnally, N. R., and Richard E. Witmer, 1970b, "Remote Sensing for Land-Use Studies," *Photogrammetric Engineering,* 36:449-453.

Olson, C. E., 1967, "Accuracy of Land-Use Interpretations from Infrared Imagery in the 4.5 to 5.5 Micron Band," *Annals of the Association of American Geographers,* 57:382-388.

Organization of American States, 1969, *Physical Resource Investigations for Economic Development,* Organization of American States, Washington, D.C.

Pawnall, L. L., 1950, "Aerial Photographic Interpretation of Urban Land Uses in Madison," *Photogrammetric Engineering*, 26:414-426.

Peplies, R. W., 1968, "Land Use and Regional Analysis," *Earth Resources Aircraft Program Status Review*, NASA/MSC, vol. I, Houston, Tex.

Place, John L., 1972, "An Automated Map and Model of Land Use in the Phoenix Quadrangle," *Fourth Annual Earth Resources Program Review*, vol. III, NASA/MSC, Houston, Tex., pp. 71-1 to 71-19.

Rabben, E. L., 1960, "Fundamentals of Photo Interpretation," Chapter 3 in *Manual of Photographic Interpretation*, R. N. Colwell, ed., American Society of Photogrammetry, Washington, D.C., pp. 99-168.

Ratclaff, J. R., and David S. Simonett, 1969, *The Question of Resolution in Land Use Studies from Spacecraft Photography*, University of Kansas, Center for Research, Inc., Lawrence.

Reynders, J. J., 1962, "The Analysis of Shifting Cultivation Areas," *Symposium on Photo Interpretation*, Delft, Netherlands, 14:171-176.

Rib, H. T., and R. D. Miles, 1969, "Automatic Interpretation of Terrain Features," *Photogrammetric Engineering*, 35:153-164.

Richter, D. M., 1965, "An Airphoto Index to Physical and Cultural Features in the Eastern United States," *Photogrammetric Engineering*, 31:896-914.

Richter, D. M., 1969, "Sequential Urban Change," *Photogrammetric Engineering*, 35:764-770.

Roscoe, J. H., 1955, "Symposium Photo Interpretation Keys," *Photogrammetric Engineering*, 21:703-719.

Rosenfeld, A., 1962, "Automatic Recognition of Basic Terrain Types from Aerial Photography," *Photogrammetric Engineering*, 28:115-132.

Rudd, R. D., 1971, "Macro Land-Use Mapping with Simulated Space Photos," *Photogrammetric Engineering*, 37:365-372.

Samol, J. D., 1968, *Rural Land Use Analysis via Ektachrome Infrared Photo Interpretation*, Technical Report 4, East Tennessee State Remote Sensing Institute, Johnson City.

Schepis, E. L., 1968, "Time-Lapse Remote Sensing in Agriculture," *Photogrammetric Engineering*, 34:116-1179.

Schneider, S., 1967, "The Problem of Natural Regions in Relation to Air Photo Interpretation," in *Photo Interpretation for Rational Use and Conservation of Biological Resources*, report of the Commission on Interpretation of Aerial Photographs, International Geographical Union, to UNESCO, pp. 54-59.

Schwarz, D. E., and F. Caspall, 1968, "The Use of Radar in the Discrimination and Identification of Agricultural Land Use," in *Proceedings of the Fifth Symposium on Remote Sensing of Environment*, Institute of Science and Technology, University of Michigan, Ann Arbor, pp. 233-247.

Schwarz, D. E., D. S. Simonett, G. F. Jenks, and J. R. Ratzlaff, 1969, "The Construction of Thematic Land Use Maps with Spacecraft Photography," in *The Utility of Radar and Other Remote Sensing in Thematic Land Use Mapping from Spacecraft,* second annual report, USGS Contract No. 14-08-001-10848, CRES, University of Kansas, Lawrence.

Shelton, R. L., 1968, "Air Photo Interpretation and Computer Graphics for Land Use and Natural Resources Inventory," *Papers from the Thirty-Fourth Annual Meeting, American Society of Photogrammetry,* Washington, D.C., pp. 198-204.

Simonett, D. S., 1968, *Land Evaluation Studies with Remote Sensors in the Infra-red and Radar Regions,* USGS Interagency Report NASA-126; also in G. A. Stewart, Ed., *Papers of a CSIRO Symposium Organized in Cooperation with UNESCO,* Macmillan of Australia, Canberra, pp. 349-366.

Simonett, D. S., 1969a, "Thematic Land Use Mapping: Some Potentials and Problems," *Second Annual Earth Resources Aircraft Program Status Review,* NASA/MSC, Houston, Tex., section 13, also published as a CRES Report, University of Kansas, Lawrence.

Simonett, D. S., 1969b, *The Utility of Radar and Other Remote Sensors in Thematic Land Use Mapping from Spacecraft,* CRES Publication, University of Kansas, Lawrence.

Simonett, D. S., et al., 1967, *The Potential of Radar as a Remote Sensor in Agriculture,* Technical Report 61-21, NASA Contract NAR 17-004-003 and NASA Grant NSR NSG-298, Center for Research in Engineering Science, University of Kansas, Lawrence.

Simonett, D. S., F. Henderson, G. Jenks, and J. Ratzlaff, 1970, *Thematic Land Use Mapping with Spacecraft Photography in the Dallas-Fort Worth Area, Texas,* University of Kansas, Department of Geography and Center for Research, Inc., Lawrence.

Sridas, S., 1966, "Interpretation and Mapping of Rural Land Use from Air Photographs in Ceylone," *Photogrammetria,* 21:77-83.

Steiner, D., 1964, "A World-Wide Survey of the Applications of Air Photographs to Interpreting and Mapping Rural Land Use," paper presented at UNESCO Conference on Integrated Aerial Surveys, Department of Geography, University of Zurich.

Steiner, D., 1965, "Use of Air Photographs for Interpreting and Mapping Rural Land Use in the U.S.," *Photogrammetria,* 20:65-80.

Steiner, D., 1966, "Investigation of Seasonality as a Factor Affecting the Photo-Interpretation of Rural Land Use," *Actes du Ile Symposium International de Photo-Interpretation,* Paris-Editions Technip, Paris, pp. II-67 to II-80.

Steiner, D., 1967, *Index to the Used Aerial Photographs for Rural Land Use Studies,* Commission on Interpretation of Aerial Photographs, International Geographical Union, Bad Godesberg, Germany.

Steiner, D., 1968, "Aerial Photography for Land Use Mapping, Cattle Inventories, Yield Forecasting and Crop Disease Determination," *Transactions of the Third International Agricultural Aviation Congress,* Anaheim 1966, International Agricultural Aviation Centre, the Hague, pp. 334-365.

Steiner, D., 1969, "Using the Time Dimension for Automated Crop Surveys from Space," *Technical Papers from the Thirty-Fifth Annual Meeting, American Society of Photogrammetry,* Washington, D.C., pp. 286-300.

Steiner, D., and H. Maurer, 1967, "Toward a Quantitative Semi-Automatic System for the Photo-Interpretation of Terrain Cover Types," *Actes du Ile Symposium International de Photo-Interpretation,* Paris-Editions Technip., Paris, pp. III-51 to III-54.

Steiner, D., and H. Maurer, 1969, "The Use of Stereo Height as a Discriminating Variable for Crop Classification on Aerial Photographs," *Photogrammetria,* 24: 223-241.

Stewart, G. A., 1968, "Land Evaluation," in G. A. Stewart, Ed., *Papers of a CSIRO Symposium Organized in Cooperation with UNESCO,* Macmillan of Australia, Canberra.

Stone, K. H., 1956, "Air Photo Interpretation Procedures: Report of Commission VII, Photographic Interpretation, to International Society of Photogrammetry," *Photogrammetric Engineering,* 22:123-132.

Thrower, N. J. W., 1972, "Satellite Photography as a Geographic Tool for Land Use Mapping," *International Geography, 1972: Papers Submitted to the Twenty-Second International Geographical Congress, Canada,* Montreal, pp. 984-986.

Thrower, N. J. W., and L. W. Senger, 1970, *Satellite Photography as a Geographic Tool for Land Use Mapping of the Southwestern United States,* Technical Report 69-3, USGS Contract No. 14-08-0001-12009, Commission on Geographic Applications of Remote Sensing, Association of American Geographers, Washington, D.C.

Vidal, R. S., 1967, "Land-Use Mapping in Chile," *Photogrammetria,* 22:153-159.

Wellar, B. S., 1968, "Utilization of Multiband Aerial Photographs in Urban Housing Quality Studies," *Proceedings of the Fifth Symposium on Remote Sensing of Environment,* University of Michigan, Ann Arbor, pp. 913-926.

Wellar, B. S., 1971, "Monitoring and Reporting Change in Urban Housing and Its Environment," *Papers from the Thirty-Seventh Annual Meeting of the American Society of Photogrammetry,* Washington D.C., pp. 174-203.

Witenstein, M. M., 1954, "Photo-Sociometrics--The Application of Aerial Photography to Urban Administration and Planning Problems," *Photogrammetric Engineering,* 20:419-427.

Witenstein, M. M., 1955, "Uses and Limitations of Aerial Photography in Urban Analysis and Planning," *Photogrammetric Engineering,* 21:566-572.

Witenstein, M. M., 1956, "A Report on Application of Aerial Photography to Urban Land-Use Inventory, Analysis and Planning," *Photogrammetric Engineering,* 22:656-663.

Wray, J. R., 1960, "Photo Interpretation in Urban Area Analysis," Chapter 12 in *Manual of Photographic Interpretation*, R. N. Colwell, Ed., American Society of Photogrammetry, Washington, D.C., pp. 667-716.

Wray, J. R., 1972a, "The Census Cities Project: A Status Report for 1971," *Fourth Annual Earth Resources Program Review*, vol. 3, NASA/MSC, Houston, Tex., pp. 73-1 to 73-21.

Wray, J. R., 1972b, "A Remote Sensing System for Detecting Gross Land Use Changes in Metropolitan Areas," *International Geography, 1972: Papers Submitted to the Twenty-Second International Geographic Congress, Canada*, Montreal, pp. 968-970.

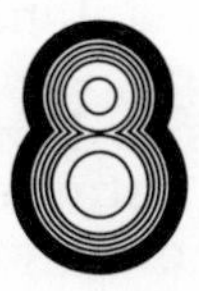

Remote Sensing of Agricultural Resources

Randolph R. Thaman
University of California, Santa Barbara

Although discussed to a certain extent under land use, agriculture merits attention in its own right. Domesticated plants and animals provide food, fibers, and other raw materials needed to sustain human life and culture. An expanding human population requires that these living resources be effectively inventoried and monitored on a global scale to facilitate management tasks. Remote sensing systems are regarded as potential sources of the accurate and timely data needed to meet these requirements, since existing conventional ground survey methods are proving inadequate for the present magnitude of the task. This chapter examines possible applications of remote sensing technology to agricultural surveys with respect to (1) agriculture information requirements, (2) remote sensing capabilities, (3) agricultural surveys where the use of remote sensing techniques is at an operational level, and (4) research projects in agricultural remote sensing.

The aim of this chapter is to present the reader with an idea of the usefulness of remote sensing techniques for generating data on the world's agricultural resources. Major themes that are included in this discussion concern: (1) the present means of generating agricultural data, (2) how the use of remote sensing techniques might improve the generation of such data, (3) the advantages and limitations of remote sensing in the agricultural information context, (4) factors which should be considered in the implementation of agricultural surveys using remote sensing techniques, and, (5) operational surveys and research conducted in the field of agricultural remote sensing. Throughout the chapter an attempt has been made to focus on the use of remote sensing in both developed and developing areas of the world.

Agricultural surveys are presently conducted throughout the world in order to gather information and associated statistics on crops, rangeland, livestock, and other agricultural resources. The importance of such agricultural surveys is reflected by the great number of countries conducting these surveys, and the volume of data that is generated each year.

In the United States and other developed countries, agricultural surveys of one type or another have been conducted for more than a hundred years (Luney and

Dill, 1970). In developing countries in Africa, Asia, South America, and Oceania, however, such surveys are of comparatively recent origin and leave much to be desired in terms of the reliability of the data.

There is a great diversity in the types of information needed from agricultural surveys, ranging from very generalized land-use information (such as cropland versus grazing land or forest) to very specific information (such as the identity and location of certain insects and/or diseases which may affect certain crops). Other specific examples of data requirements are (1) total cropland, (2) crop types, (3) crop vigor, (4) crop yield, (5) planting dates, (6) harvesting dates, (7) types of irrigation systems, (8) soil characteristics, (9) disaster damage assessment, (10) total rangeland, (11) range carrying capacity, (12) total livestock population, (13) sex of animals, (14) total rural population, and (15) number and types of farm or ranch structures. These data are of utmost importance for the implementation of effective management decisions at local, regional, national, and even global levels.

With increasing population pressure throughout the world and the concomitant need for increased agricultural production (food and fiber crops as well as livestock), there is a definite need for improved management of the world's agricultural resources. In order to accomplish this, it is first necessary to obtain reliable data on not only the types, but also the quality, quantity, and location of these resources. The acquisition of these data is the objective of agricultural surveys. Not only do such surveys provide valuable data on which management decisions can be based, but they also provide a benchmark against which future agricultural development can be measured.

The implementation of meaningful agricultural surveys is a very involved process; and, at present, systems of generating these data could be improved upon considerably. The author believes that the use of remote sensing techniques has been, and will continue to be, a very important factor in the improvement of the present systems of acquiring and generating agricultural data. The balance of this chapter will examine this belief through discussions of (1) present methods for acquiring agricultural data, (2) remote sensing techniques as they apply to agricultural surveys, (3) operational agricultural surveys conducted using remote sensing techniques, and (4) the status of remote sensing research in agriculture with respect to crops, rangeland, and livestock.

PRESENT SYSTEMS FOR GENERATING AGRICULTURAL DATA

A great majority of all agricultural data which is collected throughout the world is done by governments or government-sponsored agencies, not only on a local, regional, or national level, but also to some extent on an international level. One agency which is instrumental in providing the funds and/or personnel for many agricultural surveys is the United Nations.

The Food and Agricultural Organization (FAO) branch of the United Nations conducts a World Census of Agriculture every ten years, the latest being in 1970. This is an attempt to present a worldwide picture of production of agricultural commodities, and to gather detailed information on subjects such as land tenure, land use, crop types, acreages, livestock populations, farm populations, rural transportation, and irrigation and drainage resources (FAO, 1970). Other statistical data apart from the World Census of Agriculture are distributed by the

FAO in the form of publications such as the *Production and Trade Yearbook*, the *Monthly Bulletin of Agricultural Economics*, and the *State of Food and Agriculture*.

The United Nations Special Fund has also been instrumental in conducting agricultural surveys in the Sudan, Kenya, Togo, Nigeria, Egypt, Honduras, Nicaragua, and Paraguay (Dill, 1967). The studies carried out under the Special Fund are generally very extensive in nature and are concerned with general agricultural land-use mapping, soil surveys, and water resource inventories. Numerous other agencies, such as the Organization of American States and the Land Resources Division of the Overseas Development Administration in the United Kingdom, also sponsor and provide personnel to carry out agricultural surveys in developing countries.

Some countries have developed comparatively sophisticated systems for generating and processing more detailed agricultural data. These include Japan, Canada, Australia, the Netherlands, and the United States. In the United States alone, more than $40 million is spent annually on agricultural censuses and statistical data acquisition (Hoffer et al., 1967). Although some of these data are collected by local and state governments and various other agencies such as the U.S. Bureau of the Census, U.S. Department of Commerce, the U.S. Geological Survey, and the U.S. Department of the Interior, a majority of the data are collected under the auspices of the U.S. Department of Agriculture. Agencies within the Department of Agriculture responsible for collecting agriculturally oriented data are the Statistical Reporting Service, Economic Research Service, Agricultural Stabilization and Conservation Service, and the Bureau of Land Management.

From this extensive program of agricultural information acquisition, more than 700 reports are published annually, covering topics such as agricultural land-use change, planting times, crop acreages, weekly yield forecast, harvesting times, total production, livestock inventories, grain reserves, and farm labor population (Kelly, 1970). The reporting cycle of these reports ranges from weekly forecasts of crop yields and monthly reports of range feed, cattle, and sheep in 17 Western and Midwestern states (Luney and Dill, 1970), to the U.S. Census of Agriculture which is published every five years. The data generated by these agencies form the basis for important management decisions affecting the planting, harvesting, processing, storage, and disposal of U.S. agricultural products, not to mention decisions regarding optimum broad-scale land-use planning on a regional basis.

Problems in Data Collection

The primary question that has been, and continues to be, the concern of agricultural statisticians the world over is "How do we improve the methods of collection and quality of the data?" The three aspects of agricultural surveys which are most often discussed in this respect are (1) reliability, (2) cost and benefits, and (3) timeliness. It is anticipated that remote sensing data may provide solutions to these particular problems.

Reliability of Data. Most agricultural data are presently collected by methods such as (1) census records, (2) mailed questionnaires, (3) personal interviews, (4) on-the-ground observations, and (5) office estimations. In more developed countries, such as the Netherlands, Canada, the United States, and Russia, sophisticated sampling techniques are used to minimize sampling bias and increase the statistical reliability of the resultant data. However, in many developing countries, a great deal of the information is obtained from government officials, chiefs, or headmen, who, in many instances, not only do not know the desired information but also are often too busy to find out.

Regardless of the sampling techniques, most methods employ some form of subjective sampling, such as questionnaires or interviews, which tend to bias the data. An example of this type of bias was encountered by the author in Tonga (South Pacific) while conducting a survey of Tongan agricultural land use. When the acreage estimages made by farmers were compared with measurements taken in the field, the farmers' estimates were often found to be off by as much as 400 percent. In an agricultural census carried out in Nepal in 1962, similar errors were believed to be the result of imprecise units of measurement, incomplete coverage, and perhaps deliberate underreporting by a suspicious peasantry (Kelly, 1970). These types of discrepancies (bias) may be the result of many factors; nevertheless, they exist, and better means of gathering the required agricultural data are needed.

The reliability of agricultural survey data is also dependent on the sampling frame of the survey. Whereas some countries choose their sampling units on a statistically correct random or stratified sampling basis, the best available sampling frame in many developing countries is a simple list of villages compiled as part of the population census. Moreover, by virtue of the fact that a "sample" takes into account only a portion of the entire "universe" under consideration, a certain amount of bias can be expected regardless of the sampling frame used. Larger sample sizes would minimize bias; and, if it were possible to use the entire universe as the sample size, the problem could be obviated. Unfortunately, in a consideration of the present techniques used for generating agricultural statistics, such a complete survey would be far too costly and would require considerable manpower.

Cost of Data. The cost of implementing agricultural surveys on a world scale is almost impossible to estimate. However, the estimated cost for surveys conducted in the United States (more than $40 million annually) is an indication of the great expense involved.

The high cost of agricultural surveys is often the result of the great amount of time and manpower required for the planning, data-acquisition, data-reduction, and data-distribution phases. In many countries, surveys are carried out under research and development sponsorship, while in others operational surveys have reached a level where the direct or indirect benefits of the data compensate for the cost of the surveys.

Timeliness of Data. Programs in agriculture and agricultural development are heavily dependent on timely information for management decisions. Consequently, the greatest shortcoming of the present system of agricultural surveys is, in all likelihood, the lack of timeliness of the data. The time period between data acquisition and data availability to the user is crucial when considering the net value of the information. For example, information about the existence of wheat rust in a farmer's wheat field is of little or no value if it is received after the time that control measures might have been effectively implemented. In order for any information to be of optimum utility in improving management decisions, it must be received at the most opportune time.

The Use of Remote Sensing for Agricultural Surveys

The use of remote sensing techniques for certain kinds of agricultural inventories has already proved to be of great value, and the techniques will probably have much broader applications in the not-too-distant future. Some of the more optimistic proponents of the use of remote sensing techniques have envisioned the use of satellites for purposes such as gathering data on the total acreages and yields of all major food and fiber crops on a worldwide basis; the location of fields of marijuana and opium poppies in Mexico and Middle East (Bulban, 1972); and the detection of moisture stress in crops and the subsequent automatic activation of sprinkler systems in affected areas. Obviously, these potential applications will not be realized for some time, if at all. However, it should be kept in mind that, as far-fetched as these applications appear at present, there is a distinct possibility that applications such as these may be operational in the near future.

The importance attached to the future uses of remote sensing techniques by some agriculturalists is evidenced in a statement made by Luney and Dill, of the Economic Research Service, USDA:

> Although in the United States forecasting and estimating yields of major crops has been carried on for a hundred years, present methods produce results that are often at variance with the real situation. The use of multiband sensing techniques in conjunction with repetitive overflights to provide data on crops more rapidly may reduce the lag between observation and data reduction by at least 50 percent and improve accuracy. Further, a remote sensing system will permit quick response to any major disaster that calls for an adjustment in the forecast. (Luney and Dill, 1970)

Table 8-1 is a list of some of the possible remote sensing applications to the informational needs of agriculturalists. Regardless of the specific application, remote sensing techniques can be used for (1) detection, (2) identification, (3) measurement, and (4) monitoring of agricultural phenomena. The detection of agricultural phenomena (such as cropland, disease, infestations, and rangeland) is the most easily accomplished; but the subsequent identification, measurement, and monitoring of these phenomena may be more difficult.

Advantages of Utilizing Remote Sensing Techniques in Agricultural Surveys

With the primary aim of improving the present means of generating agricultural data, a number of specific advantages may result from the use of remote sensing techniques.

Vantage Point. Because the agricultural landscape depends upon the sun as a source of energy, it is exposed to the aerial view and, consequently, is ideally suited to remote sensing techniques.

Coverage. With the use of high-altitude sensor platforms, it is now possible to record extensive areas on a single image. When extensive coverage was needed in the past, aerial photo mosaics were prepared; today, with the advent of high-flying aircraft and satellites, single high-quality images covering thousands of square miles are obtainable. The synoptic view afforded by such imagery not only allows the image analyst to view an integrated picture of the landscape but

TABLE 8-1

Possible applications of remote sensing techniques for agricultural surveys.

A. Areas of general applications:

agricultural land-use mapping	rural transportation network
agricultural land-use change	soil surveys
agricultural population distribution	water resource surveys
land-use potential	

B. Areas of specific applications:

1. Applicable to crop surveys:

crop identification	irrigation effectiveness
crop acreage	drought prediction
crop vigor	weed concentrations
crop density	nematode infestations
crop maturity	insect infestations
growth rates	disease infestations
yield forecasting	location of disease-resistant species
actual yield	frost damage
planting dates	storm warning
harvesting dates	flood warning
soil fertility	fire surveillance
areas of fertilizer application	fire control
effects of fertilizers	damage assessment
soil toxicity	water availability
soil moisture	location of canals
excessive salinity	detection of heat in silos, etc.
water quality	
irrigation requirements	

2. Applicable to range surveys:

forage-species identification	soil fertility
delineation of forest types	soil moisture
condition of range	weed infestation
carrying capacity	insect infestations
forage yield	disease infestations
growth rates	wildlife inventory
times of seasonal change	effects of wildlife
development potential	rodent damage
location of water	fire surveillance
water quality	fire control
drought prediction	trafficability
extent of erosion	conditions of fences
identification of toxic species	

3. Applicable to livestock surveys:

cattle population	distribution of animals
sheep population	animal behavior
pig population	health of animals
poultry population	disease identification
age-sex distribution	types of farm buildings

also makes it possible to conduct surveys of inaccessible areas where transportation networks may be lacking. The coverage afforded by remote sensing imagery may also facilitate the complete sampling of an entire area, eliminating biases resulting from insufficient sampling sizes.

Permanent Record. After an image is obtained, it serves as a permanent record of a landscape at a point in time and as a datum from which agricultural changes can be monitored and evaluated.

Mapping Base. Certain types of remote sensing imagery are, in essence, pictorial maps of the landscape and, after rectification (if needed), allow for precise measurements (such as field acreages) to be made on the imagery, obviating time-consuming on-the-ground surveys. These images may also aid ground data sampling by serving as a base map for locating agricultural features while in the field, and also as a base for the selection of ground sampling points or areas.

Cost Savings. Utilizing remote imagery,mapping can often be accomplished quickly by skilled interpreters in the office. Areas where further ground checking is needed can also be determined on the imagery.

Real-Time Capability. The rapidity with which imagery can be obtained and interpreted may help to eliminate the lack of timeliness which plagues so many agricultural surveys.

Possibility of Automation. There is a distinct possibility that remote sensing data can be analyzed automatically. This would speed up the data reduction stage and would, in turn, permit the collection of greater volumes of sampling data, thus increasing statistical reliability.

At present, all the advantages listed above have been demonstrated either operationally or experimentally; and, as a result, agencies at all levels are beginning to utilize remote sensing techniques in order to improve their data-collection techniques.

Limitations of the Utilization of Remote Sensing Techniques in Agricultural Surveys

A number of factors limit the increased use of remote sensing techniques in agricultural surveys. Most of these may be either directly or indirectly attributed to the relative recency of use of remote sensing techniques. Some of these limitations, many of which may be eliminated in the near future, are as follows:

Lack of Imagery. Although many developed countries have complete photographic coverage, often on a sequential basis, many of the developing countries have outdated imagery that may not even provide continuous area coverage. Moreover, most of this imagery is limited to small-scale, black-and-white photography. In some countries, the use of photographs may be restricted to the military and the coverage which does exist is not available to civilian agencies (Dill, 1967).

Diversity of Agricultural Landscape. It is difficult to adopt standardized remote sensing procedures owing to the diversity of agricultural environments, agricultural practices, crop types, and seasonal variations throughout the world.

Even on the local scale, the diversity of cropping practices, tillage variations, crop types, etc., make it difficult to develop reliable remote sensing models.

Dynamic Nature of the Agricultural Landscape. Owing to the rapidly changing nature of agricultural features, imagery often becomes out of date in a relatively short period. This problem may not be of vital significance for agricultural land-use studies, but it is a major concern for applications such as monitoring the spread of a crop disease or the ripening of fruit.

Sensor Calibration. Many sophisticated sensors have not been calibrated for optimal returns when imaging agricultural landscapes. Most of these sensors, developed for military purposes, are just now being tested over agricultural landscapes.

Lack of Ground-Truth Data. In order to determine the exact nature of a given signature on an image, a great many ground-truth data must be collected, preferably coincident with the remote sensing overflight. At present, the effect of different parameters (such as row direction, soil temperature, soil moisture, percent cover, and salinity) on the resultant signature is not fully understood. Considerable ground-truth data have been collected, but a continuing need exists for accurate interpretation and subsequent correlation of ground-truth data with signatures on remote sensing imagery.

Cost. Since many surveys are presently supported by research and development funds, accurate cost/benefit analyses are needed to ascertain the economic operational feasibility of a given program. However, the determination of the costs and benefits of agricultural surveys is often difficult because some of the benefits may be indirect.

Manpower Utilization. Many of the developing countries, as a result of low standards of living and a surplus of available manpower, find it more economical to utilize conventional means and a large labor force to gather agricultural data rather than use more expensive remote sensing techniques. This is particularly true when a high degree of accuracy is not mandatory.

REMOTE SENSING TECHNIQUES FOR AGRICULTURAL SURVEYS

Given the above advantages and disadvantages, two general sets of factors influence the use of remote sensing in agricultural surveys: (1) the characteristics of the agricultural landscape and (2) characteristics of the remote sensing devices used for the survey.

Detection, identification, measurement, and monitoring of agricultural phenomena are predicated on the assumption that agricultural landscape features (e.g., crops, livestock, crop infestations, and soil anomalies) have consistently identifiable signatures on a given type, or types, of remote sensing imagery.

Some of the parameters which may cause these identifiable signatures include crop type, state of maturity, crop density, crop height, crop geometry, crop vigor, crop moisture, crop temperature, percent cover, soil type, soil moisture, soil temperature, row spacing, tillage practices, irrigation practices, harvest practices, type and size of livestock, and numerous other unique agronomic practices. If an image analyst can correlate a certain signature with one of these many characteristics, he may be able to detect or identify a given feature.

Owing to the diversity of both the possible applications of remote sensing techniques to agricultural surveys and the characteristics of plants which affect the signatures on remote sensing imagery, it is important to consider briefly the significance of choosing the appropriate sensor system, as well as the scale and/or resolution requirements that will yield optimum benefits for a given survey objective. Whereas some features may be detectable using one particular sensor or a given resolution, these same features may be undetectable if an alternative choice is made. Consequently, in the planning of an operational agricultural survey utilizing remote sensing techniques, several considerations must be kept in mind. These considerations include (1) image characteristics,(2) image resolution, (3) image scale, and (4) choice of sensors.

Image Characteristics

Image characteristics which enable the interpreter to detect, measure, identify, and/or differentiate agricultural features on remote sensing imagery are tone, hue, texture, shape, shadow, boundaries, and location. The significance of each of these image characteristics varies with the type, scale, and resolution of the imagery used. Some features may be distinguished using one sensor on the basis of textural or tonal differences apparent on the imagery, while these same features may not be identifiable if another sensor were used.

Image Resolution

In considering the choice of sensors, the problem of resolution will be considered first. For the purposes of this chapter, resolution is defined (unless otherwise specified) as the ground resolvable distance (GRD); that is, the size, length, or area of the smallest object discernable on an image, taking into account the difference in contrast ratios across an image. An important consideration is that, as resolution becomes progressively poorer, the information content of an image decreases. As resolution decreases, size, shape, pattern, shadow, and texture decrease in importance as interpretative aids until a point is reached where resolution is so poor that only tone and hue can be used as interpretative aids (Thaman and Lauer, 1971).

The image resolution necessary for a particular survey depends upon the size of the features that are to be surveyed. For instance, a range manager might need a photographic image with a ground resolvable distance of 6 inches in order to determine the extent of rodent damage, while the agricultural land-use planner might need only imagery with a ground resolvable distance of no better than 100 feet to map the boundary between cropland and rangeland. For the accurate estimation of crop yields, it has been suggested that plots as small as an acre may need to be resolvable (Shay, 1966). Figure 8-1 shows both Apollo 9 satellite photo and a high-altitude photography to illustrate why better resolutions will probably be needed for yield forecasting.

Image Scale

The choice of optimum image scale is also important. Given a constant format, say 9 inches by 9 inches or 70 mm by 70 mm, and a sensor with given resolution capabilities (e.g., resolving power of the lens and film if using a photographic

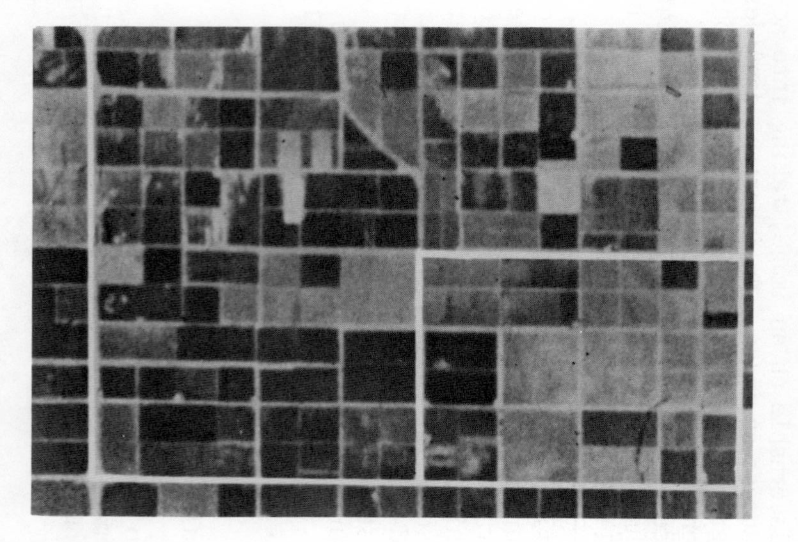

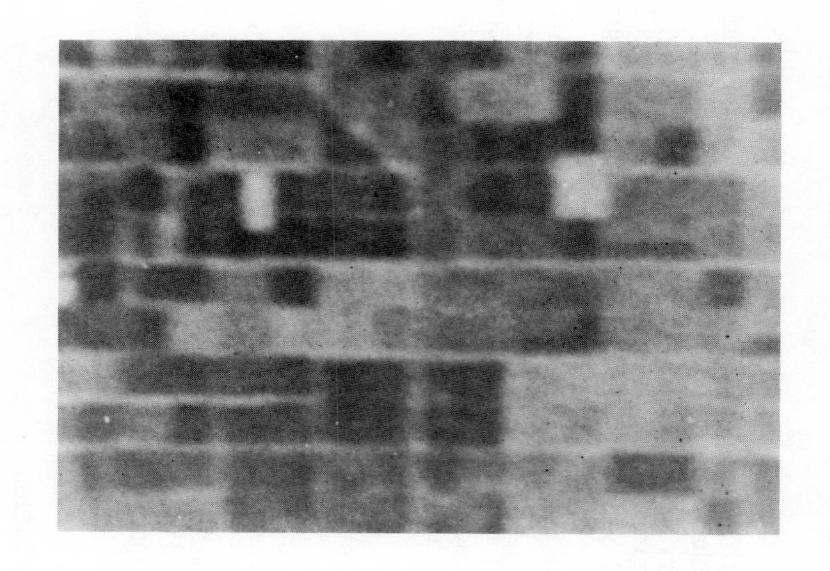

Figure 8-1. The NASA high altitude photograph on the left (taken from an altitude of approximately 70,000 feet) and the Apollo 9 photograph on the right (taken from an altitude of approximately 129 nautical miles) illustrate why higher resolutions are needed for the prediction of crop yields than are needed for crop identification. The satellite photograph is of insufficient resolution to show "weak spots" and differences in vigor within individual fields, whereas on the high-altitude photograph this information (upon which yield estimates can be based) is readily obtainable. However, the satellite and high-altitude photographs are of almost equal utility for the identification of crop types, since interpretation is based primarily on tonal differences.

system), the image scale is (1) inversely proportional to the area covered by an image and (2) directly proportional to the ground resolvable distance on the image. In other words, the smaller the scale, the greater the area imaged and the poorer the ground resolvable distance. Another important consideration is that, in most cases, the smaller the scale of imagery, the lower the acquisition cost per unit area. The final choice, then, for the scale of imagery, in order for it to be of optimal use for a given survey, would depend on (1) required image detail, (2) areal extent of study area, and (3) the amount of money available.

In the past, the range of scales of imagery was limited by the altitude at which conventional aircraft could fly. With the advent of the satellite, it is now possible to acquire imagery ranging from scales greater than 1:1 to scales smaller than 1:1,000,000. This new dimension in the range of possible scales has opened further avenues for the implementation of different types of surveys. Moreover, this great range of scales provides for alternatives, especially if cost constraints preclude the use of large-scale, high-resolution imagery covering an entire test site. The alternative choice here is to obtain complete coverage of an area at a small scale, and then obtain larger-scale imagery for selected sites. This use of a number of increasingly larger scales in concert with the small-scale overall coverage, to improve both interpretability and the information content of a survey, is termed multistage sampling.

Choice of Sensor

Probably the most important consideration in the use of remote sensing techniques is the choice of the optimum sensing device. Because different agricultural features exhibit varying energy returns in various portions of the electromagnetic spectrum, the choice of the best sensor is of great significance. Sensors which will be discussed here are (1) photographic sensors, (2) multispectral scanners, (3) active microwave sensors (side-looking airborne radar, SLAR), and (4) passive microwave radiometers.

Photographic Sensors. With respect to the present level of technological development, photographic sensors are by far the best. At the present time, almost all of the operational surveys that have been conducted throughout the world have utilized photographic sensing systems.

Some of the advantages of photographic systems include (1) a wide range of film-filter combinations; (2) metric quality imagery (i.e., imagery that can be rectified so that accurate measurements can be made); (3) high spatial resolution; (4) ability to be viewed stereoscopically; (5) relatively low cost; (6) the similarity of the imagery to the on-the-ground situation, hence facilitating human interpretation; and (7) ease of information extraction, both by humans and/or machines.

Most operational uses of photographic systems have been confined to black-and-white film emulsions. Uses include general agricultural land-use studies, soil surveys, and crop acreage measurements. However, more recently, the use of color photographic emulsions, both conventional color and color infrared, has proved valuable in increasing the potential information content of a given photograph. In particular, the use of color infrared film (which is sensitive to reflected infrared energy) has proved of significant value in detecting loss of vigor in vegetation. The additional cost of color photography, even if it is taken at the same scale as black-and-white, is often offset by the increased information content of the imagery.

Multispectral Scanners. The use of multispectral-scanner imagery has certain advantages for agricultural surveys. These include (1) the number of spectral bands and regions which can be utilized simultaneously; (2) in-flight (real-time) monitoring; (3) simplified data storage system; (4) potential for direct electronic transmission of data to earth-based stations; (5) potential lower (than photography) net cost for coverage of very large areas, when considering the ability of satellites to telemeter imagery as opposed to total cost of similar area coverage by recoverable film satellites; and (6) the possibility of day-or-night operation in the thermal infrared portion of the EM spectrum.

In the reflectance portion of the EM spectrum, the imagery obtained from a multispectral scanner records the same type of energy responses from the agricultural landscape that photographic sensors do. Consequently, the resultant images exhibit similar signatures for given phenomena. However, in the thermal infrared portion of the EM spectrum, signatures on the imagery are not dependent upon reflected, but rather on emitted energy from objects on the earth's surface. Certain factors, such as soil moisture, excessive salinity, and disease, have been shown to cause temperature differences or gradients which are detectable on thermal infrared imagery.

Although the use of scanner systems has certain advantages over the use of photographic systems, limitations exist. These include (1) poor resolution,(2) image distortion, and (3) expensive and complicated nature of the system requiring skilled operators. Despite these disadvantages, scanner imagery in time may prove to be of great value in conducting certain types of agricultural surveys.

Active Microwave. Active microwave (side-looking airborne radar, SLAR) systems have certain advantages for agricultural surveys. Among these are (1) day-or-night capability; (2) nearly all-weather capability; (3) wide area coverage on a single image with essentially uniform resolution; (4) crop and tree cover may be penetrated to show soil cover, underlying cultivation, or drainage networks; and (5) multiband, multipolarization radar imagery may be obtained (Holter et al., 1970). The use of SLAR data has been shown to be of value for identification of bare soil and of crops such as corn and sugar beets, but, at present, the overall accuracy for other crops is not of acceptable standards for statistical reporting purposes (Haralick et al., 1968; Simpson, 1969). It has also been shown that side-looking airborne imagery may be of considerable value for soil surveys and soil-moisture studies (Morain and Campbell, 1972). The only major operational use of radar with potential application to agricultural surveys has been in broad-scale land-use studies on a national level in tropical areas such as Panama and Brazil, where it is almost impossible to obtain complete photographic coverage owing to persistent cloud-cover conditions in these areas.

The disadvantages of using radar are somewhat similar to those mentioned for scanners, but an added factor creates problems when interpreting SLAR imagery. Whereas the signatures on both photography and scanner imagery are the result of reflected and emitted energy from surface features, SLAR systems actively provide their own source of target illumination. This self-illuminating feature, in addition to the variables which affect object signatures, makes interpretation of the "less familiar" data more difficult.

As mentioned earlier, only limited research has been conducted on the applicability of other sensor systems (e.g., Fraunhoffer line discriminators) to agricultural surveys. Hence, they are not considered here. At the present time, it seems that the use of photographic sensors will continue to be of most value for agricultural surveys, with multispectral imagery and side-looking airborne radar taking on greater importance on an operational basis in the future.

Passive Microwave. There is only limited information concerning the use of passive microwave radiometers for the collection of agricultural resource data. The information that is available, however, indicates that, although passive microwave is of little value for crop identification, it is probably the most valuable sensor for detecting soil moisture and for studying water resources.

Multidate Imagery. One final consideration with respect to the choice of sensors is the use of "multidate" or "sequential" remote sensing imagery (see Figure 8-2). Because of the dynamic nature of the agricultural landscape, it may be necessary to obtain data at frequent intervals in order to effectively monitor changes taking place. The timeliness and accuracy required for many surveys necessitates the development of systems which can rapidly generate current information about phenomena such as the growth cycles of plants, movement of livestock, or the rate of agricultural land-use change. Numerous investigations have shown that sequential imagery (photographic, infrared, and SLAR) can improve crop identification, as well as other survey results, considerably (Steiner, 1970; Colwell, R. N., 1963, 1971; Schwarz and Caspall, 1968; Morain and Coiner, 1970; Thaman and Senger, 1971).

At present, cost is the main factor restricting wider use of multidate imagery. However, the development of satellites capable of acquiring high-quality sequential imagery (e.g., ERTS-1) may make the use of the multidate approach more practical.

OPERATIONAL SURVEYS

Most operational applications of remote sensing techniques to agricultural surveys have been related to general studies such as determining agricultural land-use potential, soil mapping and water-resources surveys. The first operational use of remote sensing techniques was for soil-mapping and land-classification purposes in the early 1930s. At that time, it was found that the use of black-and-white aerial photography provided for accurate and rapid mapping of earth features.

As a result of World War II and the subsequent improvements in remote sensing technology, large areas of the earth's surface had been photographed, and there was a wealth of trained photo interpreters. These advancements served to stimulate the growth of remote sensing; and, shortly after the war, a number of countries (United Kingdom, United States, Canada, Netherlands, and Australia) began using aerial photography for purposes such as general agricultural potential. In 1957, Australia, through the Commonwealth Scientific and Industrial Research Organization (CSIRO), began to use aerial photography to evaluate agricultural potential of the vast Northern Territory; and, by 1969, more than 700,000 square miles had been mapped in portions of Australia and New Guinea (Christian and Perry, 1969).

Apart from these general agricultural land-use studies, the use of remote

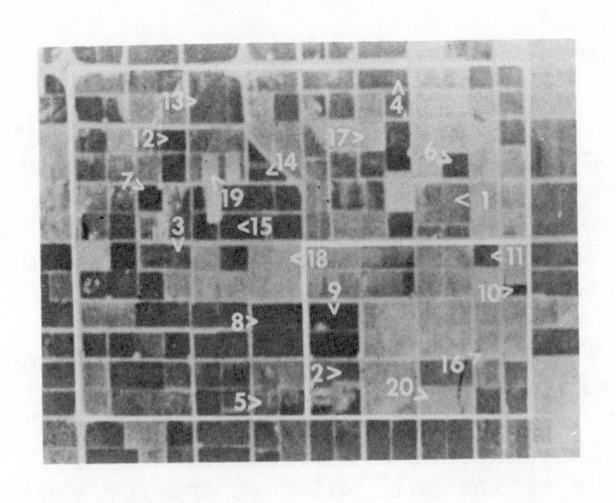

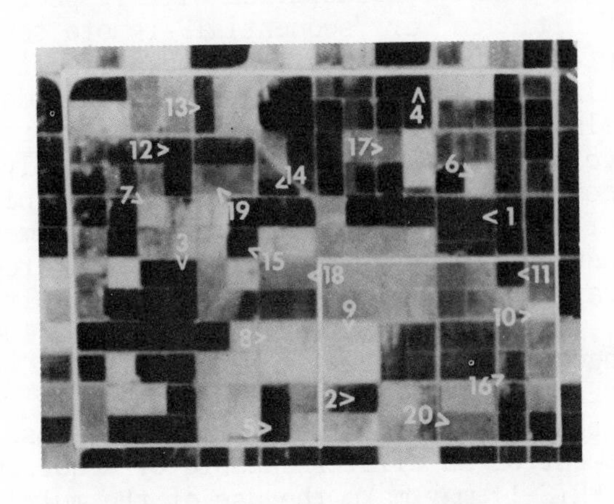

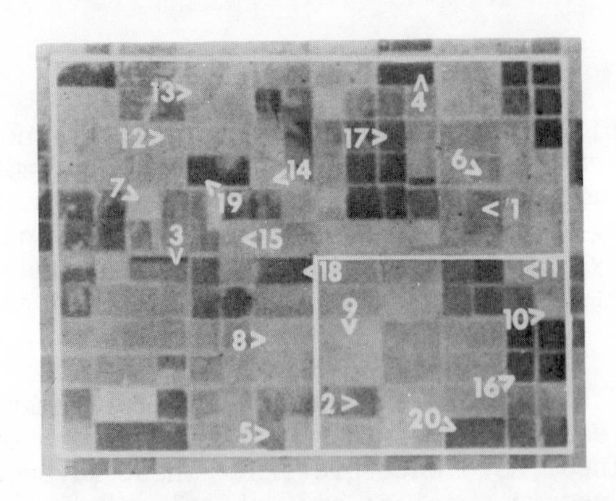

Figure 8-2. Multidate high altitude photographs (top - March 8, 1969; middle, May 21, 1969; bottom, August 5, 1969). Full caption appears on following page.

Figure 8-2. The three black-and-white NASA high altitude photographs taken over a twelve square-mile test area in the Imperial Valley, California on March 8, May 21 and August 5, 1969 illustrate the usefulness of multidate photography for improving the accuracy of crop identification. On the March photograph, alfalfa (fields 1-5), barley (fields 6-10), and sugar beets (fields 11-15) were almost impossible to differentiate, whereas cotton (fields 16-20) was just being planted and the fields resembled bare soil in appearance. On the May photograph, however, the barley (which was dark in tone in March and similar in appearance to the alfalfa and sugar beets) is now bright white owing to dessication prior to harvest. The alfalfa and sugar beets are still almost undifferentiable. The cotton, which has been planted by this time, now ranges in tone from light grey to grey. On the August photograph, the sugar beets have been harvested and the resultant bare soil gives a much brighter signature than the alfalfa fields, which are generally cut periodically throughout the year, but not harvested. The cotton which is nearing maturity now has a dark signature. Thus, on the basis of the length and time of growing periods and phenological changes, the use of these three dates provides for almost 100 percent identification of these four crops. This is in marked contrast to single date identification where interpretation accuracies of over 50-75 percent are difficult to obtain. (Photos courtesy of NASA Manned Spacecraft Center, Houston.)

sensing techniques in agricultural surveys progressed slowly. As recently as the early 1950s, the only specific use made of aerial photographs was for the determination of field acreages (USDA, 1966).

By the late 1950s, aerial photographs were used to delineate utilization strata and select sampling areas as a part of annual agricultural survey programs (Kelly, 1970). At the present time, agencies under the aegis of the USDA which utilize aerial photography (for purposes such as base maps for making boundary delineations and for in-the-field mapping) include the Agricultural Stabilization and Conservation Service (ASCS), the Soil Conservation Service (SCS), the Forest Service (FS), the Statistical Reporting Service (SRS), and the Economic Research Service (ERS) (USDA, 1968). Stereoscopic photo interpretation has also been used by the ERS to map cropland, pasture land, and forest lands, utilizing little or no field work (Frey, 1967).

Most of the photography used in the United States is flown by the ASCS. These photos are normally panchromatic black-and-white, at a scale of 1:20,000, with a 9-inch-by-9-inch format. Some 80 percent* of the nation's land area and virtually all the cropland are covered by the photography, and most areas have been photographed three or four times since the late 1930s (Frey, 1967).

This photography forms the basis for most of the general agricultural land-use studies and soil surveys that have been carried out in the United States. Canada has similar capabilities and has a collection of more than 3 million vertical, oblique, and trimetrogon photographs at the Canadian National Air Photo Library (Dill, 1967).

General land-use studies with somewhat of an agricultural orientation (using remote sensing techniques) have also been carried out in areas outside of the United States and Canada. Of more recent nature are those that are being undertaken in developing countries. Among these are Ghana, Malawi, Kenya, Nigeria, Sudan, and Morroco in Africa; Costa Rica, Chile, Ecuador, Peru, Nicaragua, Argentina, Brazil, and Grand Cayman in Latin America; India, Indonesia, Thailand and Ceylon in Asia; Spain and Italy in Europe; and Fiji and Tonga in Oceania (Dill, 1967; Rains and Brunt, 1972; Huson, 1970). These projects include (1) soil surveys, (2) water resource studies, (3) location of suitable areas for irrigation, (4) detection of excessive soil erosion, and (5) general land-use and cadastral surveys. The data obtained from these studies are very important with respect to agricultural reform programs in most of the countries mentioned above.

The following noteworthy projects deserve special mention here, as examples of resource inventories conducted to serve as a basis for instituting land reforms.

1. A survey carried out under the auspices of the ITC (International Institute for Aerial Survey and Earth Sciences, Enschede, the Netherlands) in 1967 in the Crati River Valley, Italy, using 1:32,000-scale photography. The purpose of this was to prepare generalized maps (at scales of 1:50,000 and 1:100,000) of settlement, cropland, pastureland, and natural vegetation (Huson, 1970).

* This figure includes the 48 conterminous states and Hawaii.

2. The Projecto Aerofotogrametrico, OEA (Organizacion de los Estados Americas), in Chile, completed in 1963, under the joint sponsorship of the Organization of American States and the Chilean government. This project was designed to classify land in an effort to improve the tax base and bring idle land into agricultural production. Using black-and-white photography at scales of 1:20,000 and 1:50,000, maps were made of general land use, soils, property divisions, and irrigation systems. An atlas was produced as part of the project, and the survey reportedly paid for itself within five years (Swami, 1972; Aero Service, 1967).

3. Surveys conducted by the Overseas Development Administration of the United Kingdom using black-and-white aerial photography (color photography was also used for comparative purposes), ranging in scale from 1:10,000 to 1:50,000, to map land-use systems, soils, vegetation, and land-resources potential. These surveys were the basis for making recommendations regarding the most appropriate types of development for Ghana, Kenya, Malawi, Nigeria, Fiji, and Grand Cayman (Rains and Brunt, 1972).

4. Project RADAM, in which synthetic-aperture, side-looking airborne radar is being used to provide a data base for planning development of the Amazon Basin. Data will be generated in the form of 1:250,000-scale radar-image mosaics for approximately 4.5 million square kilometers, and will include (data on) geology, geomorphology, hydrology, vegetation, soil types, and land-use potential (Miller, 1972; Colwell, J. E., 1972).

Although all the surveys mentioned here are generalized and not solely agricultural in nature, these and similar surveys form the bulk of agriculturally oriented surveys which have reached the operational stage.

RESEARCH PROJECTS

There are numerous institutions and agencies, in the United States and elsewhere, carrying out research related to the use of remote sensing techniques for agricultural surveys. In 1968, a five-year research program was initiated under joint funding by the National Aeronautics and Space Administration (NASA) and the United Stated Department of Agriculture (USDA). The program provided for the use of five aircraft, a funding level of $8 million the first year and $5 million for each succeeding year, to study the use of remote sensing techniques for natural-resource inventories with special emphasis on agriculture (Laboratory for Agricultural Remote Sensing, 1968). Brief descriptions of the research carried out under this program and others will be broken down under the subheadings crop surveys, range surveys, and livestock surveys.

Crop Surveys

Some of the research programs oriented toward the use of remote sensing techniques for crop surveys, and brief descriptions of the research, are as follows:

Spectral Data. Spectral data must be obtained and analyzed in order to optimize the use of remote sensing imagery and to determine which physiological characteristics and environmental factors affect reflective, thermal, and other energy responses recorded on remote sensing imagery. Use has been made of spectroradiometers, temperature probes, ground-based cameras, and other scientific instruments to gather data on the reflection and emission properties of plants, soils, and other agricultural features. At present, knowledge concerning the spectral characteristics of different agricultural features is improving. It has been shown that differences in spectral response can make possible the detection and measurement of phenomena such as soil moisture, moisture stress in plants, tillage practices, excessive salinity, vigor of selected crop species, and the occurrence of certain diseases (Myers et al., 1966; Wiegand et al., 1968; Von Steen et al., 1969).

Crop Identification (single date). Studies to determine the feasibility of identifying crop species and varieties, using single-date remote sensing imagery, have been carried out in Illinois (Goodman, 1959); Kansas (Simonett et al., 1967; Brooner et al., 1971; Morain and Coiner, 1970); California (Johnson et al., 1969; Thaman, 1969; Spansail, 1969; Colwell, R. N., 1971); and Arizona (Carneggie et al., 1969; Colwell, R. N., 1971). Outside the United States, similar research has been performed in Switzerland (Steiner, 1970). These studies have included the use of conventional photography, satellite photography, thermal infrared imagery, and side-looking airborne radar imagery. Some of the studies were based on simple photographic evaluations, some entailed the use of photo-interpretation tests administered to more than 30 skilled interpreters (Colwell, R. N., 1971), and some were performed using scanning densitometers.

Results from these studies indicate that (1) color and color infrared photography, and possibly optical multi-image enhancements, yield the best results; (2) the accuracy for overall crop identification rarely exceeded 70 percent for all categories; (3) bare soil and cropland could be identified with a high degree of accuracy; and (4) some individual crops, such as barley on conventional photography and corn and sugar beets on radar, could be identified with a reasonably high degree of accuracy, often approaching 90 percent (Simonett et al., 1967; Haralick et al., 1968; Simpson, 1969). Studies have also been performed to determine the ability to identify orchard crops using aerial photography (Colwell et al., 1966). It was found that different orchard crops in the San Joaquin Valley, California, such as figs, stone fruit, and oranges, could be successfully identified on the basis of row spacing and crown shape, as well as other evidence (e.g., pruning holes in the center of the crown).

Crop Identification (multidate). As a result of studies using single-date imagery, it was hypothesized that the use of sequential or multidate imagery taken at different times during the growing season would improve identification accuracy. Studies using multidate imagery have been performed both in Switzerland (Brunnschweiter, 1957; Steiner, 1970) and in the United States (Schwarz and Caspall, 1968; Thaman and Senger, 1969; Morain and Coiner, 1970; Colwell, R. N., 1971; Draeger et al., 1971). These studies (using photographic, thermal infrared, and side-looking airborne radar imagery), ranging from subjective appraisals to statistically significant photo interpretative tests, show that correct overall identification for crops can be improved considerably over results obtained using only single-date imagery. Accuracies of better than 90 percent were possible in many instances (Thaman and Senger, 1969; Colwell, R. N., 1971) (see Figure 8-2). The use of multidate photography also provided the basis for a semioperational inventory of wheat, barley, and alfalfa for approximately half a million acres of cropland in Maricopa County, Arizona. Accuracy achieved by three skilled interpreters, using 1:120,000-scale multidate color photography, approached 90 percent for the entire county (Draeger et al., 1971).

Yield Estimates. Estimation of yield is closely associated with the ability first to identify crop types and second to identify certain crop characteristics such as maturity, density, vigor, incidence of disease, etc. With these considerations as the basis, techniques for determining yields of wheat, rice, and sugar cane have been developed for use with high-altitude aerial photography (Mark Systems, Inc., 1966). These techniques involve collecting historical crop-yield data, then subtracting yield-reducing factors such as low crop density, disease, and excessive salinity (all of which can be detected on the aerial photography) from the potential yield. Using this system it was found that reliable results were obtainable.

Research has also been performed to determine the effectiveness of using aerial photography as an aid in yield forecasting during the raisin-grape harvest in the San Joaquin Valley, California (Colwell, R. N., 1962, 1963, 1965). It is of utmost importance to secure frequent and accurate estimates of how the harvest is progressing so that the farmers will know whether it will be more profitable to pick and dry grapes for the raisin market or divert them to wine production. These studies, which covered approximately 1,000 square miles of the San Joaquin Valley, utilized high-resolution, black-and-white, 1:17,000-scale photography flown seven times during the six-week harvest season. Results of the study showed that by counting raisin trays, which were laid between the rows of vines, it was possible to improve existing forecasting procedures.

Automated Data Reduction. A number of groups have conducted experiments to determine the feasibility of automated image interpretation (Laboratory for Agricultural Remote Sensing, 1968; Morain and Coiner, 1970; Steiner et al., 1969; Wiegand et al., 1968). Most of these studies utilized scanning densitometers which digitally recorded differences in optical density across a given photo (Figure 8-3). Some systems, however, work directly off analog tape recovered from airborne scanners. Some preliminary studies have achieved results as high as 80 percent correct identification (Marshall et al., 1969). Because of the great amount of data that can be generated using high-flying aircraft and satellites, the use of automated data reduction systems would provide for more timely and more frequent information. At present, the main limitation of automated interpretation techniques is the almost complete reliance on tone as an identifying feature. For improved results, there is a need for a better interface with spatial analytical techniques based on site, texture, patterns, etc.

Disease Detection. Since 1956, when it was demonstrated that aerial photography could be used to detect diseased wheat, oats, barley, and rye (Colwell, R. N., 1956), a number of groups have conducted experiments which have shown that other crop diseases can be detected, some before visual symptoms occur. The basis for most of these studies has been the change, resulting from loss of vigor, in the normal signature of a given crop on the remote sensing imagery. Although conventional photographic and thermal infrared imagery have proved of some value in detecting diseases, the sensor which shows the most promise is color infrared film. The reason for this is that diseases seem to have a profound effect in decreasing the infrared reflectance in plants. Notable studies which illustrate the use of remote sensing techniques in disease detection are (1) the previously mentioned study of grain-crop diseases by R. N. Colwell (1956); (2) the detection of fields of sugar beets in eastern North Dakota and Minnesota, which were infested with *Cercospora* leaf spot disease (Meyer and Calpouzos, 1968); (3) the detection and monitoring of the late blight fungus of potatoes on infrared photography in the Fenland area of England (Brenchley, 1966) and in Aroostook County, Maine (Manzer and Cooper, 1967); (4) the detection and monitoring of

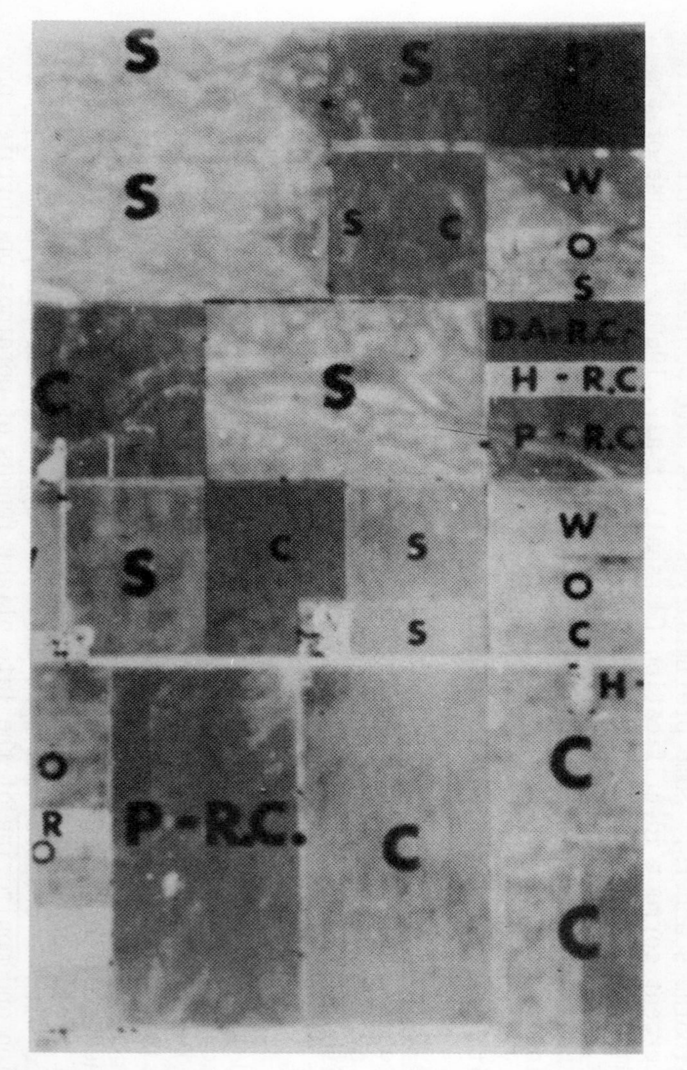

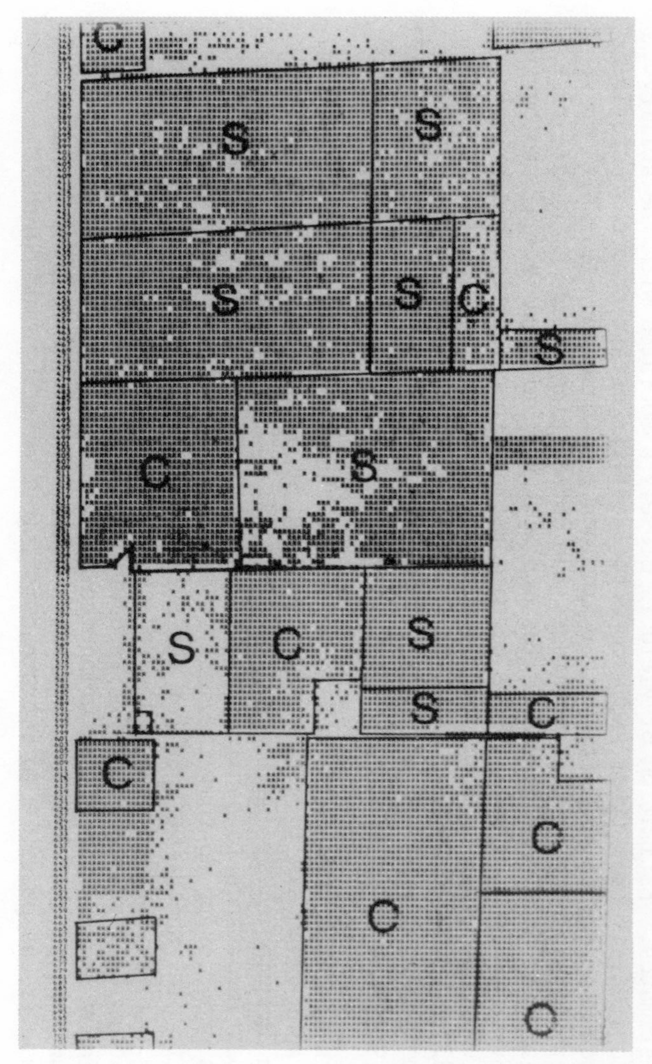

Figure 8-3. Automatic computer classification results showing the aerial photomosaic on the left, and the corresponding computer printout with the automatic identification for corn (c) and soybeans (s) on the right. (Courtesy Laboratory for Agricultural Remote Sensing, Purdue University.)

moderate-to-severe damage caused by corn blight in the seven cornbelt states in the United States (MacDonald et al., 1972); (5) the use of infrared photography for studying disease and decline in citrus trees in Florida (Norman and Fritz, 1965) and in Texas (Gausman et al., 1970); and (6) the use of low-altitude color infrared photography for the previsual detection of coconut wilt in the state of Kerala in southwestern India (Dakshinamurti et al., 1971; Roberts, 1972). Studies have also been performed showing that the effect of insect infestations can be detected on multiband photography (Meyer and Chiang, 1971). All these studies show how disease can be detected, often before visual symptoms occur; some of them, although not undertaken on an operational basis, have had some financial benefits.

Detection of Edaphic Problems. Studies have shown that, on the basis of visible soil differences, crop densities, or differences in tonal signatures of different crops (e.g., cotton), problems related to excessive salinity can be detected with the use of remote sensing imagery (Thomas et al., 1966; Wiegand et al., 1968; Thaman, 1971). Laboratory tests also indicate that nitrogen deficiency affects the reflectance characteristics of certain crop species (Thomas et al., 1966). Another study has demonstrated that fertilization trails on coconuts produce a marked spectral response on color infrared film when nitrogen concentration in the soil is increased (Dakshinamurti and Summanwar, 1972).

Problems Related to Agricultural Land Use. Most of the research described has been oriented toward those problems associated with midlatitude cropping systems. Although these studies are not totally inapplicable to the situation in developing nations, there is need for more research with reference to these countries' particular informational needs in the field of agricultural surveys. In most developed countries, the presence of large fields, relatively uniform field sizes, and the predominance of single-crop-to-a-single-field cropping practices are a distinct advantage for the application of remote sensing technology to crop identification, yield estimates, disease detection, etc.

In many developing nations, however, fields are small, fragmented, and two or more crops may be grown in the same area under a system of shifting or semipermanent cultivation. This poses a definite problem for the use of remote sensing technology in studies which are beyond the scope of general land-use studies, soil surveys, etc. Before the application of remote sensing can go beyond these general studies, there is a need for a reorientation of techniques and typologies. In an effort to orient remote sensing techniques toward developing nations, typologies have been constructed which are tailored to the informational needs of these areas. Studies of the agricultural systems of Puerto Rico, Tanzania, and Vietnam (Knight and Harnapp, 1971), Indonesia (Thaman, 1973),Jamaica (Collins, 1966) and the Kingdom of Tonga (Thaman, 1972), using conventional aerial photography, have shown that, although it is not possible to identify all crops, it is possible to accurately identify such agricultural land-use types as commercial livestock, annual and perennial peasant gardens, commercial crops (such as sugar cane, corn, tobacco, rice, sorghum, pineapples,and bananas), commercial coconut plantations, and various stages of bush fallow. In the study by Knight and Harnapp, the classification was based not only on visible landscape features, but also on socioeconomic factors related to developing countries. In Collins' study, 21 different crops or land-use types were identified and particular emphasis was placed on defining underutilized areas.

Range Surveys

The range resource, which encompasses nearly one-half of the earth's total land mass, includes a great variety of environments: tundra, semiarid areas, mountains, meadows, open forests, and perennial and annual savannas (Carneggie, 1968a). The importance of this resource is exemplified by the United States, where 35 million cattle, out of a total population of some 107 million, are grazed on rangeland. An improvement of only 10 percent in carrying capacity, through the application of remote sensing techniques, could mean an increase of 3.5 million annually (Hoffer et al., 1967). Optimum management of the range resource is important not only to domestic livestock production but also to the well-being of wildlife species.

Because the rangeland resource covers such vast areas and is very sensitive to environmental changes and management practices, the use of remote sensing techniques, especially multidate imagery, seems to be ideally suited for range resource inventories. Apart from broad-based rangeland mapping projects, comparatively little detailed research has been accomplished with reference to the range resource. Some of the studies that have been performed are discussed here.

Location and Delineation of Rangeland. Studies involving the delineation of rangeland have been conducted both in Australia and the United States, using high-altitude and satellite photography. Studies conducted in the Northern Territory, Australia (Perry, 1961; Colwell, R. N., 1968), and in Arizona (Carneggie et al., 1969; Poulton et al., 1969), show that it is possible, using satellite and high-altitude photography, to accurately map valuable rangeland areas. On Gemini satellite photography imaged over the Northern Territory of Australia, it was found possible to distinguish between areas of *Spinifex* grassland and Mitchell grass, the latter being far more valuable as browse for livestock. In Arizona, using Apollo 9 satellite photography, it was possible to differentiate between scrub vegetation types and valuable grazing areas with a high degree of accuracy. Similar applications of remote sensing techniques could very well lead to the location of optimal grazing areas throughout the world.

Species Identification. In order to successfully evaluate the range potential of an area, knowledge of the presence of both valuable fodder species and toxic plants is needed. Research conducted in Australia (Carneggie et al., 1971) and northern California (Carneggie, 1968a, 1968b) have demonstrated that the use of large-scale and color infrared photography (70 mm format, a scale of approximately 1:600, and preferably with stereoscopic coverage) is extremely useful for identification of forage species versus other undesirable nonnutritive and toxic plants. Complete reliance, however, cannot be placed on the use of photography alone, and limited ground checking is often required.

Range Condition and Carrying Capacity. The condition and carrying capacity of a given range area varies considerably as a function of time, owing to changes in moisture availability, species composition, forage density, soil types, slope, and grazing intensity. A number of studies have demonstrated that many of these variables and resultant changes can be monitored using various remote sensing techniques (Carneggie, 1968a, 1968b; Carneggie et al., 1971). Results of these studies have shown that (1) differences in moisture regimes can be detected as a result of temperature differences on thermal infrared imagery and as a result of vegetation reflectance characteristics on photographic imagery; (2) relative estimates of plant cover and forage density classes can be rapidly obtained using photo interpretive techniques; (3) the carrying capacity can be monitored successfully and some indication of yield can be arrived at using multidate photography; (4) by virtue of signatures on color infrared photos of annual grassland range, it is possible to discriminate range units which have been moderately and lightly grazed or are ungrazed; in large scale photography, it is even possible to see which plants have been grazed on, as well as recent fecal droppings (Carneggie, 1968a); (5) soil erosion is easily detected on most types of imagery; (6) the effects and frequency of burning can be studied on thermal infrared imagery owing to the absorption properties of charcoal; (7) color and color infrared photography seem to be most useful for the majority of surveys, especially for detecting changes in vigor, although black-and-white photography in two or more bands, scanner imagery (especially thermal infrared), and side-looking airborne radar data may all be of some use for soil and moisture studies; and, (8) because the condition of rangeland is so variable from year to year, the choice of time of photography is a critical consideration.

Infestations. Less work has been carried out with respect to the detection of disease, insects, or insect infestations, but it has been demonstrated that the effects of rodent activity as well as overgrazing by wildlife (e.g., deer or kangaroo depending on the area under consideration) can be monitored using remote sensing techniques (Carneggie, 1968a; Newsome, 1965; Parker, 1972).

Livestock Surveys

At present, livestock surveys are still conducted using somewhat unreliable conventional sampling techniques. However, a number of studies have evaluated the use of aerial photography and thermal infrared imagery for livestock surveys. The three main areas of research have been related to (1) the feasibility of inventorying total livestock populations; (2) the identification of the breed or type of animal; and (3) the study of animal behavior. Following are summaries and results of some of these studies.

Livestock Inventory. From 1966 to 1968, studies of areas in northern California and Idaho were conducted, using color and black-and-white films, in order to determine the usefulness of aerial photography for livestock inventories (Colwell, R. N., Estes, et al., 1966; Colwell, et al., 1966; Huddleston and Roberts, 1968). The imagery was interpreted by skilled interpreters, and the results were checked in comparison with ground-truth data collected coincident with the remote sensing overflight. The results of these studies indicated that (1) the results from photo-interpretation techniques were almost always within 5 percent of the true count in open environments; (2) the interpretation results were less accurate when there was more than 20 to 30 percent cover of woody vegetation or numerous barnyard structures which obscured the animals from the aerial view; (3) the optimum photographic scale for enumerating livestock was about 1:6,000; (4) from a cost/benefit standpoint, black-and-white photography was preferred to color; (5) conventional photography, both black-and-white and color, was preferred to both black-and-white and color infrared photography; (6) stereoscopic coverage (60 percent overlap) was necessary to make accurate counts; (7) the optimum season for photography was in the spring, while the grass was still green and provided optimum contrast between animals and background vegetation; (8) early-morning and late-afternoon photography was preferred because, during the heat of the day, the animals often stay in the shade of trees or other structures; (9) although sheep and cattle could be consistently identified, horses were more difficult to identify; and (10) thermal infrared imagery may have possible application for livestock inventories because of its day-or-night capability and its ability to discriminate between animals and their background or among the animals themselves on the basis of radiometric temperature variations (see Figure 8-4).

More recently, an experiment designed to eliminate interpretive problems in counting livestock, where there were numerous barnyard structures,was conducted using black-and-white, 1:12,000 photography flown over southern Ontario (Ryerson and Wood, 1971). Indirect methods were used, involving the study of features such as the types and acreages of different fodder crops and the size and types of milking stalls and other farm structures. These features were used as surrogates of the number and type of cattle (dairy or beef),and overall accuracies of better than 92 percent were obtained.

Identification of Breeds and Species of Animals. Results from a study carried out by R. N. Colwell, Estes et al. (1966) indicated that (1) it was possible to differentiate sheep, cattle, and horses on color and black-and-white photography at scales greater than 1:6,000; (2) in order to differentiate animals such as pigs, jackasses, and goats, as well as make breed, sex, and age differentiations, large-scale imagery, such as 1:500, should be utilized; (3) color photography provided much more information for making such determinations; and (4) stereoscopic coverage was important.

The Study of Animal Behavior. A number of studies have been carried out to determine the behavior of rangeland animals,particularly in Australia with large-scale photography (Dudzinski and Arnold, 1967; Low, 1972). Most of these studies have focused on the distribution of range animals in relation to range type and productivity, water, and climate.

CONCLUSION

The belief that remote sensing techniques will, in the future, have an increasingly important role to play in the execution of agricultural surveys has been based on four assumptions: (1) that present data collection and dissemination programs are worth the cost incurred, (2) that some of the limitations of the present programs are particularly amenable to improvement using remote sensing techniques, (3) that many new remote sensing techniques showing promise in the research and development stage will soon be operational, and (4) that improvements resulting from the application of remote sensing techniques will result in either direct or indirect dollar benefits to the agricultural economy.

At present, the bulk of evidence points to the fact that these assumptions are well founded. First, the very continuance of broad-scale agricultural surveys throughout the world indicates that the direct or indirect benefits of these surveys meet the cost incurred. Second, limitations, such as the lack of a uniform sampling frame, the subjective basis for many surveys, the costliness of on-the-ground surveys, the relative inaccessibility of many undeveloped agricultural areas, and the lack of timeliness, are particularly amenable to improvement using remote sensing techniques. Third, the use of color infrared films, multidate imagery, multistage sampling, satellites, and other remote sensing systems, techniques, and platforms which have been shown to be a great

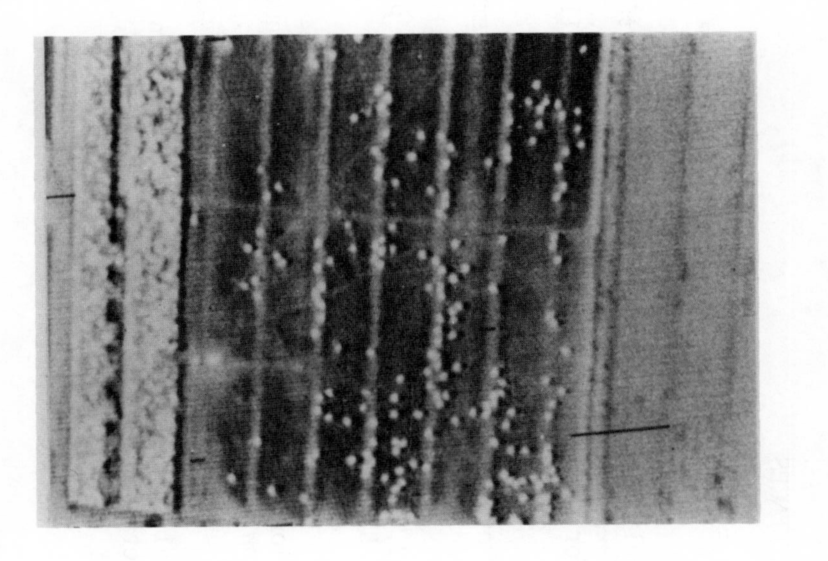

Figure 8-4. The thermal infrared image on the left of a cattle feedlot in the Imperial Valley, California illustrates the possible applications of this type of imagery for livestock surveys. The warmer bodies of the animals show up brighter in contrast to the darker background. Nevertheless, the use of conventional black-and-white photography, such as the photograph on the right taken in Davis, California, still offers the best possibilities with reference to cost effectiveness. (Infrared image courtesy of HRB-Singer, Inc.; the image on the right courtesy of the Forestry Remote Sensing Laboratory, University of California, Berkeley.)

value in numerous research projects, may be operational in the very near future. Finally, if the use of such techniques can improve only slightly the survey techniques employed in programs such as range improvement, disease detection, or weed control, the dollar benefits may be considerable. For example, the annual loss to major crops in the United Arab Republic from disease and insects amounts to $168 million (Luney and Dill, 1970); in the northern half of Africa, the Near East, India, and Pakistan, invasions of the desert locust caused losses totaling $42 million from 1949 to 1957 (despite intensive and costly control programs); and, in the United States, the annual cost of weed control in agriculture is estimated to be $3.8 billion (Hoffer et al., 1967). If the application of remote sensing techniques to agricultural surveys of these phenomena allowed for only a 10 percent reduction of the damage, the dollar savings for the three instances above would be $16.8 million, $4.2 million, and $380 million, respectively.

These are only a few of the possible applications of remote sensing to agricultural surveys in the future. There is a distinct possibility of other types of projects, such as estimating the extent of frost damage to orange groves or the inventory of cropland for taxation or compliance control purposes. Nevertheless, the greatest value of the application of remote sensing techniques may very well be for very general agricultural land-use mapping in developing countries, where there is virtually no land-use information. Remote sensing, particularly from satellite platforms, may provide an answer to this need, since many of these countries are limited by financial constraints and area inaccessibility.

REFERENCES

Aero Service Corporation, 1967, *Chile Survey Pays for Itself in Five Years*, Philadelphia, Pennsylvania.

Belcher, D. J., E. E. Hardy, R. L. Shelton, and E. L. Schepis, 1967, *Potential Benefits to Be Derived from Applications of Remote Sensing of Agricultural, Forest, and Range Resources*, Center for Aerial Photographic Studies, Cornell University, Ithaca.

Brenchley, G. H., 1966, "The Aerial Photography of Potato Late Blight Epidemics," *Journal of the Royal Aeronautical Society*, 70:1082-1085.

Brenchley, G. H., and C. V. Dadd, 1962, "Potato Blight Recording by Aerial Photography," *N.A.A.S. Quarterly Review*, 57:21-25.

Brooner, W. G., R. M. Haralick, and I. Dinstien, 1971, "Spectral Parameters Affecting Automated Image Interpretation Using Bayesian Probability Techniques," *Proceedings of the Seventh Symposium on Remote Sensing of Environment*, vol. III, University of Michigan, Ann Arbor, pp. 1929-1949.

Brunnschweiter, Dieter, 1957, "Seasonal Changes of the Agricultural Pattern: A Study in Comparative Airphoto Interpretation," *Photogrammetric Engineering*, 17(5):759-771.

Bulban, E. J., 1972, "Space Technology," *Aviation Week and Space Technology*, Jan. 31, pp. 33-36.

Carneggie, D. M., 1968a, *Analysis of Remote Sensing Data for Range Resource Management*, Annual Progress Report, Forestry Remote Sensing Laboratory, University of California, Berkeley.

Carneggie, D. M., 1968b, "Applying Remote Sensing Technology for Improving Range Resource Inventories," *Proceedings of the Fifth Symposium on Remote Sensing of Environment*, University of Michigan, Ann Arbor, pp. 373-385.

Carneggie, D. M., L. R. Pettinger, C. M. Hay, and S. J. Daus, R. N. Colwell et al., 1969, "Analysis of Earth Resources in the Phoenix, Arizona, Area," in *Analysis of Earth Resources on Apollo 9 Photography*, University of California, Berkeley.

Carneggie, D. M., D. G. Wilcox, and R. B. Hacker, 1971, *The Use of Large Scale Aerial Photographs in the Evaluation of Western Australian Rangeland*, Technical Bulletin 10, Department of Agriculture, Perth, Western Australia.

Charter, S., 1959, "An Introduction to Infrared Aerial Photography in Agriculture," *Agriculture and Food Chemistry*, 7(8):536-539.

Christian, S. S., and R. A. Perry, 1969, "Arid Land Studies in Australia," W. G. McGinnies, and B. J. Goldman, Eds., in *Arid Lands in Perspective*, American Association for the Advancement of Science, Washington, D.C., and University of Arizona Press, Tucson.

Collins, W. G., 1966, "Aerial Photography Applied to Tropical Land Use," *Chartered Surveyor*, England, pp. 253-259.

Collins, W. G., 1972, "The Application of Remote Sensing to Locating and Monitoring Under-Utilized Land in Jamaica," *Proceedings of the Eighth International Symposium on Remote Sensing of Environment*, University of Michigan, Ann Arbor, Oct. 2-6 (in press).

Colwell, John E., 1972, "Uses of Remote Sensing in the Inventory of Agricultural Crops," University of Michigan, Willow Run Laboratories, Ann Arbor, pp. 34.

Colwell, R. N., 1956, "Determining the Prevalence of Certain Cereal Crop Diseases by Means of Areal Photography," *Hilgardia*, 26(5):223-286.

Colwell, R. N., 1960, "Some Uses and Limitations of Aerial Color Photography in Agriculture," *Photogrammetric Engineering*, 26, pp. 220-222.

Colwell, R. N., 1962, *The Development of a System for Making Raisin-Lay Surveys with High-Altitude Panoramic Photography*, Forestry Remote Sensing Laboratory, University of California, Berkeley.

Colwell, R. N., 1963, *Spectrozonal Aerial Photography as an Aid in Detecting and Counting Raisin Trays in California Vineyards*, Forestry Remote Sensing Laboratory, University of California, Berkeley.

Colwell, R. N., 1965, *Determining the Usefulness of Ektachrome, Panchromatic and Infrared Aerial Photography for the Inventory of Vine Crops and Raisin Trays*, Forestry Remote Sensing Laboratory, University of California, Berkeley.

Colwell, R. N., 1968, "Remote Sensing of Natural Resources," *Scientific American*, 218(1):54-69.

Colwell, Robert N., 1972, Personal Communication, Earth Satellite Corporation, Berkeley, California.

Colwell, R. N., Ed., 1971, *Monitoring Earth Resources from Aircraft and Spacecraft*, NASA SP-275, National Aeronautics and Space Administration, Washington, D.C.

Colwell, R. N., J. E. Estes, C. E. Tiedemann, and J. E. Flemming, 1966, *The Usefulness of Thermal Infrared and Related Imagery in the Evaluation of Agricultural Resources*, vols. I and II, Forestry Remote Sensing Laboratory, University of California, Berkeley.

Colwell, R. N., D. T. Lauer, and E. H. Roberts, 1966, *Aerial Photo Interpretation of Livestock and Fruit and Nut Crops*, U.S. Department of Agriculture/California Department of Agriculture, Training Syllabus.

Culver, R. N. and C. E. Poulton, 1968, *Application of Ecology and Remote Sensing in the Analysis of Range Watersheds*, Oregon State University, Corvallis.

Dakshinamurti, C., B. Krishamurthy, A. S. Summanway, P. Shanta, and P. R. Pisharoty, 1971, "Remote Sensing for Coconut Wilt," *Proceedings of the Seventh International Symposium on Remote Sensing of Environment*, vol. I, University of Michigan, Ann Arbor, pp. 25-29.

Dakshinamurti, C., and A. Summanwar, 1972, "Remote Sensing of Coconut Plants in Kerala (India)," *Eighth International Symposium on Remote Sensing of Environment: Summaries*, University of Michigan, Ann Arbor, pp. 135.

de Azevedo, L. H. A., 1962, "Radar in the Amazon," *Proceedings of the Seventh Symposium on Remote Sensing of Environment*, vol. III, University of Michigan, Ann Arbor, pp. 2303-2306.

de Azevedo, L. H. A., 1972, "Radar in the Amazon," *Proceedings of the Seventh International Symposium on Remote Sensing of Environment*, vol. III, University of Michigan, Ann Arbor, pp. 2303-2306.

Dill, H. W., Jr., 1959, "Use of the Comparison Method in Agricultural Airphoto Interpretation," *Photogrammetric Engineering*, 25:44-49.

Dill, H. W., Jr., 1967, *Worldwide Use of Airphotos in Agriculture*, Agriculture Handbook 344, Economic Reporting Service, Washington, D.C.

Dill, H. W., Jr., and R. C. Otte, 1971, "Urbanization of Land in the Northeastern United States," *USDA Economic Research Bulletin ERS-485*, U.S. Department of Agriculture, Government Printing Office,Washington, D.C.

Donner, P., 1965, *Issues in Land Reform: The Chilean Case*, Discussion Paper 5, Land Tenure Center, University of Wisconsin, Madison.

Draeger, W. C., L. R. Pettinger, and A. S. Benson, 1971, "The Use of Small Scale Aerial Photography in a Regional Agricultural Survey," *Proceedings of the Seventh International Symposium on Remote Sensing of Environment,* vol. II, University of Michigan, Ann Arbor, pp. 1205-1217.

Dudzinski, M. L., and G. W. Arnold, 1967, "Aerial Photography and Statistical Analysis for Studying Behavior Patterns of Grazing Animals," *Journal of Range Management,* 20:77-83.

FAO, 1970, *Program for the 1970 World Census of Agriculture,* Food and Agriculture Organization of the United Nations, Rome, Italy.

FAO Statistics Advisory Committee of Experts, 1969, *Problems Encountered in Compilation and Publication of Agricultural Production Statistics, Fourth Session,* Food and Agriculture Organization of the United Nations, Rome, Italy.

Fischnich, O. E., 1972, Personal Communication, Assistant Director, General Agriculture Department, Food and Agriculture Organization of the United Nations, Rome, Italy.

Frey, H. T., 1967, "Agricultural Application of Remote Sensing--The Potential from Space Platforms," *Agricultural Information Bulletin 328,* Economic Research Service, U.S. Department of Agriculture, Washington, D.C.

Frey, H. T., O. E. Krause, and C. Dickason, 1968, *Major Uses of Land and Water in the United States: With Special Reference to Agriculture,* Agricultural Economic Report 149, Economic Research Service, U.S. Department of Agriculture, Washington, D.C.

Gates, D. M., H. J. Keegan, J. C. Schleter, and V. R. Weidner, 1965, "Spectral Properties of Plants," *Applied Optics,* 4(1,2):11-20.

Gausman, J. W., W. A. Allen, R. Cardenas, and R. L. Bowen, 1970, "Detection of Root Rot Disease of Grapefruit Trees with Infrared Color Film," *Journal of the Rio Grande Horticultural Society,* 24:36-42.

Goodman, M. S., 1959, "A Technique for the Identification of Farm Crops on Aerial Photographs," *Photogrammetric Engineering,* 25:131-137.

Haefner, J., 1967, "Airphoto Interpretation of Rural Land Use in Western Europe," *Photogrammetria,* 22:143-152.

Haralick, R. M., 1968, "Adaptive Pattern Recognition of Agriculture in Western Kansas by Using a Predictive Model in Construction of Similarity Sets," *Proceedings of the Fifth International Symposium on Remote Sensing of Environment,* University of Michigan, Ann Arbor, pp. 343-356.

Haralick, R. M., F. Caspall, R. K. Moore, and D. S. Simonett, 1968, *A Statistical and Conditional Probability Study of Crop Discrimination Using Radar Images,* Technical Memorandum 133-5, University of Kansas, Center for Research in Engineering Science, Lawrence.

Harnapp, V. R., and C. G. Knight, "Remote Sensing of Tropical Agricultural Systems," *Proceedings of the Seventh International Symposium on Remote Sensing of*

Environment, vol. I, University of Michigan, Ann Arbor, pp. 409-433.

Henderson, F. M., 1971, *Local Level Agricultural Practices and Individual Farmer Needs as Influences on SLAR Imagery Data Collection,* Technical Report 177-15, University of Kansas, Center for Research, Inc., Lawrence.

Hill, Howard L., 1972, Personal Communication, Acting Director, Natural Resource Economics Division, Economic Research Service, Washington, D.C.

Hoffer, R. M., R. A. Holmes, and J. R. Shay, 1966, "Vegetative Soil and Photographic Factors Affecting Tone in Agricultural Remote Multispectral Sensing," *Proceedings of the Fourth Symposium on Remote Sensing of Environment,* University of Michigan, Ann Arbor, pp. 115-134.

Hoffer, R. M., C. J. Johannsen, and M. F. Baumgardner, 1967, "Agricultural Applications of Remote Multispectral Sensing," *Proceedings of the Indiana Academy of Science for 1966,* 76:386-395.

Holter, M. R., et al., 1970, "Imaging with Nonphotographic Sensors," in *Remote Sensing with Special Reference to Agriculture and Forestry,* National Academy of Sciences, Washington, D.C., pp. 73-163.

Huddleston, H. F., and E. H. Roberts, 1968, "Use of Remote Sensing for Livestock Inventories," *Proceedings of the Fifth International Symposium on Remote Sensing of Environment,* University of Michigan, Ann Arbor, pp. 307-323.

Hunting Technical Services Ltd., 1960, *Report on a Pilot Survey for Agricultural Census in Northern Ghana,* Report to Ghana Ministry of Food and Agriculture, London, England.

Huson, J. J., 1970, *Land Utilization in the Crati Valley (Calabria, Italy): A Study on the Applicability of Medium Scale Aerial Photographs,* I.T.C., Delft, The Netherlands.

Johnson, C. W., R. W. Pease, and L.W. Bowden, 1969, *A System of Regional Agricultural Land Use Mapping Tested Against Small Scale Apollo 9 Color Infrared Photography of the Imperial Valley, Technical Report 5,* Department of Geography, University of California, Riverside.

Kelly, B. W., 1970, "Sampling and Statistical Problems," *Remote Sensing with Special Reference to Agriculture and Forestry,* National Academy of Sciences, Washington, D.C., pp. 324-353.

Knight, C. G., and V. R. Harnapp, 1971, *Remote Sensing of Tropical Agricultural Systems,* University of Kansas, Center for Research, Inc., Lawrence.

Knipling, E. B., 1967, *Physical and Physiological Basis for Differences in Reflectance of Healthy and Diseased Plants,* A Report of U.S. Army CREEL, Hanover.

Kohn, C. F., 1952, *An Essay Key for the Photoindentification of Farm Crops at Several Intervals During the Growing Season in Northern Illinois,* Office of Naval Research Contract No. N7onr45-005, Technical Report No. 3, Department of Geography, Northwestern University, Evanston.

Krumpe, P. F., 1972, *Remote Sensing of Terrestrial Vegetation: A Comprehensive Bibliography,* Ecology Department, University of Tennessee, Knoxville.

Laboratory for Agricultural Remote Sensing, 1968, *Remote Sensing in Agriculture,* Research Bulletin 844, Purdue University, Agricultural Experiment Station, Lafayette, Ind.

Lauer, D. T., 1968, "Remote Sensing in Agriculture: Techniques, Equipment and Outlook," paper presented at the Texas Agricultural Experiment Station Annual Conference, Texas A & M University, College Station.

Lauer, D. T., and R. R. Thaman, 1971, "Information Content of Simulated Space Photographs as a Function of Various Levels of Image Resolution," *Proceedings of the Seventh International Symposium on Remote Sensing of Environment,* vol. III, University of Michigan, Ann Arbor, pp. 17-21.

Low, W. A., 1972, "Behavioral Aspects of the Ecology of Arid Zone Mammals, with Particular Reference to Cattle," in A. D. Wilson, Ed., *Studies of the Australian Arid Zone,* CSIRO, Canberra.

Luney, P. R., 1965, "Benefits and Problems in Agriculture as Related to Aerial Photography," prepared for seminar on "The Role of Aerial Studies in Agricultural Development," October 24-26, Cornell University, Ithaca, N.Y.

Luney, P. R., and H. W. Dill, Jr., 1970, "Uses, Potentialities, and Needs in Agriculture and Forestry," in *Remote Sensing with Special Reference to Agriculture and Forestry,* National Academy of Sciences, Washington, D.C.

Luybx, N., 1965, "A Demonstration Project on the Use of Aerial Photography in Planning in Developing Countries," presented at the seminar on "The Role of Aerial Studies in Agriculture Development," October 24-26, Cornell University, Ithaca, N. Y.

MacDonald, R. B., R. Allen, J. W. Clifton, M. E. Bauer, D. Landgrebe, and J. D. Erickson, 1972, "Results of the 1971 Corn Blight Watch Experiment," *Proceedings of the Eighth International Symposium on Remote Sensing of Environment,* University of Michigan, Ann Arbor, October 2-6, (in press).

Manzer, F. E., and G. R. Cooper, 1967, *Aerial Photographic Methods of Potato Disease Detection,* Bulletin 646, Maine Agricultural Experiment Station, University of Maine, Presque Isle.

Mark Systems, Inc., 1966, *Investigations on the Feasibility of Determining Yield of Rice, Wheat, and Sugar Cane by Means of High Altitude Aerial Photography,* Final Technical Report on Project ACRE, Cupertino, California.

Marshall, R. E., N. Thomson, F. Thomson, and F. Kiegler, 1969, "Use of Multispectral Recognition Techniques for Conducting Rapid, Wide-Area Wheat Surveys," *Proceedings of the Sixth International Symposium on Remote Sensing of Environment,* vol. I, University of Michigan, Ann Arbor, pp. 3-21.

Meyer, M. P., and L. Calpouzos, 1968, "Detection of Crop Diseases," *Photogrammetric Engineering,* 34:554-557.

Meyer, M. P. and H. C. Chiang, 1971, "Multiband Reconnaissance of Simulated Insect Defoliation in Corn Fields," *Proceedings of the Seventh International Symposium on Remote Sensing of Environment*, vol. III, University of Michigan, Ann Arbor, pp. 1231-1234.

Miller, B., 1972, "Side-Looking Radar Plays Key Role in Mapping," *Aviation Week and Space Technology*, 97(3):44-46.

Morain, S. A., and J. B. Campbell, 1972, "Soil Mapping from Radar Imagery: Theory and Preliminary Applications," Unpublished manuscript.

Morain, S. A., and J. Coiner, 1970, *An Evaluation for Making Agricultural Determinations*, Technical Report 177-7, University of Kansas, Center for Research, Inc., Lawrence.

Myers, V. I., D. L. Carter, and W. J. Rippert, 1966, "Photogrammetry and Temperature Sensing for Estimating Soil Salinity," International Committee on Irrigation and Drainage, Fourth Congress, New Delhi, India, Question 19:39-49.

Myers, V. I., C. L. Wiegand, M. D. Heilman, and J. R. Thomas, 1966, "Remote Sensing in Soil and Water Conservation Research," *Proceedings of the Fourth Symposium on Remote Sensing of Environment*, University of Michigan, Ann Arbor, pp. 801-813.

Nalepka, R. F., H. M. Horwitz, and N. S. Thomson, 1971, "Investigations of Multispectral Sensing of Crops," *Report NASA CR-WRL 3160-30T*, NASA Manned Spacecraft Center, Houston, Tex.

National Academy of Sciences, 1970, *Remote Sensing with Special Reference to Agriculture and Forestry*, National Academy of Sciences, Washington, D.C.

Newsome, A. E., 1965, "The Abundance of Red Kangaroos, *Megaleia rufa* (Demarest) in Central Australia," *Australian Journal of Zoology*, 13:269-287.

Norman, C. G., and N. L. Fritz, 1965, "Infrared Photography as an Indicator of Disease and Decline in Citrus Trees," *Proceedings of the Florida State Horticultural Society*, 78:59-63.

Park, A. B., 1969, "Remote Sensing of Time Dependent Phenomena," *Proceedings of the Sixth International Symposium on Remote Sensing of Environment*, vol. II, University of Michigan, Ann Arbor, pp. 1227-1236.

Parker, B., 1972, "Remote Sensing in the CSIRO Division of Wildlife Research," paper presented at the CSIRO Remote Sensing Symposium, Sydney, N.S.W., September 20-22.

Perry, R. A., 1961, "Pasture Lands of the Alice Springs Area: Map 1:1,000,000," Division of Land Research and Regional Survey, CSIRO, Melbourne, Australia.

Philpotts, L. E., 1965a, *Farmers' Estimates of Acreage in Comparison with Measurements from Aerial Photos, Manitoba, 1961*, Resource Development Section, Economic Branch, Canada Department of Agriculture, Ottawa.

Philpotts, L. E., 1965b, "The Use of Aerial Photography in the Canada Department of Agriculture," presented at a seminar on "The Role of Aerial Photography in Agricultural Development," October 24-26, Cornell University, Ithaca, N.Y.

Poulton, C. E., E. Garcia-Moya, J. R. Johnson, and B. J. Schrumpf, 1969, *Inventory of Native Vegetation and Related Resources from Space Photography*, Department of Range Management, Agricultural Experiment Station, Oregon State University, Corvallis.

Rains, A. B., and M. A. Brunt, 1972, "An Evaluation of Air Photography for Land Resource Surveys in the Tropics," *Proceedings of the Seventh International Symposium on Remote Sensing of Environment*, vol. III, University of Michigan, Ann Arbor, pp. 2319-2324.

Roberts, E. H., 1972, Personal Communication, Forestry Remote Sensing Laboratory, University of California, Berkeley.

Rohde, W. G., and C. E. Olson, Jr., 1971, "Estimating Foliar Moisture Content from Infrared Reflectance Data," *Proceedings Third Biennial Workshop on Color Aerial Photography in Plant Sciences*, American Society of Photogrammetry, pp. 144-164.

Ryerson, R. A., and H. A. Wood, 1971, "Air Photo Analysis of Beef and Dairy Farming," *Photogrammetric Engineering*, 37:157-169.

Schwarz, D. E., and F. Caspall, 1968, "The Use of Radar in the Discrimination and Identification of Agricultural Land Use," *Proceedings of the Fifth Symposium on Remote Sensing of Environment*, University of Michigan, Ann Arbor, pp. 233-247.

Shay, J. R., 1966, "Some Needs for Expanding Agricultural Research," *Proceedings of the Fourth Symposium on Remote Sensing of Environment*, University of Michigan, Ann Arbor, pp. 33-36.

Simonett, D. C., J. E. Eagleman, A. B. Erhart, D. C. Rhodes, and D. E. Schwarz, 1967, *The Potential of Radar as a Remote Sensor in Agriculture: A Study with K-Band Imagery in Western Kansas*, CRES Report 61-21, University of Kansas, Center for Research, Lawrence.

Simpson, Robert B., 1969, "APQ-97 Imagery of New England: A Geographic Evaluation," *Proceedings of the Sixth Symposium on Remote Sensing of Environment*, vol. II, University of Michigan, Ann Arbor, pp. 909-925.

Spansail, N., 1969, Personal Communication, Willow Run Laboratories, University of Michigan, Ann Arbor.

Steiner, D., 1965, "Use of Air Photographs for Interpreting and Mapping Rural Land Use in the United States," *Photogrammetria*, 20(2):65-80.

Steiner, D., 1970, "Time Dimension for Crop Surveys from Space," *Photogrammetric Engineering*, 36:187-194.

Steiner, D., K. Baumberger, and J. Mauer, 1969, "Computer-Processing and Classification of Multi-Variate Information from Remote Sensing Imagery," *Proceedings of the Sixth International Symposium on Remote Sensing of Environment*, vol. II, University of Michigan, Ann Arbor, pp. 895-907.

Swami, Sri, 1972, Personal Communication, Aero Service Corporation, Beverly Hills, Calif.

Thaman, R. R., 1967, *A Study of the Feasibility of Mapping Vegetation on a World Scale Using Satellite Imagery,* Master's Thesis, Department of Geography, University of California, Berkeley.

Thaman, R. R., 1969, "Analysis of Agricultural Resources in the Imperial Valley, California Area," Chapter 4 in R. N. Colwell, Ed., *An Evaluation of Earth Resources Using Apollo 9 Photography,* Forestry Remote Sensing Laboratory, Berkeley, Calif., vol. 2.

Thaman, R. R., 1971, "Monitoring the Effects of Excessive Salinity," in *Monitoring Earth Resources from Aircraft (NASA Sp-275),* National Aeronautics and Space Administration, Washington, D.C., pp. 89-92.

Thaman, R. R., 1972, "A System for Land Use Studies: Tongatapu, Tonga, *Journal of the Arizona Academy of Science* (Abstract of paper presented at Sixteenth Annual Meeting, May 5-6), 7:29-30.

Thaman, R. R., 1973, "The Use of Multispectral Photography for Resource Surveying Southeast Asia: An Indonesian Example," paper presented at the 27th Annual Meeting of the California Council for Geographic Education, San Jose, May 4-5,1973.

Thaman, R. R., and L. W. Senger, 1969, "Evaluation of the Agricultural Resources of the Imperial Valley: Model for Crop Identification, Utilizing Cyclical Field Patterns and Vegetation Phenological-Reflectance Characteristics," in L. R. Pettinger, Ed., *Analysis of Earth Resources on Sequential High Altitude Photography,* Forestry Remote Sensing Laboratory, Berkeley, Calif., pp. 4-1 - 4-44.

Thaman, R. R., and L. W. Senger, 1971, "Analysis of Agricultural Resources in the Imperial Valley, California," in *Monitoring Earth Resources from Aircraft and Spacecraft,* (NASA Sp-275), National Aeronautics and Space Administration, Washington, D.C., pp. 65-82.

Thomas, J. R., V. I. Myers, M. D. Heilman, and C. L. Wiegand, 1966, "Factors Affecting Light Reflectance of Cotton," *Proceedings of the Fourth Symposium on Remote Sensing of Environment,* University of Michigan, Ann Arbor, pp. 305-312.

USDA, 1966, *Remote Sensing in Agriculture/Forestry,* Agricultural Research Service, U.S. Department of Agriculture, Washington, D.C.

Von Steen, D. H., R. W. Leamer, and A. M. Gerbermann, 1969, "Relationship of Film Optical Density to Yield Indicators," *Proceedings of the Sixth International Symposium on Remote Sensing of Environment,* vol. II, University of Michigan, Ann Arbor, pp. 1115-1122.

Welch, R. I., 1963, "Photointerpretation Keys for Classification of Agricultural Crops," paper presented at symposium on "Uses of Aerial Photography in Agriculture," Sacramento, Calif.

Wiegand, C. L., M. D. Heilman, and A. H. Gerbermann, 1968, "Detailed Plant and Soil Thermal Regime in Agronomy," *Proceedings of the Fifth Symposium on Remote Sensing of Environment,* University of Michigan, Ann Arbor, pp. 325-342.

Wiegand, C. L., R. W. Leaner, D. A. Weber, and A. H. Gerbermann, 1971, "Multibase and Multiemulsion Space Photos for Crops and Soils," *Photogrammetric Engineering*, 37:147-156.

Wilson, Wendell, 1972, Personal Communication, Mathematical Statistician, California Crop and Livestock Reporting Service, Sacramento, Calif.

Urban Applications of Remote Sensing

David T. Lindgren
Dartmouth College

Apart from agriculture, the other major component of land use accorded special treatment in this book is the urban environment. Urban areas represent a complex association of population concentrations, intensive economic activities, and diverse lifestyles. They are a microcosm of human activity, and frequently experience rapid changes that need to be monitored and understood. This chapter is concerned primarily with specific urban applications of remote sensing, while the following chapter by Horton emphasizes the relationship of remote sensing to urban information requirements. Lindgren's discussion centers upon urban land-use mapping, transportation studies, engineering projects, municipal inspection, and population estimation.

One of the major tasks confronting planners and other municipal officials is the acquisition and analysis of information upon which the efficient administration of cities and towns depends. Although most American cities are attempting to establish some type of information system, efforts in this direction have been largely unsuccessful. Present methods of data acquisition and analysis continue to be time-consuming, costly, and extremely inefficient. In an effort to improve the effectiveness of urban information systems, research is being undertaken to determine possible urban applications of remote sensing. To date results have been very encouraging (see Chapter 10).

So far research into the urban applications of remote sensing has involved primarily photographic sensor systems, in particular black-and-white, color, and false color (color infrared) photography. Although research has primarily involved photographic sensors, nonphotographic sensors have not been entirely ignored. Two in particular, radar and thermal infrared, have displayed potential urban applications. Mention will be made of both. From these systems, two general types of data have been obtained--directly observable and indirectly observable (Manji, 1968). By definition, the former are phenomena which can actually be viewed on the photography--e.g., the number of dwellings within a given area. Indirectly observable data, on the other hand, are phenomena which cannot be seen directly on the photograph, but which can be inferred from the presence of other observable phenomena. An estimation of dwelling units within a number of residential structures would be an example of the indirectly observable data.

On the basis of directly observable data, a number of urban applications have been developed which, for the sake of convenience, have been combined into four categories: (1) urban land use mapping, (2) transportation studies, (3) engineering projects, and (4) municipal inspection. Two broad types of applications have been developed from indirectly observable data: (1) estimation of dwelling units and population and (2) housing-quality analysis.

DIRECTLY OBSERVABLE DATA

Urban Land-Use Mapping

Perhaps the map most commonly used by planners is the land-use map. This category of map, which is basically an inventory of how land is presently being utilized, illustrates the spatial relationships of various land uses. If accompanied by quantitative summations, it can also illustrate how much land is devoted to each use. Furthermore, the land-use map shows the extent of the transportation network and, more importantly, the relationship of the transportation network to land use.

Traditionally land-use surveys have been conducted by teams in the field. This method, however, is both costly and time-consuming; as a result, land-use data frequently become outdated. Research has demonstrated that urban land-use surveys now can be conducted from aerial photography. Furthermore, employing time sequential photography, changes in the use of urban space can be monitored.

There are limits, however, to the use of photo-interpretation techniques for land-use mapping. If land-use data are required only on a block basis, they can be satisfactorally derived from aerial photography of scales as small as 1:100,000. However, if land-use data are required on a parcel basis, as they are by most municipal planners, aerial photography cannot provide them regardless of scale. In the case where parcel data are needed, additional sources of information are almost always necessary to supplement photo-derived information (Howard and Dracht, 1971).

Unquestionably, the most ambitious effort to evaluate the applicability of photography from high-altitude aircraft and earth-orbiting satellites for urban land-use change detection is the Census Cities Project. This project is supported by the National Aeronautics and Space Administration (NASA) through the Geographic Applications Program (GAP) of the U.S. Geological Survey (USGS). Initially, 26 cities were named as test sites; and, for 20 of them, the U.S. Air Force Weather Service and NASA's Manned Spacecraft Center acquired multispectral, high-altitude photography. The overflights were made at the time of the 1970 census in order to render change detection data from both sources (photography and census) compatible (Wray, 1972).

The basic data from the overflights were color infrared photographs taken by an RC-8 camera at an image scale of 1:100,000 or 1:120,000 depending upon the aircraft's altitude. Color infrared film was used for two reasons. First, since color infrared film is sensitive to longer wavelengths of electromagnetic radiation than normal color film, it has a high haze-penetration capability. This film type is particularly useful over most U.S. cities, where haze and smog create problems for the acquisition of normal color photography. A second reason for employing this film type is that vegetation is highly reflective in the infrared and appears reddish on color infrared film; cultural features, on the other hand, appear blue. The contrast, then, between cultural and vegetative features is pronounced and has important implications for Eastern metropolitan regions where urban/woodland mix is common.

The ultimate goal of the Census Cities Project is to produce an Atlas of Urban and Regional Change. The atlas will be looseleaf and will accommodate many kinds of data presentation including photo mosaics, conventional maps, computer-printed maps, computer-tabulated data, and text. It has been designed with user applications in mind.

In the Boston study (Simpson et al., 1970), which served as one of the prototypes for the Census Cities Project, the purpose was to prepare a land-use map and a computerized data base for the entire metropolitan region from 1:120,000-scale aerial photography. The land-use map was compiled directly from the photography (on overlays), with a minimum of field checking required. The land-use classification system consisted of 24 categories. A minimum cell size of about 10 acres for mapping was established in order to make it comparable with the anticipated resolution of ERTS-1. The authors concluded from their study that it was practical to prepare an urban land-use map from high-altitude aerial photography, and that such a map would have utility for state and regional planners.

An additional objective of the Boston study was to prepare a computerized data base. Accordingly a UTM-addressable grid was constructed with a cell-scale equal to 0.2 kilometer (approximately 650 feet) on a side. The grid was placed over the completed land use map and land use was recorded for the centerpoint of each cell, of which there were 90,000 for the metropolitan Boston region. The land-use data were input to a computer and, to make them compatible with the 1970 census data, were made retrievable by census tract. One of the by products of the data was a series of computer-generated maps illustrating the spatial arrangement of land uses, either individually or in combination (see Figures 9-1, 9-2, and 9-3).

Test sites studied thus far under the Census Cities Project, in addition to Boston, include Cedar Rapids, New Haven, Pontiac, San Francisco, and Washington.

The Census Cities Project was envisioned as a bridge between the low-altitude urban land-use mapping projects of the past and the newer multicity approach initiated with the launching of the ERTS-1 satellite. Although ERTS-1 imagery* is only now being evaluated, Dartmouth scientists have already produced a land-use map of Rhode Island from it. Mapping at a scale of 1:250,000, using a four-times magnification of a 1:1,000,000 ERTS-1 image (see front cover for typical ERTS-1 scale image), they were able to identify eight major categories of land use. Difficulties were encountered in distinguishing between single-family and

---

* The ERTS satellite is imaging in four bands of the electromagnetic spectrum--green, red, and two near-infrared bands. In addition, a color infrared composite can be produced by combining the green, red, and one of the near-infrared bands.

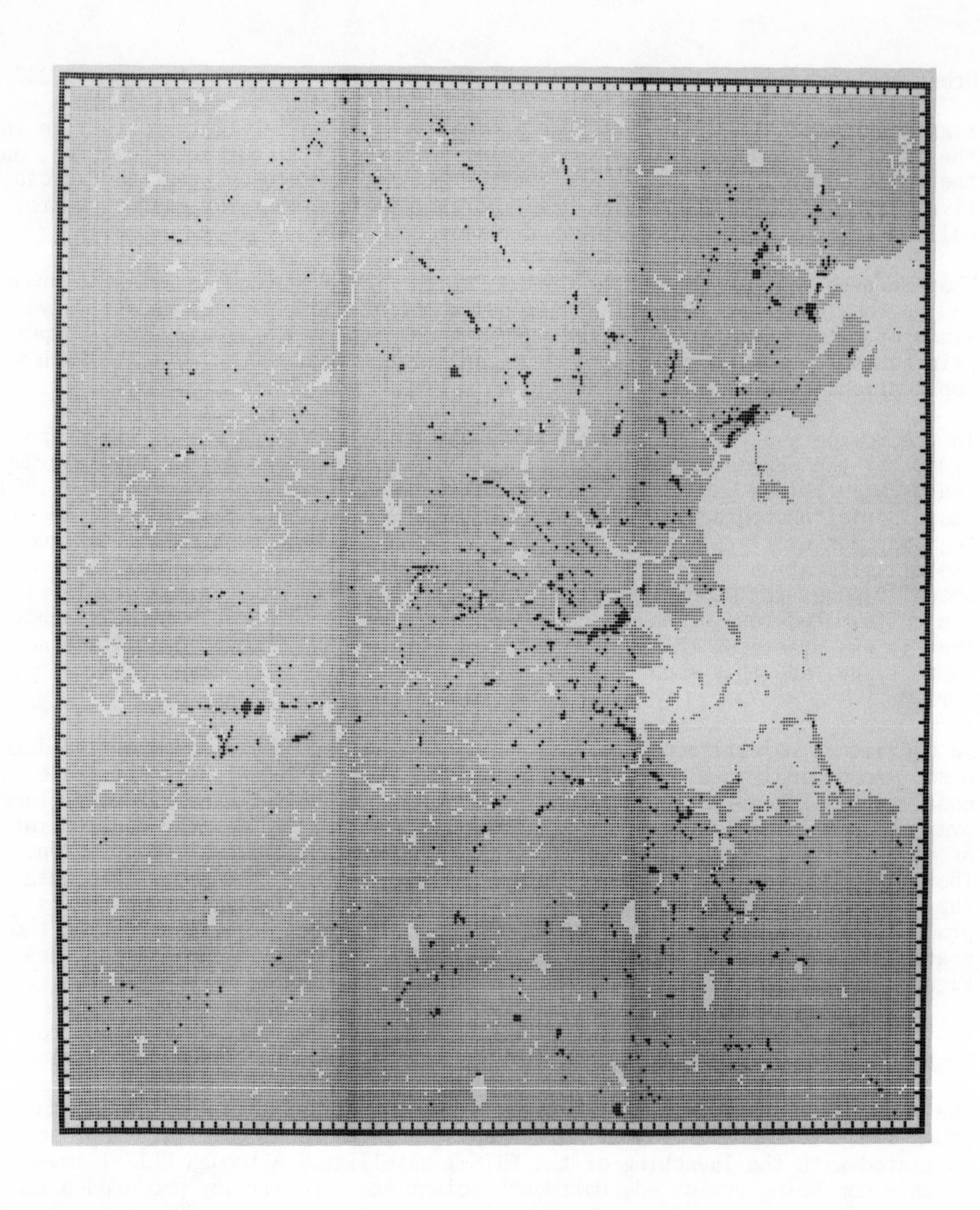

Figure 9-1. Commercial Land Use (1.7% of total area). Most conspicuous are the ribbon developments which radiate outward from the city of Boston.

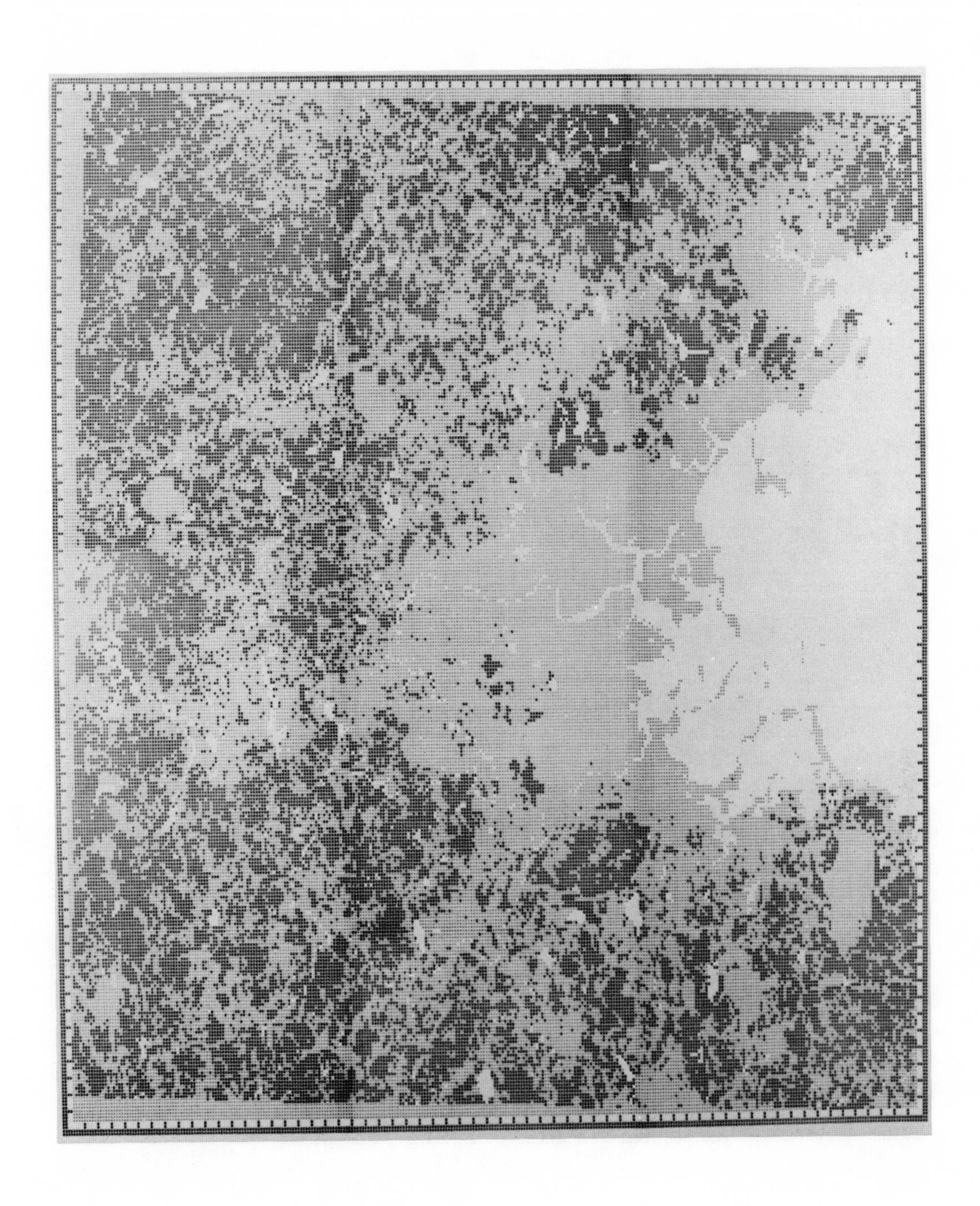

Figure 9-2. Woodland (41.6% of total area). Surprisingly the dominant land use within the Metropolitan Boston area is woodland.

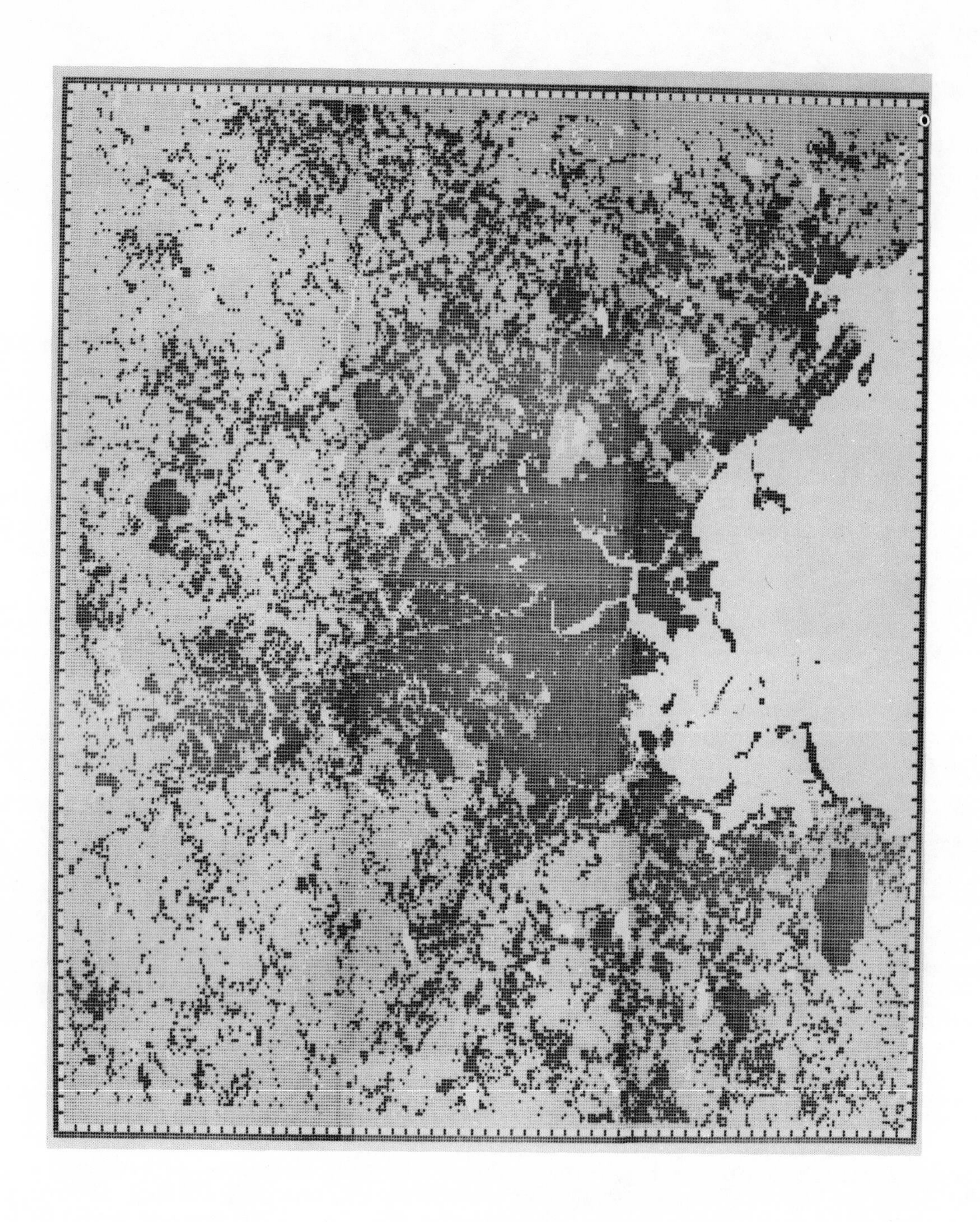

Figure 9-3. Combination of "Built-Up" Categories (40.5% of total area). Only agriculture, woodland, and vacant land are excluded from this category. The "built-up" area corresponds closely to "Urbanized Area" of 1970 census.

multifamily residential areas and in separating commercial, industrial, and institutional land uses (Simpson, 1972). Nevertheless, the land-use map derived from the ERTS-1 image appeared to meet standards set by Connecticut in its state land-use map published in 1960.

Transportation Studies

Nowhere has aerial photography been utilized for such a long period, and as successfully, as in the area of transportation studies. For more than 20 years, the Bureau of Public Roads has been encouraging the use of photo interpretation in transportation studies through research and education. It has urged highway organizations to use Highway Planning and Research funds available to them for research in this area. Due in large part to this program, a survey of major highway organizations revealed that 65 to 75 percent of the organizations polled utilized aerial photography in highway planning, although only 15 to 30 percent of those replying used them extensively (Rib, 1966). The applications of remote sensing to transportation studies fall broadly into four categories--highway planning, traffic studies, parking assessment, and highway inspection.

Although the era of major highway construction within urban centers may be drawing to a close, the role played by aerial photography in the design of such highways has been significant. Photogrammetric techniques have provided highway engineers with qualitative and quantitative data about (1) ground surface required for route location, (2) preliminary survey and design, (3) location survey, and (4) construction stages of urban highway projects. Furthermore, the first three stages can be completed before the ground survey team even begins its work (MacLeod, 1966).

Traffic studies are undertaken to provide comprehensive traffic information for use in connection with transportation planning and the determination of general traffic conditions over large areas. Aerial photography has been used to pinpoint areas of congestion and to provide information on traffic flow in these areas. Flying at altitudes under 5,000 feet, fixed-wing and hover craft have provided data on the speed, concentration, and flow of traffic on a lane-by-lane basis as well as on the adequacy of traffic light cycles. On the George Washington Bridge and others, the Port of New York Authority has utilized aerial photography to smooth out traffic flow on the approach and exit ramps (Dickens, 1964).

More specialized studies regarding traffic flow have sought to determine the alternative routes frequently used by commuters and truckers seeking to avoid city traffic congestion. Often these routes are along side streets never designed for heavy use, thereby creating a safety hazard.

Assessment of traffic flow is also important in the location of new municipal buildings (Branch, 1971). Fire departments, for example, must not enter onto streets choked with traffic, but onto streets relatively free and clear. Highway departments cannot have heavy trucks constantly passing through the center of town or past schools or playgrounds. Aerial photography can be a useful tool in each of these instances.

For many years, American cities have been plagued with parking problems, as each morning thousands of autos descend on the central business district.For planners assessing the availability of parking, aerial photography can be an indispensable tool (Quinn, 1952). Photography can reveal where the heaviest concentrations of automobiles are, and where additional parking areas may be needed. Where parking is not sufficient, photography can reveal where the excess autos are parking--along what streets, in what empty lots, or even in what private yards or ways. Aerial photography can also be used to determine where such parking represents a hazard.

Finally, for cities which have hundreds of miles of streets and highways to maintain, it may be possible to utilize aerial photography for highway maintenance (Pryor, 1954). In other words, where are the heavily used highways whose pavement is cracking or where potholes are appearing? Are these areas that simply are not receiving proper maintenance? And in winter, what is the quality of snow removal from city streets? Are there areas where snow is not being removed properly and which, as a result, are creating traffic bottlenecks and fire hazards? Admittedly, more research is necessary in this area.

Special Engineering Projects

For many years, aerial photography has been utilized for a variety of engineering projects. For example, aerial photos have been successfully used in the development of water distribution systems since they can provide most of the necessary data--the number of homes to be served, the distance between homes, vacant land, and the types of land usage (residential, commercial, or industrial). In a similar manner it has been demonstrated that aerial photography can be an important aid in the planning of sewage collection systems and treatment plants. In addition to providing information on the number of homes and types of land use, aerial photographs can also provide information on gradient, an important factor in sewage collection systems. Finally, it is perhaps the most practical and economical method for designing the layout of pipelines, pumping stations, and force mains (Warnick, 1954).

Photogrammetric surveys are almost always conducted for the laying of long-distance pipelines and high-voltage transmission lines. They have also been used in the construction of microwave transmission towers which require a line-of-sight alignment. Tower heights, too, have been determined from the photos. Finally, they have been utilized to determine the best approach zones for airports in areas where the topography is particularly uneven.

The list of engineering applications is literally endless, and no attempt has been made here to name them all.

Municipal Inspection

Plagued by insufficient funds and manpower, many municipal agencies are unable to constantly inspect the activities for which they are responsible. There appear to be a number of areas where remote sensing would be useful, although as yet it is not being utilized to any significant degree. Nevertheless, brief mention should be made of some possible applications.*

* This information can be found in a more complete form in Branch (1971).

Zoning boards are constantly faced with having to make decisions on proposed zoning changes. Particularly where there is a shortage of manpower, aerial photographs can be effectively utilized in the decision-making process. The zoning board needs information on surrounding land use, structures, and circulation patterns. They must decide what will be the relationship of the proposed zoning change to the neighborhood and to the community as a whole. The only practical way of providing such information is through the use of aerial photographs.

Aerial photography can also be a valuable tool in the evaluations of and action upon subdivisions. Subdivisions must have an orderly arrangement of structures, proper transportation facilities, and sufficient open space. Furthermore, the spatial arrangement of the subdivision must be consistent with the local terrain, soils, and drainage. Finally, the subdivision must fit well within the overall community in terms of land use, traffic patterns, and public facilities. There is perhaps no better way to evaluate these factors than with aerial photography.

In rapidly growing urban and suburban communities, it is often extremely difficult for taxing authorities to keep their information on personal property up-to-date. Aerial photographs can quickly reveal the presence of new buildings; swimming pools, landscaping, and paving--each of which adds to the value of property (Rex, 1963).

An increasing area of concern, for which new agencies have been created in many cities, is the quality of the urban environment. Specifically, the concern is for the quality of the atmosphere and water bodies, with a somewhat secondary interest in such things as the health of shade trees. While the use of remote sensors to monitor the quality of the urban environment is still in the research stage, a few municipal agencies have already begun to utilize remote sensors for this purpose.

In the area of atmospheric monitoring, two techniques have been developed for data acquisition and analysis. In the first, aerial photographs were taken of a polluted air mass using color film with a polarizing filter. Then the polluted air mass was mapped as an overlay to a USGS topographic map; information included the horizontal extent of the air mass, as well as the elevation of the smoke above sea level. Quantitative measurements of extent and elevation were derived using a microdensitometer, which scanned the photo through the image of the polluted air layer and the neighboring ground (Veress, 1970).

The second technique entailed using a correlation spectrometer to determine the amount of nitrogen oxides and sulphur oxides present in the atmosphere. The technique makes use of characteristic absorption spectra exhibited by virtually all gases. Nitrogen oxides and sulphur oxides, which absorb in the ultraviolet and visible spectra, can be sensed remotely using natural daylight as the source of illumination. The feasibility of placing a correlation spectrometer on a spacecraft is presently being studied (Barringer et al., 1968).

In the area of water quality, several sensors seem capable of providing necessary data. Color and false color films can frequently indicate the location and extent of effluents discharged into a water body. Furthermore, where the effluent is responsible for excessive algae growth, detection is made relatively easy through the use of color infrared film. The latter can also be used to detect the presence of large quantities of sediment, which may have been washed into a stream or other water body from surrounding unprotected landscape (Strandberg, 1969).

Increasingly, thermal pollution has become a major problem for urban and rural areas. Thermal infrared imaging systems have proven to be particularly useful in detecting the sources, as well as areal extent, of warm-water discharges.

It is not anticipated that remote sensors will completely replace present ground surveillance systems for monitoring the quality of our nation's rivers and streams. However, since present ground surveillance systems can monitor less than 25 percent of our water sources, it would appear that remote sensing could augment ground methods, thereby saving time and money. Indeed, both the United States Coast Guard and the Environmental Protection Agency have major capability development programs underway in this area.

The ability of color infrared film to indicate disease in trees has been recognized for several years. Recently, however, cities have begun to use color infrared film in an attempt to monitor the health of shade trees. Denver has effectively used color infrared photography in a program to defend its shade trees from an attack of Dutch elm disease. The elms, which number over 200,000, represent about 60 percent of the city's shade trees. When the disease struck in 1969, color infrared photography was used to detect the dead and dying trees. The rapid removal of stricken trees has had the effect of slowing down the spread of the disease (Lindgren, 1971a). Other cities have begun to monitor the impact of smog and salt upon the health of their trees with remote sensing techniques.

For many types of inspection, then, remote sensing can be a valuable too. While seldom eliminating the need for ground surveys, it can save time, manpower, and money by providing direction for inspectors in the field.

INDIRECTLY OBSERVABLE DATA

Dwelling-Unit and Population Estimation

A necessary element of any urban information system would have to be a method for acquiring demographic data. At present, such data are obtained primarily by a federal census which takes place every ten years. Unfortunately the census data become out-of-date after several years and are, therefore, of limited value for planning and development purposes. While there is growing support within Congress and elsewhere to require a federal census every five years, there is a need, nevertheless, for a technique capable of providing demographic data quickly and inexpensively. Research suggests remote sensors may be capable of providing many of the necessary data.

The basic technique for estimating population from aerial photography entails estimating the number of dwelling units within a specified area and multiplying that figure by the average family size of the population within that area. Perhaps the first attempt to estimate dwelling units in an urban area was Green's study of Birmingham, Alabama (Green, 1956). Using 1:7,500-scale black-and-white photography, Green examined 17 residential subareas of Birmingham, recording several categories of housing types. His housing categories included single-family, double-family, multifamily (3 to 5), multifamily (6 to 8), and multifamily (9 to 11). Identification of housing types was based on criteria such as form and structure of roof; yards and courts; driveways and entranceways; and size, shape, and height of structures. Three major errors were revealed by this study. First, dwelling units per block were underestimated by 7 percent; second, single-unit detached structures were overestimated by 8 percent; and third, the amount of error increased in areas having a higher prevalence of multiunit structures.

Similar results were found in a study of Chicago (Binsell, 1967). Dwelling units were underestimated by 15.7 percent, single detached dwellings were overestimated by 4.3 percent, and the degree of error was found to increase with the prevalence of multiunit residential structures.

In a more recent study of Boston (Lindgren, 1971b), it was found that dwelling-unit estimates could be made from aerial photographs of a much smaller scale than had been employed in the past. Using 1:20,000-scale color infrared transparencies, dwelling-unit estimates were shown to be statistically significant at the 99 percent confidence level. A further conclusion to the study was that color infrared photography is an effective medium for dwelling-unit estimation because of its haze penetration capability and the contrast it provides between cultural and natural features.

The application of aerial photography to dwelling-unit and population estimation would appear to have particular utility to developing countries where rates of urban and population growth are unusually great. Demographic data in such countries are frequently inadequate for planning purposes, since national censuses have been few and the results obtained often inaccurate. Aerial photographic techniques could be extremely useful in this situation.

Housing-Quality Studies*

Within the United States there are numerous agencies and individuals responsible for gathering and utilizing data on housing quality. The U.S. Bureau of the Census conducts a decennial Census of Housing, and the American Public Health Association (APHA) acquires housing data on a continuous basis as do scores of state and local housing authorities. Present methods of acquiring housing-quality data, however, are extremely time-consuming; and, as a result, the data themselves rapidly become outdated. While few housing agencies have attempted to utilize aerial photo-interpretation techniques for housing-quality data acquisition, the results of research in this area have been encouraging.

As one means of evaluating the capability of aerial photography for providing housing quality data, Wellar (1968) compared the information extracted from multiband aerial photographs directly with the information contained on the APHA appraisal forms. For the most part, data derived from the aerial photography correlated well with ground-truth data obtained from the APHA appraisal forms. A variety of features related to housing-quality analysis were identified on the aerial photography, including several not covered by APHA. Identifiable features included (1) building frontages, (2) open or vacant land, (3) unpaved

---

* For additional information, see Chapter 10 by Horton.

versus paved parking lots, (4) amount of on-street parking, (5) proportions of multifamily and single-family dwellings in an area, (6) architectural style, (7) landscaping, (8) condition of lawns,(9) presence of litter, and (10) lack of curbing along parkways. In the determination of housing quality, the surrounding landscape was found to be an important criterion; aerial photographs are useful because they show dwellings in relation to surrounding features.

These same techniques have been employed to acquire socioeconomic data on the urban poor. Large-scale photography (1:10,000) was found capable of revealing a number of features associated with poverty, including structural deterioration; debris; clutter; and the lack of vegetation, walks, and paved streets. A strong correlation was found between urban poverty and residential areas located adjacent to the CBD, industry, and major transportation arteries. On the basis of other studies, such areas were found to correlate with low income, unemployment, low education achievement, family crowding, crime, low health status, and lack of community facilities (Mumbower and Donoghe, 1967).

Another important indicator of poverty was brought out in a study of Lexington, Kentucky, which attempted to map urban poverty areas from 1:6,000-scale black-and-white photography. Although initially no one particular environmental variable was given greater weight than any other, it became evident that housing density was the most significant criterion for the identification of substandard housing on the photographs. And when the maps of urban poverty areas derived from the aerial photographs were compared with those compiled by the City-County Planning Commission, they were found to be about 80 percent accurate (Metivier and McCoy, 1971).

Far more work is necessary not only in testing the capability of different sensors to provide housing-quality data, but also on the housing-quality classification schemes used by various agencies. Nevertheless, it is not anticipated that remote sensing techniques will ever by capable of replacing ground surveys. On the contrary, remote sensing may one day supplement traditional techniques and surveys by (1) providing certain types of data better revealed by aerial photographic means; (2) by providing data at intercensal periods; and, (3) perhaps most importantly, by portraying the city as a single system and the area under study as an integral part of that system.

NONPHOTOGRAPHIC SENSORS

Radar

The all-weather capability of radar has stimulated interest in its possible applications for urban analysis. Although research is still at a preliminary stage, three types of urban-related projects have been identified for which radar can be an aid: (1) the collection of data when postponement of overflight owing to bad weather would be intolerable, (2) analysis of gross land-use patterns for large cities, and (3) surveys of large regions to determine location and areal extent of small urban centers (Moore, 1968).

Of the three types of projects listed above, research has primarily been concerned with land use and the identification of small urban centers. For land-use studies, K-band radar has demonstrated a capacity to provide data on linear transport features as well as on gross patterns of industrial, residential, and vacant-land uses. However, attempts to identify commercial land uses have not been successful (Moore, 1968).

In another attempt to evaluate K-band imagery, a map of gross land use was prepared for the city of Lawrence, Kansas. Well-defined areas, such as the CBD and major industrial districts, were accurately delimited, but light industrial, commercial, and areas of mixed land uses were almost impossible to separate (Peterson, 1969).

As a tool for identifying built-up (urban) areas, radar displays somewhat greater utility. In one test of radar imagery, it was found that experienced photo interpreters could identify all cities of over 7,000 inhabitants, 80 percent of settlements over 800 in population, and 40 percent of settlements between 150 and 800 population (Simpson, 1969). The value of this capability appears to be in relationship between areal size and population. In other words, an increasing number of people generally requires an expansion in the area providing their homes (Sabol, 1966). If such a relationship can be established, rapid population estimates could be made over large areas. This would have great utility to many countries of the developing world.

Thermal Infrared (IR)

Research into potential applications of thermal IR sensor systems for urban data acquisition is presently at a preliminary stage. In part this may be a result of the imagery itself, which is generally of inferior quality for such a purpose. Nevertheless, empirical analyses have revealed the capability of thermal IR to provide urban data in at least two areas--land use and transportation.

The information provided by thermal IR on land use is very gross. For example, while a city's CBD is usually quite distinguishable on thermal IR imagery, it cannot always be clearly differentiated from surrounding multistoried apartment buildings. Major outlying shopping centers are distinguishable, but areas of mixed commercial-industrial-residential land use are not. Although individual houses are usually visible, there is in essence little land-use data provided by thermal IR that cannot be obtained more easily from conventional aerial photography (Wellar, 1968).

The same is basically true of thermal IR's capacity to provide transportation data. Roads, railroads, and water courses can be identified, although not directly. Their location can be interpolated from buildings and trees which tend to line such features. Considerable mention has been made of thermal IR's capability of providing data on traffic flow, particularly at night, but little research has been conducted to substantiate this hypothesis.

As yet the utility of thermal IR to provide urban data has simply not been fully tested. However, in a study evaluating the relative utility of radar, thermal IR, and conventional photography for discriminating built-up from non-built-up areas, it was concluded that only under special operating conditions relating to weather, cost, and the like, would one select radar or thermal IR in preference to conventional aerial photography (Simpson, 1970).

CONCLUSION

On the basis of research conducted thus far, it would appear that remote sensing should play an important role in any urban information system. Plagued with shortages in money and manpower, cities should find in remote sensing a valuable tool for data acquisition. Remote sensing can take the place of present data collection procedures, which may be inefficient, or, as is more likely to be the case, provide an important supplement to these methods. However, with but few exceptions, municipal agencies do not appear to be utilizing aerial photographic techniques to any great extent. Researchers in the field of remote sensing, therefore, must work more closely with municipal officials, not only to keep the officials abreast of their research but also to make the results of their research more applicable to municipal problems.

REFERENCES

Anschutz, G., and A. H. Stallard, 1967, "An Overview of Site Evaluation," *Photogrammetric Engineering*, 33:1381-1396.

Barringer, A. R., B. C. Newbury, and A. J. Moffat, 1968, "Surveillance of Air Pollution from Airborne and Space Platforms," *Proceedings of the Fifth Symposium on Remote Sensing of Environment*, University of Michigan, Ann Arbor, pp. 123-155.

Binsell, Ronald, 1967, *Dwelling Unit Estimation from Aerial Photography*, Northwestern University, Remote Sensing Laboratory, Department of Geography, Evanston, Ill.

Branch, Melville C., 1971, *City Palnning and Aerial Information*, Harvard City Planning Studies 17, Harvard University Press, Cambridge, Mass.

Chaves, J. R., and R. L. Schuster, 1968, "Color Photos for Highway Engineering," *Photogrammetric Engineering*, 34:375-379.

Collins, W. G., and A. H. A. El-Beik, 1971, "Population Census with the Air of Aerial Photographs: An Experiment in the City of Leeds," *Photogrammetric Record*, 7:16-26.

Dickens, J. H., 1964, "Sky Count--New System Developed for Traffic Data Acquisition," *Traffic Engineering*, 35:12-16.

Duerker, Kenneth J., 1970, *Estimating Population and Dwelling Units from Imagery*, Position Paper 1, Intra-Urban Studies, University of Iowa, Remote Sensing Project, Institute of Urban and Regional Research, Iowa City.

Estes, John E., 1966, "Some Applications of Aerial Infrared Imagery," *Annals*, Association of American Geographers, 56:673-682.

Eyre, L. Alan, Adolphus Blossom, and Monica Amiel, 1970, "Census Analysis and Population Studies," *Photogrammetric Engineering*, 36:460-466.

Green, Norman E., 1955, "Aerial Photography in the Analysis of Urban Structure, Ecological and Social," Unpublished doctoral dissertation, University of North Carolina, Chapel Hill.

Green, Norman E., 1956, "Aerial Photographic Analysis of Residential Neighborhoods: An Evaluation of Data Accuracy," *Social Forces*, 35:142-147.

Hadfield, Samuel A., 1963, *Evaluation of Land Use and Dwelling Unit Data Derived from Aerial Photography*, Urban Research Section, Chicago Area Transportation Study, Chicago.

Holz, R. V., D. L. Huff, and R. C. Mayfield, 1969, "Urban Spatial Structure Based on Remote Sensing Imagery," *Proceedings of the Sixth International Symposium on Remote Sensing of Environment*, University of Michigan, Ann Arbor, pp. 819-830.

Horton, Frank E., and Duane F. Marble, 1969, "Housing Quality on Urban Areas: Data Acquisition and Classification Through the Analysis of Remote Sensor Imagery," *Second Annual Earth Resources Program, Status Review*, vol. 1: *Geology and Geography*, NASA/MSC, Houston, Tex., pp. 15-1 - 15-13.

Howard, William A., and James B. Kracht, 1971, *An Assessment of the Usefulness of Small-Scale Photographic Imagery for Acquiring Land Use Information Necessary to the Urban Planning Function*, Publications in Geography, Technical Paper 71-2, University of Denver, Department of Geography, Denver.

Jeter, Fred, 1966, "The Annotated Photomap for Highway Planning in Congested Suburban Areas," *Highway Research Record*, No. 142, pp. 13-15, Highway Research Board, Washington, D.C.

Lindgren, David T., 1971a, *CIR: A Tool for Environmental Analysis*, Research Report, Project on Remote Sensing, Dartmouth College, Hanover, N.H.

Lindgren, David T., 1971b, "Dwelling Unit Estimation with Color-IR Photos," *Photogrammetric Engineering*, 37:373-377.

MacLeod, Malcolm H., 1966, "The Photogrammetric Method as a Means of Providing Highway Engineers with an Integrated and Complete System of Surveying," *Highway Research Record*, No. 142, pp. 28-38, Highway Research Board, Washington, D.C.

Manji, Ashraf S., 1968, *Uses of Conventional Aerial Photography in Urban Areas: Review and Bibliography*, Research Report 41, Northwestern University, Department of Geography, Evanston, Ill.

Metivier, Ernest D., and Roger M. McCoy, 1971, "Mapping Urban Poverty Housing from Aerial Photographs," *Proceedings of the Seventh Symposium on Remote Sensing of Environment*, University of Michigan, Ann Arbor, pp. 1563-1569.

Moore, Eric G., 1968, *Side-Looking Radar in Urban Research: A Case Study*, Research Report 40, Northwestern University, Department of Geography, Evanston, Ill.

Mumbower, L. E., and J. Donoghue, 1967, "Urban Poverty Study," *Photogrammetric Engineering*, 33:610-618.

Peterson, Florence, 1969, "An Urban Land Use Study of Lawrence, Kansas, Using K-Band Radar," in *The Utility of Radar and Other Sensors in Thematic Land Use Mapping from Spacecraft*, Interagency Report NASA-140, U.S. Geological Survey, Washington, D.C.

Pryor, W. T., 1954, "Highway Engineering Applications of Photogrammetry," *Photogrammetric Engineering*, 20:523-531.

Quinn, A. O., 1952, "Photogrammetry Aids Highway Engineers," *Photogrammetric Engineering*, 18:787-790.

Rex, R. L., 1963, *Evaluation and Conclusion of Assessing and Improvement Control by Aerial Assessment and Interpretation Methods*, Sidwell Studio, Inc., Chicago.

Rib, H. T., 1966, "Utilization of Photo Interpretation in the Highway Fields," *Highway Research Record*, No. 109, pp. 18-27, Highway Research Board, Washington, D.C.

Sabol, Joseph, 1966, "The Relationship between Population and Radar Derived Area of Urban Places," in *The Utility of Radar and Other Remote Sensors in Thematic Land Use Mapping from Spacecraft*, pp. 46-74, Interagency Report NASA-140, U.S. Geological Survey, Washington, D.C.

Simpson, Robert B., 1969, *Geographic Evaluation of Radar Imagery of New England*, Dartmouth College, Department of Geography, Hanover, N.H.

Simpson, Robert B., 1970, "Line-Scan vs. Optical Sensors for Discrimination of Built-Up Areas," Paper 2 in *Recognition of Settlement Patterns Against a Complex Background*, Research Report, Dartmouth College, Project in Remote Sensing, Hanover, N.H.

Simpson, Robert B., 1972, "Urban-Field Land Use of Southern New England: A First Look," paper presented at NASA ERTS Seminar, Goddard Space Center, Greenbelt, Md., October 3.

Simpson, Robert B., Robert S. Yuill, and David T. Lindgren, 1970, *Production of a High Altitude Land Use Map and Data Base for Boston*, Research Report, Dartmouth College, Department of Geography, Hanover, N.H.

Strandberg, Carl H., 1969, "Color Aerial Photography for Water Supply and Pollution Control Reconnaissance," *Proceedings First International Remote Sensing Institute Symposium*, vol. II, University of Michigan, Ann Arbor, pp. 123-132.

Veress, S.A., 1970, "Air Pollution Research," *Photogrammetric Engineering*, 36: 840-848.

Warnick, D. A., 1954, "The Application of Photogrammetry to Small Engineering Projects," *Photogrammetric Engineering*, 20:540-548.

Wellar, B.S., 1968, "Utilization of Multiband Aerial Photographs in Urban Housing Quality Studies," *Proceedings of the Fifth Symposium on Remote Sensing of Environment*, University of Michigan, Ann Arbor, pp. 913-926.

Wray, James R., 1972, "The Census Cities Project: A Status Report for 1971," paper presented at Fourth Annual Earth Resources Program Review, NASA/MSC, Houston, Tex., January 17-21.

Remote Sensing Techniques and Urban Data Acquisition: Selected Examples

Frank E. Horton
University of Iowa

Considerable research in the field of remote sensing has been directed toward the urban environment. The preceding chapter by Lindgren emphasized specific applications of remote sensing data within an urban context. The present chapter considers the relationship between remote sensing data and the requirements of urban information systems. Horton presents a theoretical and research oriented discussion related to urban data needs, change detection systems, housing quality, population estimation, and land use. The two chapters, in concert, reflect the spectrum of remote sensing research in the field of urban area analysis.

Current research related to the application of remote sensing techniques to problems of data acquisition useful for urban and regional planning, management, and research clearly indicates that a potentially powerful data acquisition system is feasible. One of the most perplexing problems facing urban planners, managers, and analysts is the dearth of pertinent, timely, and reliable information. It has been stated that "data performs a vital, two-fold task: (1) it provides a basis for testing research hypotheses 'about processes' and (2) it provides a basis for current decision-making as well as a means of monitoring the outcome of past decisions" (Horton and Marble, 1969). The collection of data concerning a variety of urban phenomena is a continuing and costly problem.

Recently there has been in this country an increasing concern with the development of information systems, data handling procedures, and data processing technology. It may be stated that our ability to handle data is much greater than our ability to collect reasonably accurate data for input to operating urban information systems. In this context, remote sensing offers a significant opportunity to help improve the effectiveness of urban management, to help guide urban growth and development, and to help maintain and improve the quality of metropolitan environments (Marble and Horton, 1969).

It should be pointed out that, of all the remote sensing technology available to us, remote sensing applications in urban environments have been primarily restricted to photographic sensors. This is not to say that others may not be more useful or that new remote sensing technologies not yet applied may not provide greater utility to urban analysts; rather this statement rests upon the fact that we have been unable, at least to date, to mount a major research program in evaluating alternative remote sensing technology applications in an urban context. In addition, and just as important, is the fact that no large-scale operational demonstration programs of the utility of remote sensing in urban data acquisition have been completed to date.

While the above statements may seem somewhat negative, they should not deter us from research goals and the development of a continuing research program; nor should they be construed to mean that positive developments in this area have not occurred. Utilizing primarily photographic sensors, and for the most part fairly primitive straightforward photo-interpretation techniques, we have learned a great deal about the amount of data which can be extracted and converted into useful information for decision makers and analysts in metropolitan areas.

In studies supported by the Geographic Applications Program, United States Geological Survey, and NASA, photographic sensors, and to a limited extent imaging radars, have been evaluated in terms of their ability to provide information about cities. These include the application of remote sensors to the acquisition of data concerning housing and population characteristics, urban travel, identification of urban land use and activities, general evaluation of urban change detection systems, utility of space photography in urban data acquisition, the identification of intraurban commercial centers and their functions, identification of the economic position of single cities with respect to all other cities within a region or nation, and, with respect to the latter, the use of that knowledge in monitoring regional economic growth.* In addition, research activities are being carried out which relate to urban geographic information systems, and the interface between imagery and operational urban information files.

SYSTEMS FOR URBAN CHANGE DETECTION**

The topic of urban change may be partitioned into changes in the physical, social, and economic subsystems of the city. Remote sensing provides a means of discerning physical changes in the distribution of activities, which in turn are related to social and economic changes within the system. Clearly an important problem area for research is the functional relationships between land use and other elements of the urban environment. In any event, imagery from remote sensors is a partial input to an overall urban change detection system. Other data, such as from surveys or administrative record keeping systems, are also important inputs to urban change detection systems. The initial research task involves evaluating all data sources related to change, identifying those indicators which describe change in a way that it is useful to those who need the information, and constructing systems which monitor those variables and report data in final form to the users.

---

* Many of these topics are discussed in detail in Marble and Horton, 1971, and in Horton, 1972.

** Material for this section is based on previous papers (Dueker and Horton, 1971b; 1971c).

Specific users have different requirements. Depending on the class of user, whether he be local, state, or federal, the urban change detection system may or may not have to be linked to local or metropolitan record-keeping functions. Thus total system design recommendations are quite different, depending upon the use and scope of the urban change detection system. If the use is primarily for intraurban area surveillance, it is imperative that the system be tied into an administrative record-keeping function. If the purpose is for comparative analysis between areas, then imagery alone may provide the necessary information. For example, urban and regional planners have a long-standing, and for the most part unmet, need for small-area data on population, employment, and other activity data. The principal need of the urban planner and manager is current information on facilities and service demand and on the facilities and services which supply those needs within small areas. Although traffic zones and census tracts have proved useful in the past, experience has proved that basic land-use data are often aggregated in several different ways (e.g., school districts, police districts); therefore, a smaller observational entity, say a city block or block face, provides the most desirable flexibility.

Population and employment are probably the most needed small-area data, yet these data are least visible from imagery. It is extremely important that better accounting methods for population and employment changes be devised. This means that an elaborate record-keeping system or a means of estimating population and employment by measuring variables that are visible, such as housing units and activity intensity, must be developed. However, care must be exercised as relationships change. For example, Des Moines, Iowa, increased its housing stock by 150 units but lost 10,555 persons in the period between 1960 and 1970. Table 10-1 is a preliminary estimate of user requirements for land-use data at various levels--local, state, and national. Table 10-1 also classifies users in the broad functional categories and attempts to determine their need for land-use data in terms of areal units and classification of land.

Urban change detection, as discussed here, focuses on the measurement of changes in the urban environment and their relationships to increased demand for urban services. This is a legitimate focus in light of the primary objectives of user groups.

The purpose of this section is to evaluate the requirements for surveillance or monitoring of urban subsystems and relate those requirements to urban information system efforts which are underway or being planned in many metropolitan areas. Thus, the emphasis is upon the surveillance component of urban information systems useful to planners, operational decision makers, and researchers concerned with urban and regional analysis.

Monitoring Urban Systems

Monitoring urban change provides a basis for the description and maintenance of the current status of urban activities. The monitoring function can take place in a variety of time cycles, i.e., annually, semiannually, monthly, daily, or continuously. Continuous monitoring would, of course, provide the greatest capability for understanding the important cyclical nature of the urban processes under examination. In general, to maintain the current status of urban activities ultimately means the recording and tabulating of urban transactions as they occur, always keeping current account of those phenomena of importance to urban

Table 10-1

User Requirements for Land Use Data
User Type versus Area Size and Classification

USER TYPE	FUNCTIONAL TYPE	AREAL UNIT	L.U. CLASSIFICATION*
NATIONAL			
	Community Development	Cities over 2,500 pop. Counties	one-digit
	Economic Development	Cities over 2,500 pop. Counties	one-digit
	Human Resources	Cities over 2,500 pop. Counties	one-digit
	Natural Resources	Counties	one-digit urban two-digit nonurban
STATE			
	Community Development	Townships	two-digit urban one-digit nonurban
	Economic Development	Cities over 100 pop.	two-digit
	Human Resources	Census tracts for cities over 25,000 pop.	two-digit urban one-digit nonurban
	Natural Resources	40-acre parcels (1/16 section)	one-digit urban two-digit nonurban
LOCAL			
	Community Development	City block	four-digit urban two-digit rural
	Economic Development	40-acre parcel (1/16 section)	four-digit
	Human Resources	City block	four-digit residential two-digit other
	Natural Resources	40-acre parcel (1/16 section)	two-digit urban four-digit nonresidential

* One-digit classification divides land use into general categories, such as residential, industrial, commercial, agriculture, etc.; two-digit classification of land use breaks each general category into subdivisions such as single-family residence, two-family structures, multifamily structures, etc.; four-digit classification provides an extremely detailed breakdown such as distinguishing among retail uses.

analysts and decision makers in cities. Monitoring urban systems by keeping current accounts of urban activities requires a broader administrative and functional framework, labeled an urban information system.

Of prime importance in specifying the nature of the operating functions of an information system is the identification and clear specification of information needed by users. In this instance, the task to be accomplished is to develop a system for urban change detection, i.e., maintaining current social, economic, and physical accounts by areal units within metropolitan regions.

Figure 10-1 illustrates, in terms of a generalized flow chart, an information system which is capable of providing information about urban change. The elements included in Figure 10-1 should allow for adequate information flow to a broad spectrum of planning processes. Figure 10-1 identifies a hardware-software system consisting of software, an input system, data files, and an output system. It also attempts to illustrate the user environment which consists of a user system, data sources, and data users. The primary basis of the input system is geocoding, which includes all forms of geographic identification of data, entity transformation, image processing, and, of course, conversion to machine-readable form. Similarly, the software system is broken down into elements of retrieval, utility, and statistical subsystems. The data file system separates data into disaggregate data, areal-units summaries, and time-cycle summaries. The output system identified forms of output such as a report generator, graphic display subsystems, mapping, and derivative machine records. Finally, potential data sources and users are identified.

Four major data sources can provide inputs to operating urban information systems. These data sources consist of primary data from operating agencies, secondary data collected and usually aggregated by others, survey data placed directly into the system, and graphic data and other data items potentially available from remote sensors.

Imagery data are of two forms: (1) maps or other forms of graphics and (2) imagery produced by remote sensing techniques. Phenomena and their attributes which can be observed directly or indirectly from imagery are numerous (see Chapter 9). The potential identification of a myriad of urban phenomena could easily tax our ability to store such information. Translating direct observation of phenomena from imagery into machine-readable form currently requires tedious coding and the definition of taxonomies necessary to define particular phenomena as well as attributes of each phenomenon. Further coding is required in order to identify locational attributes of the data items.

In many instances, imagery will provide appropriate data for describing physical aspects of the urban system. However, in many instances, data concerning a variety of socioeconomic processes are also needed. While it has been demonstrated that evaluation of variables describing the physical aspects of urban systems can provide clues about socioeconomic aspects of the system, current technology is relatively meager. Extensive financial inputs for further research into the acquisition of information related to socioeconomic processes should be given top priority.

Another data source of significance is the use of surveys, either complete inventories or sample surveys. A complete inventory, such as the United States Census of Housing and Population or urban land-use inventories, provides an

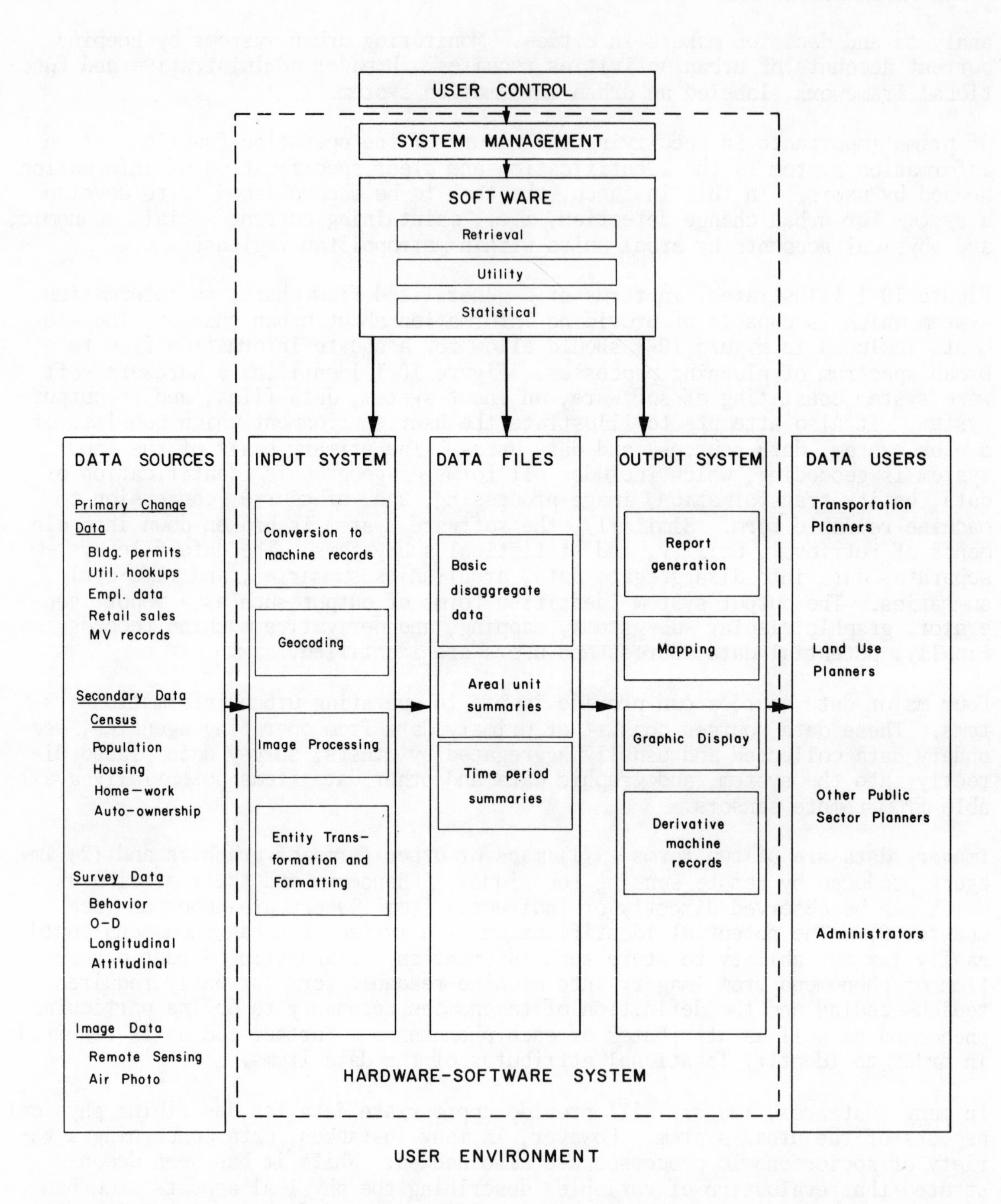

Figure 10-1. Urban Planning Information System Elements with an Emphasis on Urban Change Detection.

exhaustive data set which requires considerable monetary resources to manipulate, update, and utilize effectively. On the other hand, application of scientific sampling methodologies normally can provide reasonably accurate data about many of the phenomena of interest to urban analysts and planners. Sample surveys are particularly useful in identifying attitudes and preferences of urban inhabitants and in specifying their revealed behaviors. Attitudinal surveys attempt to anticipate people's behavior, whereas behaviorial surveys, such as the Origin-Destination Study, record the actual behavior of the respondent. Data from these types of surveys are, or should be, essential inputs into operating urban information systems, although further research could well indicate that such data might also be provided efficiently through remote sensing.

The administrative record-keeping functions of local public agencies provide a wealth of data for use in a broader planning and management context. For example, building-permit applications are used to ensure that new construction is inspected and meets the building code provisions. Similarly, building-permit applications can be used to determine areas of growth within the community and the intensity of that growth. Although it seems intuitively obvious that administrative record-keeping functions can provide useful data to planners and managers within the urban sector, these data have not been utilized in the main because of difficulty in translating administrative forms into machine-readable information and in relating street addresses to analysis areas. A major difficulty has been a lack of coordination and cooperation among various local and state agencies.

System Elements

There are three important dimensions or elements associated with urban information systems. The first is a methodology for specifying a spatial location, the second deals with temporal questions (i.e., the frequency of observation), and the third is related to the kind of phenomena being observed.

Methods of spatial location, often termed geocoding, refer to means of specifying location in a machine-readable form. Essentially there are three alternative methods for identifying location: (1) direct digitizing; (2) area unit codes; and (3) unique addresses, such as street addresses, which then must be translated to geographic coordinates or areal unit codes. Direct digitizing of observations to x and y coordinates is the usual method chosen when the data source consists of imagery, maps, or other graphics. Assignment of areal unit codes to observations is a normal procedure when conducting surveys. Depending on the type of survey and the sample size, areal units vary from individual blocks to aggregations of census tracts. Finally, a procedure which is gaining greater acceptance is the machine translation of street addresses to either geographic coordinates or to areal unit codes. The street address translation process requires a geographic base file, i.e., a directory of address ranges assigned to give an areal unit for comparison with the input address requiring translation. The street address translation process obviously allows greater utilization of administrative record-keeping files for use in urban planning and management.

An operational urban information system must have the capability to translate data from imagery, surveys, and administrative record-keeping functions and relate those data to a common geographic base. Thus, a system of small areal units based on geographic coordinates provides the most flexible means of collecting, storing, and relating separately collected data.

The frequency with which the data base is updated depends upon the use of the data and how frequently the specific phenomenon observed changes status. Determination of the appropriate frequency for acquiring new imagery, surveys, or evaluating data from record-keeping functions must be determined. Definitive decisions regarding daily, weekly, monthly, annual, or biannual updating of specific data elements is a necessity. Clearly, data items requiring constant updating and maintenance should not be obtained by reinventory methods. Rather, imagery analysis or continuous monitoring of administrative record-keeping should provide a basis for data updates. Surveys and inventories should be confined to those data which cannot be obtained by any other method.

The third information system element deals with the kind of phenomena to be measured. This element has continually plagued urban analysts, managers, and planners. While it is easy to point out that social, economic, and physical phenomena should be measured and integrated into information systems files, specific identification of needed data items and their attributes varies from place to place and from system to system. The need is for small-area data that describe the demand side for urban services and, similarly, data to describe the facilities that supply those services.

It should be apparent from the previous discussion that data sources and system elements must be integrated into an information system in order to achieve current data about social, economic, and physical variables by small areas for planning and management. This kind of integration requires that the objectives, for which the system is being designed, be explicitly stated because of the vast number of choices (with respect to data items) included and the frequency of their collection.

A System for Urban Change Detection

Given the previous element definition, a structure for an operating urban change detection system, which meets the research and planning needs for dealing with a broad range of urban subsystems, can now be formulated.

Figure 10-2 illustrates the initial development of an urban change detection system, its use, and the means by which updating the system invokes the detection of change. It is contemplated that initially the basic system would be updated annually, but that urban transactions be accumulated and reported separately for immediate needs. This is predicated on current technology and funding constraints and a judgment that annual updates are sufficient to discern changes in real-time in terms of planning needs, not sufficient in all cases as regards management needs, and probably insufficient for research activities.

Figure 10-2 clearly illustrates that urban change detection has two distinct components: (1) inventory data are compared at two points in time and (2) urban transactions that occur within a time period are aggregated. Remote sensing and other inventory methods provide a "picture" or status report at a point in time. When imagery or aggregations of transactions for two different time periods are compared, change can be described.

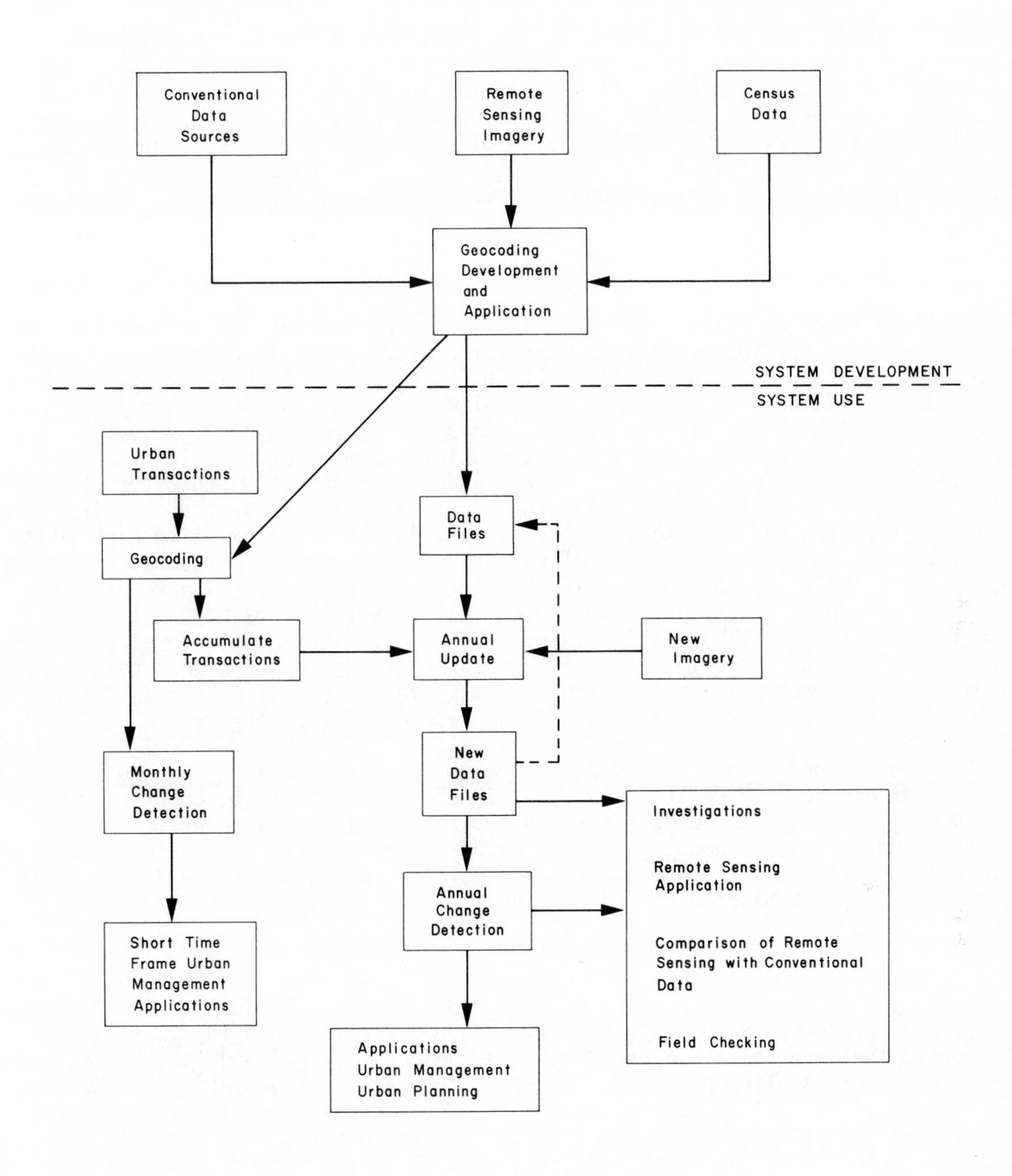

Figure 10-2. Flow Diagram of Operational Urban Change Detection System.

REMOTE SENSING DATA INPUTS IN AN URBAN CONTEXT

Given the above discussion concerning the requirements for functional urban change detection systems, it is now pertinent to turn to remote sensing inputs to urban information systems. It is becoming increasingly clear that the use of remote sensing, particularly that derived from aircraft platforms, is especially useful in providing status checks of phenomena which are important in defining the current status of urban activities. The following sections describe several specific applications of remote sensing to urban data collection.

Remote Sensing Applications to Housing Quality Definition*

Federal and local agencies have shown an increasing interest in methods for the rapid survey of housing conditions over large urban areas in order to (1) evaluate the magnitude of such problems within the city, (2) identify those neighborhoods most in need of immediate remedial action, and (3) determine those neighborhoods which qualify for federal funds for neighborhood improvement. At present,expensive ground surveys covering a large number of parcels, and involving many variables, are required. Recent investigations at Northwestern University attempted to evaluate the following hypotheses with respect to housing quality, surveys, and potential remote sensing inputs: (1) owing to high redundancy levels, an excessive number of variables are currently collected by public agencies in their attempt to identify housing quality areas; (2) a reduced set of these variables exists which are potentially observable by means of remote sensing techniques; (3) a viable classification algorithm can be developed utilizing the reduced variable set, which would quantitatively assign a particular areal unit of observation to a unique quality class; and (4) measures of the reduced variable set can be extracted from remote sensing imagery.

Analysis of Ground Data. Ground data were obtained from a survey conducted by the Los Angeles County Health Department in the spring of 1968, covering some 1,300 city blocks in three districts in the Los Angeles area (containing some of the country's worst housing). This data set constituted the basic ground-truth information for the Northwestern University participation in NASA's Earth Resources Aircraft Mission 73 and were used to explore the hypotheses noted above.

A 1 percent sample of parcels (478 parcels) was drawn from the Los Angeles housing data set (a parcel is a piece of land under single ownership). The 37 structural and environmental variables utilized are given in Table 10-2. It is unfortunate that many of these variables are subjectively defined and, hence, suffer from severe scaling problems. However, they are representative of the current state of the art in housing studies. A statistical technique called principal axes factor analysis was applied to the sample set. This analysis produced a factor structure which indicated that the basic factors produced were consistent with those found in existing public agency statements. However, this analysis also demonstrated that, for each basic housing element, the variables acting as indicators of that element tended to be highly correlated with other

* The major portion of this section has been taken from Marble and Horton, 1969. Additional information on this topic may be found in Chapter 9 by Lindgren.

TABLE 10-2

Environmental and Structural Variables
Utilized in the Los Angeles Study

1.	Land Use--Suitability for Residential Development	Environmental Variables Potentially Measurable Using Remote Sensors
2.	Condition of Street Lighting	
3.	Presence of On-Street Parking	
4.	Street Width	
5.	Street Maintenance	
6.	Street Grade	
7.	Condition of Parkways	
8.	Hazards from Traffic	
9.	Adequacy of Public Transportation	
10.	Number of Buildings/Lot	
11.	Number of Units/Lot	
12.	Condition of Fences	
13.	Adequacy of Lot Size	
14.	Access to Buildings	
15.	Condition of Sidewalks	
16.	Condition of Landscaping	
17.	Refuse	
18.	Parcel Use	
19.	Adverse Effects of Residences	
20.	Nuisances from Loading/Parking	
21.	Unclassified Nuisances from Industry, etc.	
22.	Overall Block Rating	Structural Variables Not Observable Using Remote Sensors
23.	Noise/Glare (Block)	
24.	Smoke	
25.	Condition of Accessory Buildings	
26.	Premise Rating	
27.	Noise, Fumes, and Odors (Parcel)	
28.	Construction Type	
29.	Age of Dwelling	
30.	Condition of Structure	
31.	Condition of Walls	
32.	Condition of Roofs	
33.	Condition of Foundation	
34.	Condition of Electrical Installations	
35.	Condition of Paint	
36.	Other Exterior Factors	
37.	Overall Parcel Rating	

variables within the element. This strongly suggests that a more critical evaluation is needed of the cost effectiveness of collecting data on large numbers of variables as practiced in existing housing quality studies.

Of particular interest was that, for the observations which made up the parcel sample, the structural variables emerged as a single set of variables which were uncorrelated with environmental variables. This led to the rejection, for this study area, of the notion of estimating overall housing quality (as currently defined by public agencies) at the parcel level based only upon remote sensor observation of environmental variables. It is felt, however, that such a finding may be unique to Los Angeles (or at least to cities of the Southwest), which are dominated by single-family structures with a high degree of variation in the level of maintenance of individual parcels. In other U.S. cities, particularly those of the East and Midwest, the set of relationships between structures and environment may be substantially modified in those poorer areas possessing a predominance of apartment buildings, town houses, and other kinds of multiunit structures.

Using the city block as the unit of study, a similar analysis was undertaken for observations on a 20 percent sample of blocks (268 units). The resulting factor structure was markedly different from that generated at the parcel level. Other research has indicated that simple correlations between variables tend to increase as the units of observation encompass larger and larger areas; in the several-variable case, this also results in a larger proportion of the differences being accounted for by a small number of factors and increasing correlation levels between previously uncorrelated variable sets. In particular, in the present case, the factor comprised of structural variables no longer represented an isolated variable set, but was associated with a number of environmental variables, primarily those which identified the level of upkeep of lots and the existence of land uses which are generally thought to be inappropriate for location near residential developments. This finding is extremely important, since it implies that overall housing quality may be estimated at the block level utilizing observations on environmental condition variables alone.

The results of the two analyses indicated not only that the clear factors defined at the individual parcel level had been lost at the block level, but also that the factors used to judge housing quality must be examined anew each time the observational units are made larger, such as the traffic zone or census tract. The results of this study led to a research concentration upon the assignment of blocks to housing quality classes, although remote sensor generation of environmental variables appeared most feasible.

An objective grouping of the sample blocks into five quality classes, ranging from high quality to extremely poor housing, was made based on similar profiles of factor scores derived from an analysis of observations on all 37 variables. Comparing this grouping with the subjective evaluations made by individuals working on the ground, it was found that the general trends of the two classification structures were similar, with the most deficient blocks being well identified on both; however, considerable differences existed in the drawing of boundaries between the higher-rated blocks. The objective grouping is more compact than that of the enumerators, suggesting that the latter did not utilize the full range of data recorded in making their subjective assignments. Further, it suggests that the ground enumerators tend to be somewhat conservative in assigning blocks to the highest or lowest categories.

The blocks were classified on the basis of scores generated by a factor analysis of the environmental variables. The results showed a strong agreement with those of the previous state, with 75.4 percent of the block assignments being the same in both groupings. The errors occurred in the assignment of a number of marginal blocks and do not constitute a major problem.

The final stage of the ground data analysis examined the feasibility of further reducing the set of 21 environmental variables in effecting the classification. Using a statistical method called stepwise multiple discriminant analysis, it was found that a high level of performance (82.2 percent correct assignment) could be attained using only seven environmental variables, namely measures relating to (1) on-street parking, (2) loading and parking hazards, (3) street width, (4) hazards from traffic, (5) refuse, (6) street grade, and (7) access to buildings. Table 10-3 displays the linear discriminant coefficient pertaining to each of the five quality classes.

Although it is not claimed that these results possess complete generality (in the sense that an analysis of all urban areas would result in the same variables being selected for use in classification), it is highly encouraging that the seven variables listed above, all presumably measurable using remote sensing techniques, can effect a classification of city blocks which is very similar to that obtained by using all 37 environmental and structural variables in combination. This, in itself, is an extremely important finding of the research which could lead to large financial savings in urban data acquisition.

Imagery Analysis. The imagery analysis consisted of an evaluation of black-and-white, color, and color infrared photography, obtained as part of NASA Aircraft Mission 73, with respect to the identification of the reduced variable set listed above. Color infrared photography was found to be the most useful in estimating the seven variables important in housing quality identification. (Photography was from an RC-8 camera flown at 3,000 feet.)

After some interpreter training, a subsample of 53 contiguous blocks in the Firestone area (south-central Los Angeles, California) was chosen for an evaluation experiment. Definition of the variables, and subsequent assignment using the multiple discriminant functions made up of the coefficients shown in Table 10-2 satisfactorily classified 50 percent of the blocks, when compared with the 37-variable classification, into the five housing groups. Because of the subjective nature of some of the variables, it was necessary to use three relatively inexperienced image interpreters and classify blocks on the basis of two out of three interpreters giving the same decision. Further investigation indicated that, within the area chosen, the differences between Groups 2 and 3 were not critical. Upon aggregating Groups 2 and 3, thus reducing the number of housing quality classes to four, the level of accuracy was increased to 69 percent. Thus, when remote sensor imagery was utilized to estimate the values of the seven variables, it was possible to correctly classify 69 percent of the blocks into four classes, as compared with the four-way classification based upon use of all 37 variables. Once again, this percentage is based on a two-out-of-three-interpreter agreement, with individual interpreters scoring higher and higher.

Further evaluation of the seven variables utilized suggested that a further reduction in their number would remove some which suffered from severe interpretation difficulties. The original 37-variable set was then reduced to four-- (1) street width, (2) on-street parking, (3) street grade, and (4) hazards from

TABLE 10-3

Estimated Values of Seven Variable Discriminant Function Coefficients for Five Housing Quality Classes

Variables Entered	Highest Quality Group 1	Group 2	Group 3	Group 4	Lowest Quality Group 5
Street Parking	11.98	11.71	14.30	26.83	33.83
Street Width	9.58	12.75	12.84	23.94	29.37
Street Grade	-0.10	2.27	-2.14	-8.22	-15.35
Traffic	6.30	6.97	10.26	14.83	19.92
Access to Buildings	.74	7.53	.92	4.82	-23.01
Refuse (B)	.89	.32	1.45	2.78	8.69
Loading/Parking	-0.13	.15	.06	.19	13.68
Constant Term	-14.39	-23.73	-24.20	-66.00	-179.58

traffic--by methods identical to those used in the original analysis. Comparison of the capability of the four-variable discriminant functions to classify blocks correctly with respect to the 37-variable classification showed that use of the reduced variable set led to a correct assignment in 78 percent of the cases.

When estimates of these four variables were derived from the Firestone imagery and inserted into the new linear discriminant functions, 53 percent of the 53-block test area was correctly classified.

Conclusions with Respect to Housing Quality Studies. The use of individuals with a higher degree of training in photo interpretation should significantly increase the percentage of successful classifications. Other problems which remain, but which seem to fall outside the purview of the Earth Resources Program are (1) redefinition of variables into a more objective form, (2) development of discriminant coefficients for major U.S. cities, (3) more critical evaluation of the statistical methods used in the present study, and (4) determination of sensitivity of the classification methods when giving variables different weights.

Based upon the pilot study outlined here, it seems reasonable to conclude that small-area classification of urban housing quality can definitely be accomplished by means of high-resolution aerial photography. Such surveys, at the levels of accuracy demonstrated here, can be of major utility in quick-look surveys. They will not replace ground surveys, but they can permit the ground surveys to function more efficiently by enabling them to focus on true problem areas within the city.

Total costs of the Los Angeles ground survey were more than $50 per block. Given the method outlined here, survey costs should be very significantly reduced,even when the costs of image acquisition are included. The significant time savings are of at least equal importance, since survey delays result in critical delays in implementing urgently needed social action programs. A significant amount of development and calibration work remains to be done before this approach can be considered operational in the context of the typical urban planning office, but there is little doubt of its ultimate validity.

Utility of Land Use Data*

The specific project reported on here was part of a larger project of the Geographic Applications Program of the U.S. Geological Survey, entitled "The Census Cities Project" (Wray, 1970).** The purpose was (1) to complete a one-digit land-use analysis of the Cedar Rapids metropolitan area, using a classification

* Research discussed in the following three sections will be available in full from the Geographic Applications Program and found in Horton, 1972. Joel Biggs, Kenneth Dueker, Fred Ermuth, John Mercer, Brad Pearson, and Robert Schmitt of the University of Iowa all made important contributions to the research presented in the following three section.

** For further discussion of the Census Cities Project, see Chapter 9.

scheme developed by the Geographic Applications Program staff; (2) the production of a map and a number of computer graphics showing land-use data and selected variables from the 1970 census by census tract; (3) provision of a census-tract boundary overlay for a rectified 1:62,500-scale photography of the Cedar Rapids area; and (4) submission of a written report specifying the nature of the utility of the land use and other data to the Linn County Regional Planning Commission.

The land-use information generated from this investigation has application for two major areas of the Linn County Regional Planning Commission's continuing planning program--comprehensive planning at the metropolitan regional scale and small-area planning for particular subareas within the urban region. The requirements for acceptable land-use data are generally less specific for the planning study at the larger scale. Typical comprehensive studies for Linn County, which could utilize land-use information at a fairly generalized level, include (1) analysis of existing patterns and interrelationships of land uses, (2) development of historical urban and regional growth models, and (3) perhaps regional travel demand model development.

However, the one-digit level classification of land use would seem to have rather limited utility, even for these kinds of planning studies. Perhaps this generalized level would be most appropriate for historical analysis of regional development, as illustrated by maps of existing land activities recorded at five-to-ten-year increments. In general, the larger the study area the greater the potential utility would appear to be for land-use data at this level of generality.

Planning studies which focus on small areas within Linn County generally demand a higher level of specificity of land-use information than can be provided by one-digit classification employed in the current remote sensing project. Zoning decisions, renewal area programming, neighborhood planning, and road corridor and alignment studies are a few types of planning for which more detailed land use and identification is necessary. Generally, uses need to be known at the parcel level for such studies. The remote sensing information output does not appear to have any value for planning studies of this scope.

In evaluating the potential utility of the land-use data produced by this project, the study was assessed in terms of the appropriateness of the classification scheme employed, the scale of the data assembly, data reliability, and the form of the output information. The classification scheme employed by the Geographic Applications Program employs a commercial category which may be undesirable. The number of uses classified as commercial seem inappropriate and confusing--wholesale trade, institutional, school, and church. The tabulated land-use data aggregated at the census tract level are of little use in an urban area no larger than the Linn County metropolitan area. The collection, assembly, and analysis of data as part of the Linn County Regional Planning Commission continuing planning program is conducted on a small areal basis--the traffic zone. Quantification of areas by land use for traffic zones produces a more meaningful tabulation for their purposes. However, at the smaller scale of assembly, the potential distortions of a gross classification and spatial scheme further diminish the utility and reliability of the resultant land-use summaries.

If the techniques developed in this project can be refined, especially in terms of a more detailed classification scheme, smaller areal level of detection, smaller areal basis of data aggregation, and an increased reliability of output data, greater utility for regional planning commissions can be achieved.

Comparison of Imagery-Derived Land-Use Summaries to Parcel Aggregations

The acquisition of land-use data, from sources such as tax assessor records, can be relatively expensive and time-consuming; and, quite frequently, this information is not used in its original form but is aggregated to the block group or census tract level. Much of this information can be obtained from remote sensing imagery at an appropriate scale. However, if a highly accurate land use inventory is to be conducted, the scale of the imagery used would probably range from 1:7,000 to 1:10,000. Coverage of a large area would require several hundred feet of imagery, not to mention the time involved in interpretation and tabulation of the results.

The purpose of this investigation was to evaluate the usefulness of remote sensing imagery at scales of 1:50,000, 1:100,000, and 1:382,000 in the determination of the amount of land devoted to particular uses at the census tract level of aggregation. The utilization of high-resolution imagery at these scales could reduce both the time and cost involved in securing the desired land-use information as a basic input to an urban change detection system.

The study compared two basic sets of land-use data pertaining to metropolitan Washington, D.C. The first data set was supplied by the metropolitan Washington Council of Governments (COG) and contains land-use information by census tract (1960 tract definition). These land-use data were originally collected on a parcel basis in 1968 by the participating jurisdictions.

The COG land-use data consist of the amount of land (in acres) within a census tract devoted to each of ten major land-use categories. Total tract areas are determined by summing the amount of land in each land-use category for each tract. Since the initial data were obtained from parcel records, the COG files contain no information on the amount of area devoted to street rights-of-way. The land-use classification scheme developed and used by COG is listed in Table 10-4.

The second basic data set was compiled for a sample of 26 tracts by conventional photo-interpretation techniques. Of the 26 tracts examined in this study, 16 were within the boundaries of Washington, D.C., 5 were from Montgomery County, and the remaining 5 tracts were within the boundaries of Prince Georges County. The criteria for tract selection were (1) the area enclosed by tract boundaries had to be entirely within the flight line of the imagery used, and (2) compatibility between 1960 and 1970 tract boundaries had to be maintained. After meeting these criteria, tracts were selected and the COG data file was examined to determine the quality of land-use information listed for these tracts.

The source of this second data set consisted of color infrared imagery at scales of 1:50,000, 1:100,000, and 1:382,000. This simultaneously obtained imagery covered a north-south flight line, roughly centered on the central business district (CBD) of Washington, D.C. The imagery was secured by NASA in June 1970 with a Zeiss 9-inch-by-9-inch-format mapping camera mounted in an RB-57 aircraft. The high quality of the photography used in this study enabled interpreters to identify land uses according to the ten categories mentioned previously. One of the

TABLE 10-4

Major Land-Use Categories
in Metropolitan Washington Council
of Governments Study

Code	Category
0	Residential
1	Industrial/Storage
2	Education
3	Transportation/Communication/Utilities
4	Consumer Services
5	Offices
6	Institutional
7	Public Assembly
8	Parks and Recreation
9	Underdeveloped and Resource Use

purposes of this study was to determine the accuracy of these land-use identifications.

The relevant frames of photography were placed on a light table, and census tract boundaries were drawn on mylar overlays. In most cases, the identification of boundaries presented no problem, since they are usually based on the locations of streets, railroad tracks, or rivers. However, in a few instances, boundaries were difficult to locate precisely owing to the presence of extensive areas of tree growth. It was also somewhat difficult to place tract boundaries on the 1:382,000 imagery. The total space within each tract devoted to a particular land use was identified and outlined, and the areas were calculated. The sum of these area values was then compared with the total tract area value in order to provide a check on both. If a discrepancy was found, both calculations were repeated. Since one purpose of this study is to evaluate the usefulness of various scales of imagery, interpretation of the three sets of imagery were conducted separately, and area calculations were not compared across the three scales. For example, individual and total land-use areas were determined for each of the three scales of imagery. This resulted in different values for land areas at the three scales. Generally, this resulted in larger discrepancies at the smaller scales.

The 1968 and 1970 COG and the imagery-derived land-use area values were punched on cards, and subsequent comparisons were made for census tracts between COG data and land-use interpretation at three scales.

The results of this research suggest that in certain instances, and at an approriate scale, the use of remote sensing imagery in obtaining land-use information is both useful and desirable. The problems associated with the comparison of the COG and imagery data are the result of the differential criteria upon which the two data sources are based. Each data source clearly has utility for a variety of purposes. However, land-use data can be obtained from imagery in a relatively short period and at a lower cost than the collection and aggregation of land-parcel data. If both data sources have applicability for a given purpose, the researcher should seriously consider small-scale imagery as a data source. The provision of land-use inputs for macro models of urban growth and development is both feasible and desirable, owing mainly to the relatively low costs associated with data collection.

It is difficult to evaluate the three scales of imagery examined, since each scale was not independently analyzed. There is some reason to believe that the interpreter's familiarity with the study area increased as the project progressed. This would, in part, account for the instances in which the 1:382,000 results exhibited less deviation from the COG data than the 1:50,000 results. However, the trade-off between areal coverage and interpretability within the context of land use at the tract level is somewhat balanced at a scale between 1:50,000 and 1:100,000.

Estimating Population and Dwelling Units from Imagery

Most cities do not monitor changes that occur between census surveys and have little idea as to where their city is heading and how fast. Rates and directions of change in population and housing are not known with any accuracy. Similarly, how many and what kinds of people are on the move, where they are coming from, and where they are moving to, are not known. Even more important, cities do not know what is happening in neighborhoods that are experiencing high annual move rates or in new neighborhoods that have come about since the last census.

Ideally, administrative records of the city and utility company records could be combined in ways to determine change and to maintain current accounts of important socioeconomic variables by small areas; e.g., census tracts, traffic zones, school districts, etc. However, this simple conceptual scheme has been implemented to any extent in only a few cities. The high cost of data acquisition and the concomitant problems associated with data storage and retrieval have provided a negative incentive for many metropolitan areas.

The potential usefulness of remote sensing, in obtaining certain types of change data, may provide metropolitan areas with some of the information necessary to develop viable plans for guiding the growth and development of the urban complex. However, in order to maximize the utility of remote sensing, it should be used in conjunction with other data sources. Because of its flexibility and timeliness, the use of remote sensing seems particularly appropriate for updating certain types of information, such as dwelling-unit counts, land-use change, and urban land-use development.

This investigation attempted to estimate important population variables by small area, using variables derived from remote sensing imagery. Relationships were developed between selected variables, such as housing units and population, and imagery-derived variables by means of multiple regression analysis. The general model is formulated as

$$Y = f(X_1, X_2 \ldots, X_n)$$

where:

Y = housing unit counts or population (1970 tract statistics)

$X_1, \ldots, X_n$ = imagery-derived variables such as the number of single-family structures, number of multiple-family structures, and distance to the CBD, etc.

The general model was applied using census tracts as units of observation. The model relates census-derived dependent variables to imagery-derived independent variables.

The model described above was fitted using step-wise multiple linear regression. The areal units of observation are 1970 census tracts located within the boundaries of a north-south flight line through the Washington D.C., metropolitan area. For calibration purposes, the dependent variables (Y) were derived from 1970 census data. All but one of the independent variables were obtained with an RC-8 mapping camera at a scale of 1:50,000, flown by NASA's RB-57 aircraft.

The principal shortcoming of this research is that ground-truth counts of residential structures was not possible. Use of census data for ground truth poses problems in that structures are not counted.

The objective of this investigation was to determine the feasibility of collecting selected variables from the imagery and the relative importance of these variables in predicting tract population. To the extent that the housing-unit categories of the census correspond to the categories defined by an examination of the imagery, one obtains a check on the accuracy of dwelling-unit counts derived from the imagery. While the information provided by the Census Bureau is generally straightforward, the use of imagery necessitates a careful evaluation of a variety of housing-unit categories. The development of the categories is, therefore, not arbitrary but governed by the interpreter's ability to distinguish between structures which contain a variable number of housing units. Because of the scale of imagery used (1:50,000), some identifiers, such as roof division lines and housing-unit entrance ways, were difficult to employ.

The basic method of data collection consisted of placing mylar overlays on the 1:50,000 imagery and identifying the boundaries of 51 selected tracts--the basic unit of analysis. Tract boundaries were drawn on the overlays and the total tract land area (in acres) was computed with a dot planimeter. Within the boundaries of each tract, the land devoted to residential use was identified and the residential land area computed. An effort was made to include isolated structures found in predominantly nonresidential areas. However, in areas characterized by dense settlement and mixed land uses, residential structures were somewhat difficult to identify. In some predominantly residential areas, extensive tree cover hampered the identification and accurate counting of structures. The utility of imagery in deriving structure counts would, therefore, be greatly increased if the imagery were obtained in late fall or early spring.

With the residential areas of each tract having been identified, a block-by-block structure count was made, using four categories which specified the size of structure (e.g., two to five dwelling units per structure). These categories were not totally arbitrary, but were partially dependent on the ability to identify and distinguish among structures for classification purposes. The accuracy of structure counts varied from tract to tract. Those tracts with high density, diversified development, and/or extensive tree cover presented a serious problem, resulting in substantial underreporting of structures in all categories. However, the single-family, one-unit-in-structure category counts were affected more by tree cover than by high-density development. Multiple-unit structures, located in areas of intensive land use, were extremely difficult to identify. The scale and viewing angle of the imagery did not permit adequate discrimination between multiple-unit residential structures and structures devoted to other uses. Multiple-unit planned residential structures in suburban tracts were, however, easily identified. Many of the suburban structures in this category are characterized by their physical layout and parking facility arrangement.

The census definition for "structural characteristics" provided some difficulty in relating census data to the imagery-derived counts of structures. For example, a one-unit structure may contain business units and may be attached (e.g., a row house). This sometimes makes it difficult to distinguish row houses from garden apartments and residential walk-up apartment buildings from exclusively nonresidential structures. In addition, self-enumeration census forms tend to cloud the distinction between single-family structures and multiple-family structures.

The 51 tracts were divided into two groups--central city tracts and suburban tracts. The classification of a tract into one of these groups was based on whether the tract was within the District of Columbia or not.

The population-estimation analysis consists of two regressions--one for central city and one for suburban tracts--with 1970 tract population (Y_2) as the dependent variable and the number of single-family housing units (X_2), the number of structures containing 15 or more housing units (X_3), the number of structures containing 6 to 14 housing units (X_4), the number of structures containing 2 to 5 housing units (X_5), and the distance to the CBD (X_6) as independent variables. Table 10-5 reveals the structural form of these regression equations. Surprisingly, the central-city regression accounts for more of the variation in the dependent variable than the regression for suburban tracts. A greater degree of success in predicting population for suburban tracts was expected.

The results for central-city tracts (Table 10-5) demonstrate the relative importance of the independent variables in accounting for variation in tract population. The rank of variable importance in this context corresponds to the order in which the variables are arranged in the regression equation. The magnitude of the regression coefficients associated with variables X_2, X_4, and X_5 seems to be somewhat high, but their standard errors are relatively low. For example, a unit change in the variable X_2 results in a 6.78 unit change in population. Several factors could account for this result. First, the tracts included in the analysis may exhibit some degree of overcrowding in single-family structures; second, the actual number of single-family structures may be underreported for reasons previously mentioned; and finally, variable interaction effects may have biased the coefficient values. Although somewhat conjectural, one would expect that the second factor is of primary importance in this analysis. A similar argument can be extended to variables X_4 and X_5 . However, it should be noted that the coefficient X_5 approaches the expected results.

The magnitude of the regression coefficient for variable X_3, in relation to the size of its standard error, reveals a strong tendency toward instability. One would expect this coefficient to be two and a half to three times larger than its reported value. There is strong reason to believe that this low coefficient results from a gross underrepresentation of structures containing 15 or more housing units.

All the variables mentioned thus far have been, as expected, positively related to the dependent variable. Distance to the CBD, on the other hand, is negatively related to tract population. Thus, for each unit of increase in distance, population decreases by approximately 790. While the standard error of this regression coefficient is not large, it is difficult to assess the functional stability of this variable. The population of central-city tracts tends to be extremely sensitive to changes in distance, and the particular selection of tracts may have biased the coefficient of this variable. The regression results for the suburban tracts also are shown in Table 10-5. In addition to the lower proportion of "explained" variance, the analysis for suburban tracts reveals a different order of variable importance and a marked difference in the functional form of the regression equation. However, owing to the relatively low amount of explained variance in the dependent variable, it is advisable to evaluate the results with some caution. Again, the rank of variable importance in accounting for variation in the dependent variable corresponds to the order in which the variables are arranged in the equation. Notice that X_3, the number of structures containing 15 or more units, ranks above all other variables. X_4, the number of structures containing 6 to 14 units, ranks above X_2, the number of single-family structures. Apparently, the number of larger-multiple-unit structures is a better indicator of population than duplex and single-family structures. This not totally unexpected result is somewhat contrary to general

Table 10-5

Population Estimates

Central-City Tracts:

$$Y_2 = 1522.18 + \underset{(1.61)}{6.78X_2} + \underset{(22.59)}{83.86X_4} + \underset{(10.13)}{18.48X_5} - \underset{(527.76)}{790.49X_6} + \underset{(55.43)}{19.20X_3}$$

$R^2 = .65$

Suburban Tracts

$$Y_2 = 1654.5 + \underset{(74.55)}{192.46X_3} + \underset{(7.11)}{18.12X_4} + \underset{(0.70)}{2.33X_2} + \underset{(11.28)}{23.62X_5} + \underset{(84.92)}{14.71X_6}$$

$R^2 = .54$

Y_2 = 1970 tract population (1970 census)

X_2 = the number of single-family housing units (imagery)

X_3 = the number of structures containing 15 or more housing units (imagery)

X_4 = the number of structures containing 6 to 14 housing units (imagery)

X_5 = the number of structures containing 2 to 5 housing units (imagery)

X_6 = distance to the CBD

expectations, since the predominant residential structure in suburban areas is the single-family dwelling unit.

The average error in the suburban single-family dwelling-unit count, when compared to the census one-unit-in-structure variable, is only 15.0 percent. Considering the scale of the imagery used, this value compares favorably with a 12.0 percent uncorrected total unit count reported by Hadfield (1963) and a net error in unit counts relative to total units of 12.6 percent as reported by Binsell (1967). The scale of the imagery used by Binsell was approximately 1:5,2000. Unfortunately, the effect of the 15.0 percent error associated with the present analysis on the form of the regression equation is not known. However, the combination of this error, coupled with the possible overestimation of variabes X_3 and X_4, also may have biased the relative importance of these measures in accounting for variance in tract population.

The results of this analysis are encouraging, but difficult to evaluate because of the paucity of similar studies and an uncertainty concerning the stability of the relationship between small-area population and imagery-derived indicator variables. In order to realize the full potential of this type of analysis, the errors in structure counts must be explicity specified and dealt with. If future research proves the relationship between population and indicator variables to be relatively stable ones, it would then be possible to develop a small-area population-change model based exclusively on imagery-derived information. With some modification, such a model could also be used to estimate the impact of certain policy decisions on the distribution of population. The realization of this modeling strategy, however, is dependent on several factors which must be given careful evaluation. These are (1) the provision of imagery for the entire metropolitan area at an appropriate scale for two points in time, (2) the acquisition of the imagery should be made so as to minimize the problems associated with tree cover, (3) contemporaneous data by small area is also required in order to evaluate the stability and nature of the pertinent relationships, (4) the development of an error detection system designed to provide relatively accurate adjustments in the count data, (5) calibration of the proposed model of population change, (6) the use of external data sources, imagery data, and field checks for the evaluation of model output. The present analysis, while exploratory, indicates that the development of population-change models are possible and their application may be of considerable utility in a planning context.

CONCLUDING REMARKS

It is clear, from the material included in this chapter, that the majority of the applications of remote sensing technology in urban areas have two characteristics: (1) the applications are quasi-experimental, in the sense that large-scale and continuing demonstration projects utilizing remote sensing methods have not been carried out; and (2) adjustments in interpretation techniques and data translation models often are necessary when they are applied in different cities.

The first point is important because the real cost effectiveness of remote sensing data acquisition is difficult to assess in experiments and limited applications. The second point indicates that specific interpretative techniques may have to be developed for each city for each application. In addition, it will be necessary to recalibrate translation models through use of sampling in each city. It may also be necessary to restructure the translation models through the deletion or addition of particular variables in a given metropolitan area.

The need for timely data for urban planning and management is well documented. Remote sensing offers a unique capability to provide data about many important aspects of urban growth and change. There is still a great deal of work to be accomplised before all of the cost-effective applications of remote sensing as an urban data acquisition device can be identified.

REFERENCES

Alexander, R. H., 1966, *Multispectral Sensing of Urban Environments*, Technical Report 1, Office of Naval Research, Washington, D.C., pp. 389-443.

Alexander, R. H., L. W. Bowden, D. F. Marble, and E. G. Moore, 1968, *Fifth Symposium on Remote Sensing of Environment*, University of Michigan, Institute of Science and Technology, Ann Arbor, pp. 889-991.

American Society of Photogrammetry, 1960, *Manual of Photographic Interpretation*, Washington, D.C.

American Society of Planning Officials, 1951, "Urban Mapping, Aerial Photography and Duplicating: Some Basic Elements," Information Report 29, Planning Advisory Service. Mimeographed.

Anschutz, G., and A. H. Stallard, 1967, "An Overview of Site Evaluation," *Photogrammetric Engineering*, 33:1381.

Anson, A., 1966, "Color Photo Comparison," *Photogrammetric Engineering*, 32:286.

Avery, T. E., 1962, *Interpretation of Aerial Photographs*, Burgess Publishing Co., Minneapolis, Minn.

Betak, J. F., 1967, *Object Identification in Aerial Photographs: A Preliminary Report*, Northwestern University, Remote Sensing Laboratory, Department of Geography, Evanston, Ill.

Bigelow, G. F., 1963, "Photographic Interpretation Keys--A Reappraisal," *Photogrammetric Engineering*, 29:1042.

Bill, J. T., 1952, "The Use of Aerial Photography in Urban Planning," *Photogrammetric Engineering*, 18:760-762.

Binsell, R., 1967, *Dwelling Unit Estimation from Aerial Photography*, Research Report, Department of Geography, Northwestern University, Evanston, Ill.

Boesch, H. H., and D. Steiner, 1959, *Interpretation of Land Utilization from Aerial Photographs*, Final Technical Report under U.S. Army Contract No. DA-91-591-EUC-975-01-1093-59, University of Zurich, Geographical Institute, Zurich.

Bowden, L. W., 1968, *Multi-Sensor Signatures of Urban Morphology, Function and Evolution*, Status Report II, Technical Report 2, University of California, Riverside.

Branch, M. C., Jr., 1948, *Aerial Photography in Urban Planning and Research*, Harvard City Planning Series 14, Harvard University Press, Cambridge, Mass.

Brunt, M., 1961, "Aerial Photography and Land Use Planning," *Papers of Technical Conference of Directors of Agriculture and Agricultural Institutions*, Department of Technical Cooperation, London.

Buringh, P., and A. P. A. Vink, 1962, "Aerial Photo Interpretation in Land Use Surveys," Institute Training Centre for Aerial Survey, Delft. Mimeographed.

Chisnell, T. C., and G. E. Cole, 1958, "Industrial Components--A Photo Interpretation Key on Industry," *Photogrammetric Engineering*, 24:590-602.

Cissna, V. J., Jr., 1963, "Photogrammetry and Comprehensive City Planning for the Small Community," *Photogrammetric Engineering*, 29.

Clauson, M., and C. L. Steward, 1965, *Land Use Information*, Johns Hopkins Press, Baltimore.

Colvocoressess, A. P., 1970, "ERTS-A Satellite Imagery," *Photogrammetric Engineering*, 36:555.

Data Format for Evaluation of the Utility of Remote Sensors for Geographers, Xerox copy, source unknown.

Davis, J. M., 1966, *Uses of Aerial Photos for Rural and Urban Planning*, Department of Agriculture Handbook 315, Government Printing Office, Washington, D.C.

Davis, W. O., J. P. Kuettner, 1967, "Environmental Prediction Using Orbital Sensors," Paper 67-103 presented at the American Astronautical Society, Thirteenth Annual Meeting, Dallas, Tex.

Dill, H. W., Jr., 1963, "Airphoto Analysis in Outdoor Recreation: Site Inventory and Planning," *Photogrammetric Engineering*, 29:67.

Doverspike, G. E., F. M. Flynn, and R. C. Heller, 1965, "Microdensitometer Applied to Land Use Classification," *Photogrammetric Engineering*, 31:294.

Dueker, K. J., and F. E. Horton, 1971a, *Remote Sensing and Geographic Urban Information Systems*, Technical Report 3, Remote Sensing Project, Institute of Urban and Regional Research, University of Iowa, Iowa City.

Dueker, K. J., and F. E. Horton, 1971b, "Toward Geographic Urban Change Detection Systems with Remote Sensing Inputs," *Technical Papers*, Thirty-Seventh Annual Meeting, American Society of Photogrammetry, Washington, D.C., pp. 204-218.

Dueker, K. J., and F. E. Horton, 1971a, "Urban Change Detection Systems: Status and Prospects," *Proceedings of the Seventh International Symposium on Remote Sensing of Environment*, vol. 2, University of Michigan, Ann Arbor, pp. 1523-1536.

Dueker, K. J., and F. E. Horton, (forthcoming), "The Utility of Remote Sensing Data for Urban Land Use Planning," *Proceedings, Operational Remote Sensing Conference*, American Society of Photogrammetry, Washington, D.C.

Estes, J. E., and B. Golomb, 1970, "Monitoring Environmental Pollution," *Journal of Remote Sensing*, 1(2):8.

Eyre, L. A., 1969, *An Investigation by Remote Sensing of Vacant and Unutilized Land in an Urban Coastal Area of Southeast Florida*, Technical Report 3, 14-08-001-10936, U.S. Geological Survey, Washington, D.C.

Eyre, L. A., et al., 1970, "Census Analysis and Population Studies," *Photogrammetric Engineering*, 36:460.

Fagerholm, P. O., 1959, "The Application of Photogrammetry to Land Use Planning," *Photogrammetric Engineering*, 25(4):523-529.

Falkner, E., 1968, "Land Use Changes in Parkway School District," *Photogrammetric Engineering*, 34:52.

Forte, L., Jr., 1969, "Color Aerial Photography in Transportation Analysis," *New Horizons in Color Aerial Photography*, American Society of Photogrammetry, Falls Church, and Society of Photographic Scientist and Engineers, Washington, D.C., pp. 191-195.

Garrison, W. L., 1965, *Demands for Small-Area Data: Five Papers in Remote Sensing and Urban Information Systems*, Technical Report 1, N.R., Office of Naval Research, Washington, D.C., pp. 389-442.

Garrison, W. L., et al., 1966, *Five Papers on Remote Sensing and Urban Information*, Northwestern University, Remote Sensing Laboratory, Department of Geography, Evanston, Ill.

Gimbarzcvsky, P., 1966, "Land Inventory Interpretation," *Photogrammetric Engineering*, 32(6):967-976.

Goodman, M. S., 1964, "Criteria for the Identification of Types of Farming on Aerial Photographs," *Photogrammetric Engineering*, 30:984.

Green, N. E., 1955, "Aerial Photography in the Analysis of Urban Structure, Ecological and Social," unpublished Ph.D. dissertation, Department of Sociology, University of North Carolina, Chapel Hill.

Green, N. E., 1956, "Aerial Photographic Analysis of Residential Neighborhoods: An Evaluation of Data Accuracy," *Social Forces*, 35:142-147.

Green, N. E., 1957, "Aerial Photographic Interpretation and the Social Structure of the City," *Photogrammetric Engineering*, 23:89-96.

Green, N. E., and R. B. Monier, 1953, *Reliability and Validity of Air Reconnaissance as a Collection Method for Urban Demographic and Sociological Information*, Technical Report 11, U.S. Air Force, Air University Human Resources Research Institute, Alabama.

Green, N. E., Chairman, and R. B. Monier, 1959, "Interpretation of Urban, Rural, and Industrial Structures," Report of Working Group 5, Interim Progress Report for Commission VII, *Photogrammetric Engineering*, 25:128-130.

Hadfield, S. M., 1963, *Evaluation of Land Use and Dwelling Unit Data Derived from Aerial Photography*, Urban Research Section, Chicago Area Transportation Study.

Hammond, R., 1967, *Air Survey in Economic Development*, American Elsevier Publishing Company, New York.

Hannah, J. W., 1967, "A Feasibility Study for the Application of Remote Sensors to Selected Urban and Regional Land Use Planning Studies," unpublished Master's thesis, University of Tennessee, Knoxville.

Heath, G. R., 1955, "An Associative Method of Regional Photo Interpretation," *Photogrammetric Engineering*, 21:589-598.

Heath, G. R., 1956, "A Comparison of Two Basic Theories of Land Classification and Their Adaptability to Regional Photo Interpretation Key Techniques," *Photogrammetric Engineering*, 22:144-168.

Heath, G. R., 1957, "Correlation Between Man's Activity and His Environment Which May be Analyzed by Photo Interpretation," *Photogrammetric Engineering*, 23:108-114.

Holz, R. K., D. L. Huff, and R. C. Mayfield, 1969a, "Urban Spatial Structure Based on Remote Sensing Imagery," *Proceedings of the Sixth International Symposium on Remote Sensing of Environment*, vol. II, University of Michigan, Ann Arbor, p. 819.

Holz, R. K., D. L. Huff, R. C. Mayfield, 1969b, *A Study of Urban Spatial Structure Based on Remote Sensing Imagery*, Final Report of the AAG Commission on Geographic Applications of Remote Sensing for May 1969, vol. 2, Association of American Geographers, Washington, D.C.

Honea, R. B., 1969, *Determination of Trade Areas and Traffic Flows from Remote Sensor Imagery*, Technical Report 15, East Tennessee State University, Johnson City.

Horton, F. E., 1970, "The Application of Remote Sensing Techniques to Selected Inter and Intra Urban Data Acquisition Problems," *Third Annual Earth Resources Program Review*, vol. 1, NASA/MSC, Houston, Tex., pp. 3-1 - 3-11.

Horton, F. E., 1971, "The Application of Remote Sensing to Urban Data Acquisition, *Proceedings, International Workshop on Earth Resources Survey Systems*, vol. 2, pp. 213-224.

Horton, F. E., 1972, *The Application of Remote Sensing Techniques to Inter and Intra Urban Analysis: Final Report*, Institute of Urban and Regional Research, University of Iowa, Iowa City.

Horton, F. E., and D. F. Marble, 1969a, "Regional Information Systems: Remote Sensing Inputs," *Papers from the Thirty-fifth Annual Meeting*, American Society of Photogrammetry, Falls Church, Va., pp. 259-268.

Horton, F. E., and Marble, D. F., 1969b, "Remote Sensing: A New Tool for Urban Data Acquisition," in J. D. Rickert, Ed., *Urban and Regional Information Systems: Federal Activities and Specialized Programs,* Kent State University, Kent, Ohio, pp. 252-257.

Horton, F. E., D. F. Marble, 1970, "Housing Quality in Urban Areas: Data Acquisition and Classification Through the Analysis of Remote Sensor Imagery," *Second Annual Earth Resources Program Review,* National Aeronautics and Space Administration, Houston, Tex., pp. 15-1 - 15-13.

Jacobson, A. L., E. W. Morris, and W. S. Ritter, "Measuring Housing Quality: Construction of a Quantitative Index," (817), *Study of Urban Housing in Latin America,* The Center for Housing and Environmental Studies, Cornell University, Ithaca, N.Y.

Joseph, R. D., and S. Vighione, 1966, "A Pattern Recognition Technique and Its Application to High Resolution Imagery," in *AFIRS 1966 Spring Joint Computer Conference,* Spartan Books.

Kelland, M. C. M., 1954, "The Use of Aerial Photographs in the Delimitation of the Central Business District," unpublished Master's thesis, Clark University Graduate School, Worcester, Mass.

Kiefer, R. W., 1967, "Terrain Analysis for Metropolitan Fringe Area Planning," *Journal of the Urban Planning and Development Division,* ASCE, 93 (UP4), Paper 5649, pp. 119-139.

LaCote, D. A., 1961, "A Review of Landtype Classification and Mapping," *Land Economics,* 27(3):271-278.

Landen, D., 1966, "Photo Map for Urban Planning," *Photogrammetric Engineering,* 32:136.

Lindgren, D. T., 1970, "Dwelling Unit Estimation from Color Infrared Photography," Paper No. 1 in *Recognition of Settlement Patterns Against a Complex Background,* Research Report, Department of Geography, Dartmouth College, Hanover, N.H.

Manji, A. S., 1968, *The Uses of Conventional Aerial Photography in Urban Areas: A Review,* Northwestern University, Remote Sensing Laboratory, Department of Geography, Evanston, Ill.

Marble, D. F., and F. E. Horton, 1968, "Remote Sensing and the Study and Planning of Urban Areas," *Earth Resources Program Review,* vol. 1, NASA/MSC, Houston, Tex., pp. 7-1 - 7B-2, 19-29.

Marble, D. F., and F. E. Horton, 1961, "Extraction of Urban Data From High and Low Resolution Images," *Proceedings of the Sixth International Symposium on Remote Sensing of Environment,* vol. 2, University of Michigan, Ann Arbor, p. 807.

Marble, D. F., and F. E. Horton, 1971, *Remote Sensors as Data Sources for Urban Research and Planning: Final Report,* Remote Sensing Laboratory, Northwestern University, Evanston, Ill.

Marble, D. F., and E. N. Thomas, 1966, "Some Observations on the Utility of Multispectral Photography for Urban Research," *Proceedings of the Fourth International Symposium on Remote Sensing of Environment*, University of Michigan, Ann Arbor, p. 135.

Matthes, G. H., 1927, "Aerial Surveys for City Planning," *Transactions, American Society of Civil Engineers*, 91:314-325.

Monier, R. B., (to be published), "Verification of Aerial Photographic Analysis of Urban Residential Structure: A Study of Rochester, New York."

Monier, R. B., and N. E. Green, 1953, "Preliminary Findings on the Developments of Criteria for the Identification of Urban Structures from Aerial Photographs," abstract in *Program*, Forty-Ninth Annual Meeting, Association of American Geographers, Cleveland, Ohio.

Monier, R. B., and N. E. Green, 1957a, "Aerial Photographic Interpretation and the Human Geography of the City," paper read before Association of American Geographers, Cincinnati, Ohio.

Monier, R. B., and N. E. Green, 1957b, "Report on Current Research in Aerial Photography Interpretation as Related to Urban Geographic Studies," *Annals of the Association of American Geographers*, 47(2):172.

Moore, E. G., 1970, *Application of Remote Sensors to the Classification of Areal Data at Different Scales: A Case Study in Housing Quality*, Research Paper, Department of Geography, Northwestern University, Evanston, Ill.

Moore, E. G., 1968, *Side Looking Radar in Urban Research: A Case Study*, Research Report 40, Department of Geography, Northwestern University, Evanston, Ill.

Moore, E. G., and B. S. Wellar, 1968, *Remote Sensor Imagery in Urban Research: Some Potentialities and Problems*, Interagency Report NASA-118, National Aeronautics and Space Administration.

Moore, E. G., and B. S. Wellar, 1969, "Urban Data Collection by Remote Sensor," *Journal of the American Institute of Planners*, 35:35-43.

Mullens, R. H., 1969, *Analysis of Urban Residential Environments Using Color Infrared Aerial Photography: An Examination of Socioeconomic Variables and Physical Characteristics of Selected Areas in the Los Angeles Basin*, Interagency Report NASA-153, Department of the Interior, Washington, D.C.

Mumbower, L., and J. Donoghue, 1967, "Urban Poverty Study," *Photogrammetric Engineering*, 33:610-618.

Murphy, R. E., J. E. Vance, Jr., and B. J. Epstein, 1955, *Central Business District Studies*, Clark University, Worcester, Mass. Reprinted with additions, from the following articles in *Economic Geography:* "Delimiting the CBD," 1954, 30:189-222; "A Comarative Study of Nine Central Business Districts," 1954, 30: 301-336; and "Internal Structure of the CBD," 1955, 31:21-46.

Nunnally, N. R., and R. E. Witner, 1970, "Remote Sensing for Land Use Studies," *Photogrammetric Engineering*, 36:449.

Olson, C. E., L. W. Tombaugh, and H. C. Davis, 1969, "Inventory of Recreation Sites," *Photogrammetric Engineering,* 35:561.

Pate, M., 1967, "A Feasibility Study of Remote Sensor Application to Urban and Regional Transportation Planning," unpublished Master's thesis, University of Tennessee, Knoxville.

Peplies, R. W., 1968, "Land Use and Regional Analysis," *Earth Resources Aircraft Program Status Review,* vol. I: *Geology, Geography, and Sensor Studies,* NASA/MSC, Houston, Tex.

Philbrick, A. K., 1952, "A Unit Method of Mapping Gross Land-Use Association in Urban Regions," *Proceedings of the Seventeenth International Geographical Congress of the International Geographical Union,* Washington, D.C.

Pitkin, F. A., 1948, "Aerial Photography for State and Local Planning," *Photogrammetric Engineering,* 14:532-535.

Pownall, L. L., 1956, "Aerial Photographic Interpretation of Aerial Photography to Urban Land-Use Inventory, Analysis, and Planning," *Photogrammetric Engineering,* 22:656-663.

Prochaska, J. M., 1969, "The Application of Remote Sensing in the Urban Environment," *Papers from the Thirty-fifth Annual Meeting,* American Society of Photogrammetry, Falls Church, Va., pp. 246-246J.

Rawson,E. F., and K. R. Sealy, 1957, "Air Photographs and Land-Utilization Map," *Geography,* 42(Part I):195.

Richter, D. M., 1969, "Sequential Urban Change," *Photogrammetric Engineering,* 35:764.

Rinker, J. N., 1969, "Environmental Analysis: A Challenge to the Remote Sensing Community," *Papers from the Thirty-fifth Annual Meeting,* American Society of Photogrammetry, Falls Church, Va., pp. 55-96.

Robertson, V. C., 1955, "Aerial Photography and Proper Land Utilization," *Photogrammetric Record,* 1(6):5-12.

Sabol, J., 1966, "The Relationship Between Population and Radar-Derived Area of Urban Places," unpublished paper, Department of Geography, University of Kansas, Lawrence.

Schneider, C. H. P., 1967, *Material Identification in Urban Areas from Gray Tone Variations in Multispectral Photography,* Research Report, Department of Geography, Northwestern University, Evanston, Ill.

Shephard, J. R., 1964, "A Concept of Change Detection," *Photogrammetric Engineering,* 30:648.

Simonett, D. S., F. M. Henderson, and D. D. Egbert, 1969, "On the Use of Space Photography for Identifying Transportation Routes," *Proceedings of the Sixth International Symposium on Remote Sensing of Environment,* vol. 2, University of Michigan, Ann Arbor, p. 855.

Spelt, J., 1966, "Downtown Toronto: A Look at Air Photo," *Canadian Geographer*, 10:184-189.

Stone, K. H., 1948, "Aerial Photographic Interpretation of the Anchorage Area, Alaska," *Geographical Review*, 38:465-474.

Tobler, W., "Evidence of the Central Place Theory in the Nile Delta," in *Earth Resource Surveys from Spacecraft*, prepared by the U.S. Army Corps of Engineers for Earth Resources Survey Program, NASA, Washington, D.C., vol. 1.

Turpin, R. D., 1964, "Evaluation of Photogrammetry and Photographic Interpretation for Use in Transportation Planning, *Photogrammetric Engineering*, 30:124.

Uses of Conventional Aerial Photography in Urban Areas: Review and Bibliography, 1968, Technical Letter NASA-131, NASA/MSC, Houston, Tex.

Wagner, F. A., and A. D. May, 1963, "Use of Aerial Photography in Freeway Traffic Operations Studies," Highway Research Board, *Highway Research Record*, 19: 24-34.

Wagner, R. R., 1963, "Using Airphotos to Measure Changes in Land Use Around Highway Interchanges," *Photogrammetric Engineering*, 29:645.

Wellar, B. S., 1967, *Generation of Housing Quality Data from Multiband Aerial Photographs*, Research Report 32A, Department of Geography, Northwestern University, Evanston, Ill.

Wellar, B. S., 1968, *Thermal Infrared Imagery in Urban Studies*, Research Report, Department of Geography, Northwestern University, Evanston, Ill.

Wellar, B. S., 1969, "The Role of Space Photography in Urban and Transportation Data Series," *Proceedings of the Sixth International Symposium on Remote Sensing of Environment*, vol. 2, University of Michigan, Ann Arbor, p. 831.

Witenstein, M. M., 1954, "Photo-Sociometrics--The Application of Aerial Photography to Urban Administration and Planning Problems, *Photogrammetric Engineering*, 20:419-527.

Witenstein, M. M., 1955, "Uses and Limitations on Aerial Photography in Urban Analysis and Planning," *Photogrammetric Engineering*, 21:566-572.

Witenstein, M. M., 1956, "A Report on Application of Aerial Photography to Urban Land Use Inventory, Analysis, and Planning," *Photogrammetric Engineering*, 22: 656-663.

Witenstein, M. M., 1957, "Aerial Photographic Interpretation and the Social Structure of the City," *Photogrammetric Engineering*, 23:97-98.

Woodward, L. A., 1954, "Photogrammetry in City Planning Operations," *Photogrammetric Engineering*, 20:520-523.

Woodward, L. A., 1970, "Survey Project Planning," *Photogrammetric Engineering*, 36:578.

Wray, J. R., 1957, "The Form and Function of Peoria, Illinois: An Exercise in Graphic Urban Area Analysis," Folio of maps, air photo mosaics, and tables. Distributed at the Fourth Annual Meeting of Middle Atlantic Division of Association of American Geographers, Washington, D.C., Mimeographed.

Wray, J. R., 1970, "Census Cities Project Atlas of Urban and Regional Change," *Third Annual Earth Resources Program Review*, vol. 1, NASA/MSC, Houston, Tex., pp. 2-1 - 2-16.

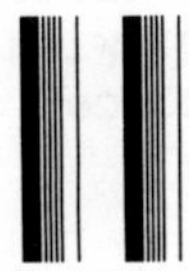

Regional Analysis and Remote Sensing: A Methodological Approach

Robert W. Peplies
East Tennessee State University

The concept of region is important within geography and other disciplines, where there is concern for the organization of patterns produced by areally distributed phenomena (land use, vegetation, landforms, etc.). A region may be an abstraction or may correspond closely to reality, and it may be composed of heterogeneous or homogeneous phenomena. Nevertheless, a region defines, in some fashion, the boundaries of a phenomenon, or phenomena, of interest. Delimitation of the region may represent the end-product of an investigation, or it may serve as a jumping-off point for further inquiry into the elements which comprise the region. Remotely sensed data can provide new perspectives on the delimitation of regional patterns, or provide the data needed to examine the component parts of a defined region. This chapter begins with a philosophical discussion of the regional concept and regional analysis, and proceeds to an examination of remote sensing possibilities for regional analysis.

In many ways, it is surprising that a significant number of geographers perceive regional analysis, and the results thereof, as the goal toward which the discipline should focus, while at the same time so much confusion surrounds the definition of a region. Undoubtedly, the fact that confusion and different opinions exist among geographers, about the nature of something which is supposedly central in their thoughts, has caused some to interpret the significance of discipline in the classification of sciences in different ways, both positively and negatively and various degrees between. The lack of accord among geographers about the nature of regions and regional analysis has been considered by some to be a healthy sign. It indicates flexibility, and absence of rigid rules to constrain researchers. Such a situation represents freedom within a science. To others, the situation of confusion and apparent dissent surrounding the terms "region" and "regional analysis" is the antithesis of the notion of a discipline, in general, and science in particular. These individuals rightfully question the existence of something which can not be agreed upon. The argument is extended even further to the point of questioning the right of geography to be considered a scholarly subject, a subject which deserves a position within the university curriculum (Tudor, 1958).

It was not the purpose of this introductory statement to open again a "Pandora's box," and engage in methodological discussion of whether regions exist or do not exist; but, rather, it is presented here to acknowledge the framework within which the concept of regions exists. Granted that extreme provocations of regional analysis are present, it would be of no purpose to "cast in the towel" about the regional analysis, for all further discussion would then cease. Instead, without engaging in further rhetoric about the philosophy and methdology of regional analysis, the approach herewith accepted is that regionalization has heretofore been practiced and has produced academic and practical results within and without geography.

Aside from engaging in methodological and philosophical debates concerning the nature of regions, it is of interest to note some of the factors which have contributed to the nature of confusion surrounding the concept of regions (Grigg, 1967). These factors have had a wide range, extending from the criteria of truthfulness and appropriateness of the regional concept to disagreement about procedures which can be followed to determine the boundaries of regions. In addition, the factors involved with regionalization are tied in with the needs of disciplines other than geography. A number of sciences have as their concern a focus on the distribution of terrestrial phenomena; and all use some form of the regionalization process to explain these. Some subjects, in addition, have accepted the notion that regions exist as concrete objects to be manipulated and worked with; cases in point are regionalism in planning, political science, and history. Thus the types of connotations that one develops when he encounters a "region" in the literature varies from naive to sophisticated and stretch across a number of discipline lines including geography. Obviously, there are significant similarities between and among concepts concerned with regions.

Although some differences of opinion exist about the methods of regional concept, these differences are not "shots in the dark." A rich and interesting history and an abundant literature exist about the regional concept. The notion was first formally introduced in the eighteenth century, but antecedents of the regional concept extend back to classical antiquity. Even after the regional concept was formally presented, it was still not completed or accepted; and since its appearance, it has continued to vacillate between use and disuse (and sometimes misuse). Each time a new generation comes forth and revisits the regional approach, new directions (in scope and function) for the concept are proposed. At times it is not known whether it is new wine in an old bottle, old wine in a new bottle, or (worse) no wine at all. Sometimes the old approaches are simply reworked and presented again. German geographers (e.g., F. Ratzel and A. Hettner) engaged in active methodological discussion about regionalism, regional concept, and regionalization throughout the latter part of the nineteenth century, and into the beginning of the twentieth. During the earliest decade of this century, one school of geographers led by V. De la Blanche engaged in regionalization of ways of life--genre de vie; others (e.g., A. Herbertson) were concerned with the division of earth according to natural regions (Grigg, 1967). Geographic instruction in American universities was strongly oriented to regional geography during the 1930s and 1940s, especially after the demise of environmental determinism as the focus of geographical thought. The sequence of interests in geography of the focuses of concerns, both from research and teaching standpoints, seem to follow accordant patterns in recent decades. For again, concomitant with the renewed interest in man-land relationships is a renewed interest in regions and regionalization. A point of note can be made of the fact that the regional concept not only has varied meanings depending on interests and purpose, but the basic approach can be changed with the passage of time. Schools of thought concerning the regional approach and regional terms are varied; the present types of regions were illustrated by Haggett (Figure 11-1) and reflect the most recent thoughts (Haggett, 1965).

In the past few decades, major guiding principles in geography and some of the other sciences have been relevance and practicality. Some revolutionary movements have risen within teaching research institutions demanding reforms. It is increasingly difficult for the research and teaching professor to cling to his ivy tower, whether it be a small college or large university, and engage in luxury-type studies, e.g., examination of the distribution and types of log cabins in some southern state. Instead the Zeitgeist of the present urges him, directs him, to plunge, or better, to SURGE forward into problems of the communities--neighborhood, local, sectional, national, and global.

The same type of demands is imposed on the approaches which exist within the sciences. Those approaches which can absorb and incorporate the pressing societal reforms are presently moving forward. Those which resist are, at least for the time being, "dying on the vine." In all fairness, it should be stated that research does tend to be cyclic and another watershed occurrence (e.g., Sputnik) may change the pattern presently developing. The four traditions of geography identified by Pattison--spatial, areal studies, man-land, and earth science--are presently being tested (Pattison, 1963). All these geographic themes incorporate the use of the regional concept as noted in Dickinson's recent review of

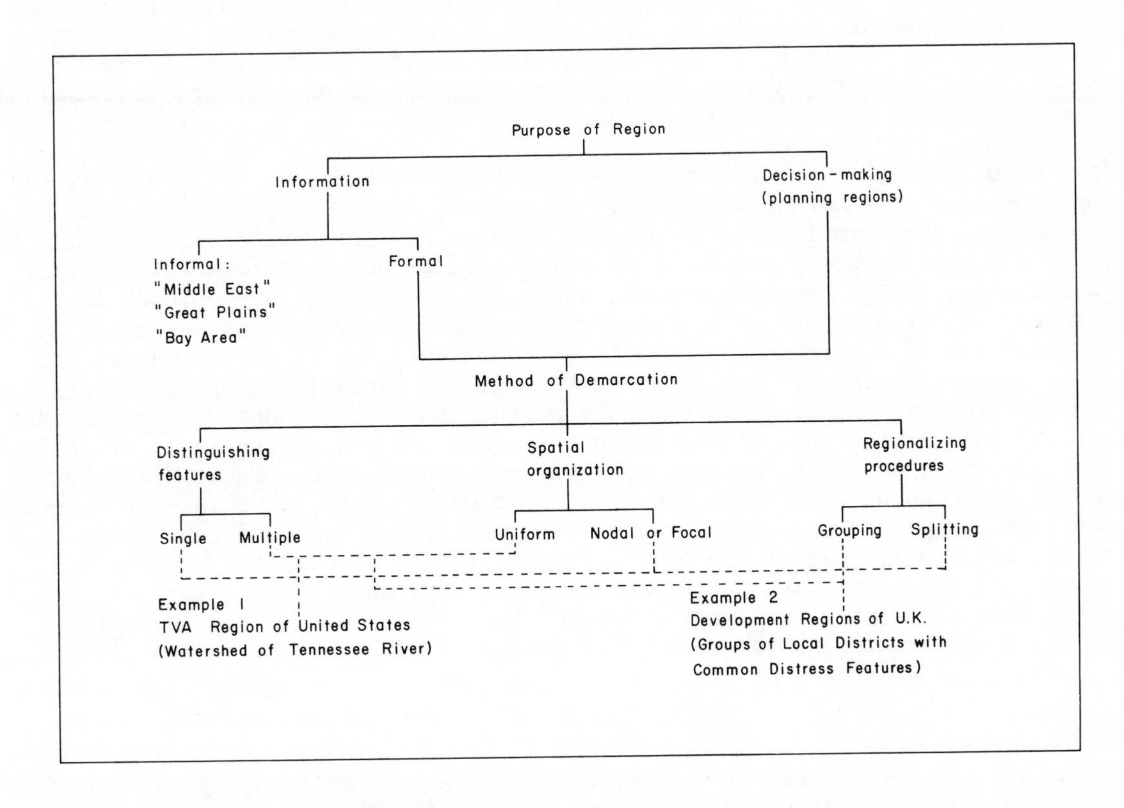

Figure 11-1. Types of Regions (Source: Haggett, 1972).

the same (Dickinson, 1970). It is also interesting to note that Dickinson deplored the fact that geographers "have not clearly developed in their student training right to the doctorate level, a clearly enumerated conceptual framework" of the regional concept for practical and pragmatic purposes. And he concludes that the regional concept "is finding ever increasing applications to practical problems in the use and organization of space, both urban and rural; the conservation of natural resources; the water supply of cities, land uses, city and country planning, marketing, business, and the reorganization of areas of local governments" (Dickinson, 1970). To quote further, from an unpublished report by James Anderson, "A major objective of regional analysis should be the solution of problems which can best be attacked on a region-wide basis" (Anderson, 1970).

As indicated earlier, there is no single regional approach, although there seem to be some general agreements as to the meaning of "region" from at least two points of reference. In popular parlance, the term "region" is used to refer to any area that is amenable to the user. The Tennessee Valley region has been defined by governmental authorities and political acts as the charge of the Tennessee Valley Authority. The Authority and its area of concern constitute what Dickinson calls regionalism as an act, "a consciousness of togetherness of human groups in particular areas and their desire and agitation for further expression and recognition of their common experience and attitudes" (Dickinson, 1970). Dickinson also notes that regionalism as an "act" must be differentiated from regionalism as a "fact." The latter, accordingly, is defined as the spatial association of peoples and places. While the former is operational, the latter is cognized and, as such, is the object of scientific study from all available facts. Both, however, are of concern to geography, especially from a standpoint of environmental perception (Broek and Webb, 1968).

In a more scientific way the region is sometimes looked upon as an area comprising some kind of sameness, especially in center, but lacking definite borders. Frequently, the term is used to delimit an area smaller than a subcontinent, but large and varied enough not to be discriminated as being uniform throughout (Whittlesey, 1954). More important, again, to the scientific approach is that a region is not accepted as a concrete object of concern but as a segment of the complexities of phenomena that can be examined in terms of their spatial and areal interrelatedness.* It is an instrument for analyzing areal groupings of complex elements on the surface of the earth. But even though Hartshorne (and others) have stated that the issue that regions are genuine entities or real objects is dead, it keeps "popping up" like an opening sore. David Grigg has recently reminded us that there are still some geographers, especially the Soviets and East Europeans, who regard regions as concrete objects and that other scientists, who employ spatial procedures (sociologists, economists, botantists) think in terms of or within the same frame of reference (Grigg, 1967). Grigg notes that the problem apparently has not been resolved and that it, perhaps, is not a matter of right or wrong, but rather simply a matter of two different

---

* The question of whether or not regions exist as concrete objects is one which concerned German geographers throughout the nineteenth century. The various themes of discussion have been reported on by Hartshorne on two occasions in English (Hartshorne, 1939, 1958).

views of the world (Grigg, 1967). A special point is made of the foregoing because it may be of significance with respect to remote sensing. For if some geographers and other scientists believe that distinct entities exist in the spatial distribution of phenomena and they can produce fruitful research results following this particular path, then remote sensing as a research tool may be of some service to them.

The data inputs for regional analysis--whether regions are mental constructs, concrete objects, or regions of "act"--are numerous and varied. Remote sensing can be helpful in regional analysis procedures in a great number of ways. Along with field work, maps, and documents, remote sensing can provide inventory inputs to regional studies. Remote sensing, along with space technology, provides for expanded data returns from three standpoints--spectral, spatial, and temporal.

Voluminous literature and tremendous amounts of research time are presently being expended on cataloging the various types of spectral signatures that exist for terrestrial objects within the various ranges of the electromagnetic spectrum. Remotely sensed data returns--ultraviolet (UV), visual (and its various subdivisions), infrared (IR), microwave, radar--provide for means whereby earth features can be identified, classified, and mapped to a better degree than before. The simple task of object interpretation is made more expansive by means of remote sensing (Robben, 1960).

Brian Berry notes that a geographic fact can be described as "a single observation recorded from the spatial point of view" or a "single characteristic at a single place or location" (Berry, 1964). More often than not, a geographic fact is one set of observations, according to Berry, of either "the same characteristic at a series of places or a series of characteristics of the same place" (Berry, 1964). Obviously, analysis of a single trait at a single location provides little challenge for investigation; and, as such, the term "geographical fact" may be somewaht pretentious. If, however, each of the two parts of Berry's statement is pluralized, either singularly or in concert, there are implied several propositions worthy of scientific endeavors. For example, if more than one characteristic exists at a place, then it can be questioned how such traits exist in relation to each other. Similarly, if a single object exists at several places, then it can be questioned how the object exists at many places--and if several of the same element-complexes exist in combination--and how they relate to their location. All these imply investigations of spatial arrangements and distribution, spatial integration, spatial interactions, and organization and spatial processes.

Whittlesey identified three classes of regions which correlate to the types of geographic facts just mentioned: the single, multiple, and total regions (Whittlesey, 1954). All these may be amenable to sensing from two, perhaps three, points of reference. Remote sensing, as already mentioned, can be used for object interpretation; but the object observed may be recognized in different manners. One approach (type I) is to consider the image produced on a remote sensing return as a direct representation of the earth object; i.e., the object is recognized in terms of some identifying characteristic generally associated with the visual range (or some other human sensory capability--hearing, smelling, tasting, and feeling). A second approach (type II) would be to consider the image as a surrogate or proxy of some earth object. The third approach (type III) is to consider the image as a direct representation of an earth object which is normally not detectable within the visual range of the electromagnetic spectrum.

To illustrate the above, the IR thermal scan imagery of Imperial Valley, California, is used (Figure 11-2). The light fluffy objects which are located on the edges of the roads in the Imperial Valley can be interpreted as trees--the type I approach mentioned above. This image could also be considered a single-feature region. Because, however, these features exist within environmental conditions which are desertlike, they can be further considered as surrogates for water, a substance which cannot be detected directly from the picture--a type II approach. Finally, because these features appear as a light image (on a return taken at night) they serve to indicate that there is a greater degree of heat present in and around the feature than there is in the surrounding environment--a type II approach. These fluffy objects are the result of the fact that the trees serve as heat sinks, and the remote sensing device serves to indicate a meteorological process which is invisible to photographic sensors or the human eye.

Point of note can be made of the fact that the regionalization process of morphologic elements, which form single, multiple, or even perhaps total regions, can be carried beyond "looks" which exist within the visual-field range. Furthermore, significant evidence about the dynamic processes associated with earth elements in their spatial setting can be detected, analyzed, and interpreted

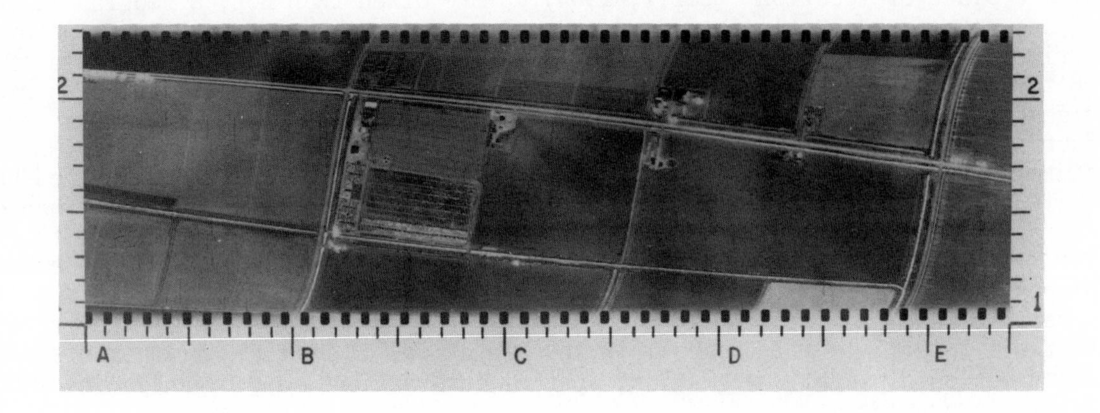

Figure 11-2. Imperial Valley, California, University of Michigan/National Science Foundation Short Course on Remote Sensing of the Environment (Prepared from imagery supplied by HRB-Singer, Inc.).

when remote sensing is used. However, to fully utilize the type II and III approaches mentioned above, the investigator must be familiar with the energy-flow profiles which are associated with the different sensor systems. He must have some knowledge of the operations, characteristics, and capabilities of remote sensing devices (see Chapter 2). It is not enough that scientists carrying out a regional procedure be able to do object-interpretation alone.*

Recently several investigators have regarded regionalization as a form of classification, and have formally presented the analogy between the two systems (Bunge, 1966). Although several researchers have "hinted" of the relationship between the two approaches, Grigg seems to have taken the forefront in this endeavor. His pronouncement rests not on the discovery of the classification procedure with respect to geography but rather on recognition of the similarities between the regionalization, especially in geography, and the manner in which classification is carried forth in some of the other sciences, e.g., biology and agronomy (Grigg, 1967).

Classification is, perhaps, the pre-science approach by which the scientist can gain some order out of that which appears to be earthly chaos. Following the classification procedure, objects which are similar in some properties are grouped together into classes, or classes are constructed of objects which maintain relationships among themselves. Individuals are the classified objects, and all individuals have one or more properties. In the classification process, a property which is designated for grouping purposes is designated as a differentiating characteristic. And the differentiation of classes of objects at the same levels produce categories. The process may be repeated until a hierarchy of classes can be produced. The classification procedure presented here can also be reversed, and this approach is known as logical division. Classification and logical division (both classification procedures) can be equated to the inductive and deductive procedures respectively (see Figure 11-3). The rules and procedures of the classification have been set down by writers from various disciplines, but especially philosophy (Harvey, 1969). It is not the present purpose to engage in the methodological discussion concerning it, but there are a number of significant implications here with respect to remote sensing in regional analysis and especially in terms of spatial and temporal aspects.

The problem to be examined here is what Harvey (1969) and Grigg (1967) call the geographical individual, while Dickinson (1970) recognizes the same as the regional cell. Dickinson clearly describes his concept as follows:

Landscape is made up of a mosaic of form units. These are entities of associated landscape elements; that is, of relief, vegetation, land use and settlement. Human groups in the various activities, economic, social, and political, are arranged in space as functional units that either correspond in their smallest

* It is at this point that I disagree with a statement made by Dickinson that "this field remote sensing is beyond the scope of undergraduate training" (Dickinson, 1970); if these techniques are to be used, then the geography student must become familiar with physics, mathematics, and all of the auxillary sciences associated with remote sensing as early in his academic career as possible.

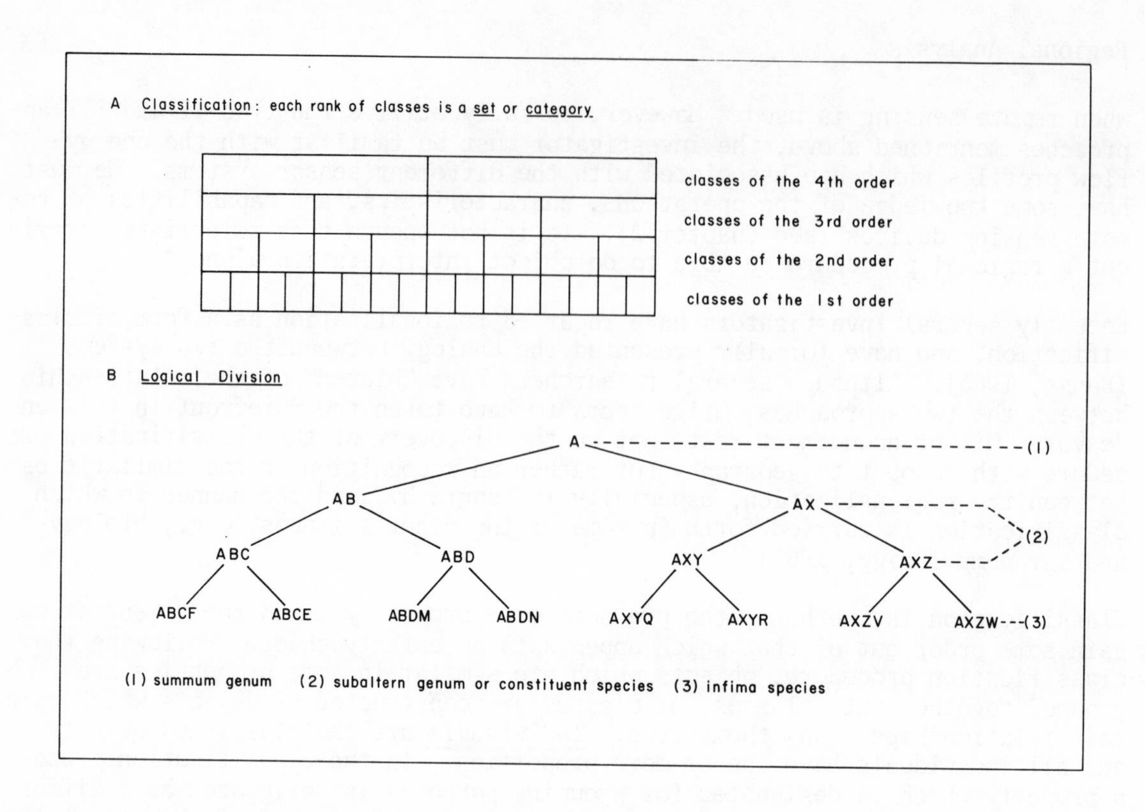

Figure 11-3. Diagrammatic Representation of Classification and Logical Division
Source: Grigg, 1967.

detail to a single form unit or to an association of section of several form units. Human societies are organized in a hierarchy of areas from these spatial units or cells, such as the farm, dwelling, or factory, to large spatial groupings of a social, economic, cultural, and polictical character. It is only in terms of these human functional groupings, the areas they cover, and how they operate as entities, that the character and areal interrelations of the elements of the landscape become understandable (Dickinson, 1970).

With respect to landscape items (regionalism as a fact), a problem arises as to identifying the individual with which the geographer or other spatial scientists must deal; i.e., the farm, block, resident, and so forth. Harvey notes that two types of languages have been developed to handle such situations. "What is termed the individuation of an object may result from (1) the properties which the object manifests, or (2) the position occupied by an object" (Harvey, 1969). He notes, furthermore, that geographers often fail to differentiate the type of language that they are using, and a tremendous amount of confusion exists, especially in regionalization. A similarity exists here, which was expressed earlier, with respect to regionalism as an act that can be defined in terms of a space-time language, e.g., TVA; the regionalism of fact may be thought of as the Tennessee Valley, a drainage system.

A significant contribution, with respect to a strategy whereby individuation can be incorporated in the process of regionalizing (classifying), has been made by Nunnally and Witmer (1970). Although their scheme, which follows the pattern suggested by Grigg, refers mainly to land use, it could be extended to any number of type elements or element-complexes on the surface of the earth. Among other things, Nunnally and Witmer suggest that a strategy for land-use mapping should be based on three tenets: (1) interpretation of land use in as great detail as is possible with complete definition of each category, (2) establishment of hierarchal categories by grouping similar or related uses, and (3) use of a uniform point sampling technique for tabulating data of large areas. They tested their strategy using low-altitude photographic remote sensing returns, and the results seem to be quite promising.

When working with large-scale imagery, especially photography, the process of object identification is not far removed from that of field work. Although a different perspective is involved, the large scale of observation permits easy recognition and identification of the objects involved. Such is not the situation when smaller-scale imagery or lower-resolution imagery is used. Haggett approaches the same problem, however, from a different direction. He notes that researchers often have difficulty in seeing the link between their field observations and smaller-scale situations--sectional, national, or global situations (Haggett, 1965). Furthermore, he notes from McCarty et al.: "In geographic investigation it is apparent that conclusions derived from studies made at one scale should not be expected to apply to problems whose data are expressed at other scales. Every change will bring about the statement of new problems and there is no basis for assuming that associations existing at one scale will also exist at another" (McCarty et al., 1956).

The keys, which are used to identify objects existing on standard or conventional low-altitude and large-scale aerial photographs, are size, shape, shadow, tone/color, texture, and pattern. Through research techniques known as the "convergence of evidence," clues are developed which also permit identification of objects. In most instances, the interpreter has some a priori knowledge of what the objects are. Such may not be the situation with hyperaltitude or orbital data. With respect to identification of objects appearing on spacecraft imagery, only tone/color, texture, and pattern appear at present to be appropriate. Some of the signatures of geographic individuals are clearly identifiable (e.g., water bodies, forest areas, and large urban places), but a tremendous number of other signatures are unrecognizable to the average person. One frame of reference which may be of some significance in defining geographic individuals on space photography or other remote sensor returns of low resolution, and may be of academic and practical worth, is the photomorphic concept.

In the past decade, several geographers have attempted to identify and explain the significance of patterns of similar tones and textures appearing on remote sensor returns. In the process of examining photo mosaics and photo maps of Chile, MacPhail (1971) noted that identifiable patterns of broad areas could be recognized. These patterns appeared to be the result of a composite of several terrestrial features--fields and fence lines, drainage, land use, superficial rock cover, vegetation, and other elements. Obviously these were many of the things with which solar radiation interacted on the surface of the earth and were recorded on film in bands allowed to filter through the sensor (camera) system. The repetitive patterns of similar image characteristics, mainly tone and texture, were called photomorphic units by MacPhail. A similar project was undertaken by Nunnally (1968) using a side-looking airborne radar (SLAR) image of the Asheville, North Carolina, area. Peplies and Wilson (1970) applied the same concept to Apollo 9 imagery of northern Alabama and analyzed the spacecraft photograph in relation to rural regional problems. They found that they could relate some of the regional problems to the photomorphic areas which they identified, especially if the images were the result, at least in part, of the earth features involved in the problem, e.g., poor drainage.

The techniques which MacPhail, Nunnally, and Peplies and Wilson used, however, were largely subjective and depended strongly on what the eye could differentiate on the return. Flynn and Peplies (1972) are attempting to provide a procedure whereby a more objective result can be obtained using the major factors of tone/color, texture, and pattern. It seems apparent to them that tonal considerations should receive first priority because (1) tone/color can be defined in terms of spectral density differences, (2) texture is the tonal repetition of objects which are too small to be discerned as individuals, and (3) pattern is macroscopic grouping of tonal variation.

Peplies and Flynn (1972) have applied the photomorphic technique to an Apollo 9 photo of the Mississippi Delta.* Photomorphic areas were first delimited subjectively following the criteria of noting tone, first; texture, second; and finally, pattern. Later, a more sophisticated analysis was attempted, using a microdensitometer and computer readouts. The problem of defining the goegraphic individual as it relates to a photomorphic area then became apparent. It was concluded that the geographic individual should take the form of a circle because of the lack of directional bias. Median density values for the circular cells were recorded at the center of the circles (the control point for an area) and compared against other cells for changes in density value which indicated boundary situations. In order that the entire photo was covered, the circles overlapped. It was concluded by Peplies and Flynn that the control area sizes may be environmentally modulated; i.e., for different areas the geographic individual may vary because of different assemblages of environmental elements. For example, assemblages of elements which compose photomorphic units in the Great Plains generally appear at large spatial intervals, in contrast to the humid East where the assemblages of elements change in short distances. A procedure was followed whereby the size of the circle was determined by expanding circles at regular size increments. The average density values for each increment was graphically plotted, and the size circle to be used was accepted when "a steady state" was reached. Several sample situations were made to validate the proper size. In the case of the Apollo 9 photo of the Mississippi Delta, the size of the circle represented 5 square miles on the earth.

The procedure described above is preliminary, for, although it can provide a "handle" which may lead to objective analysis of tonal characteristics of photomorphic units (geographic individuals), it does not describe the texture of the cell. Attempts are being made to use Fourier analysis by means of an optical bench to describe textural traits. The research designs, at this stage, are still extremely primitive.

---

* This area was used because of high correlation of patterns between a map drawn by Edward Higbee (1958) and the Apollo photo.

It may be somewhat incorrect to refer to the morphological traits which appear in proper-sized cells on a remote sensing return as geographic individuals of photomorphic units, for, until the significance of the form triats are determined, the tonal/color, textural, and pattern values are not meaningful. MacPhail and Lee (1972) have worked out a model which can be used to establish the validity of the concept of photomorphic mapping, and to determine factors responsible for contrasting characteristics of the different photomorphic patterns. The model involves selecting a group of operational variables, which represent physical and cultural traits of the urban-rural landscape and can be obtained through field work and from other sources of information. MacPhail and Lee suggest that data selected then be subjected to statistical tests to verify intramorphic and interphotomorphic patterns. The two techniques are principal components analysis and discriminant analysis.

Although the procedures described above are still tentative and preliminary, they seem to promise a methodology and technique whereby photomorphic areas can be described and can lead to one type of regional analysis. In addition to describing the procedure whereby texture and pattern can be defined, additional research needs to be directed toward explaining the temporal aspects associated with remote sensing imagery. For example, it can be observed that most image characteristics associated with spacecraft imagery have some "duration" quality. Except for meteorological traits--clouds--the majority of natural and cultural features defined on spacecraft imagery are "around" for some period of time--a week, a month, a season. In contrast, much of the significant information content detectable from large-scale imagery is of short duration. The relationships between spatial scales and resolutions have yet to be established. The regionalization process is strongly dependent on research of this type--for example, how many photographs of the Earth Resource Technology Satellite 1 (ERTS-1) or the upcoming Skylab and ERTS-2 need to be analyzed to verify the existence of photomorphic regions.

Temporal characteristics present another aspect of the regionalization process, especially in terms of uniform and nodal regions (Whittlesey, 1954). Uniform regions are similar throughout in terms of the tolerance levels permitted by the criteria used to define the areas. Nodal regions are homogeneous with respect to internal structure and organization. Each nodal region has its focal point and maintains a relationship with the surrounding area in terms of lines of circulation. Because the concept of nodality involves a dynamic system--namely, circulation of some phenomena--it implies directly a temporal element.

It is apparent that the photomorphic concept could be considered a type of uniform or formal region, and remote sensing can be used to delimit such regions. Remote sensing, on the other hand, could be used to inventory the terrestrial traits which could lead to defining nodal areas, if the terrestrial traits have morphological expression--e.g., road networks and the sizes of central business district (CBD) areas. Several researchers have followed this theme. Holz, Huff, and Mayfield (1969) used aerial photography to study 40 towns in the Tennessee River Valley in an attempt to predict the size of these central places on the basis of morphological evidence present on the remote sensing returns. Researchers at the University of Iowa have tested a model of urban distribution to facilitate spacecraft imagery interpretation. The model tested showed that locational coordinates of central places can be predicted from knowledge of larger centers and the underlying nonurban population (Hulfquist, Rushton, and Schmitt, 1971). Honea (n.d.) used remote sensor imagery to determine the size of trade

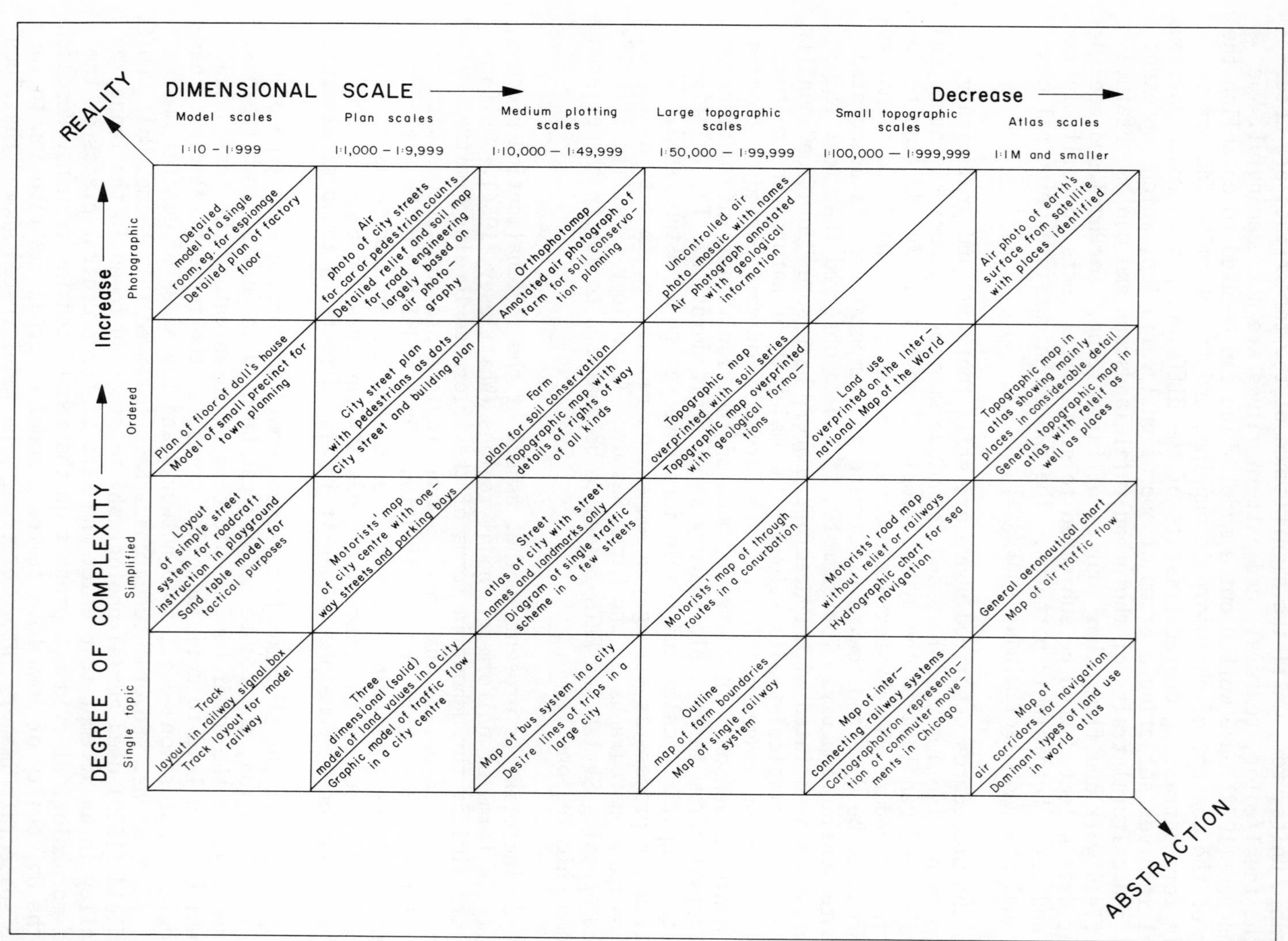

Figure 11-4. The Gradient between Reality and Abstraction Indicating Examples of Types of Maps and Remote Sensing Returns at Their Appropriate Level of Abstraction (Source: Chorley and Haggett, 1967).

areas and traffic flows. Using color infrared returns, Honea was able to determine the dominant turn-directions within an area, especially at crossroads or where driveways lead into major arteries. At locations where the turn directions reverse and focus in the opposite direction, one finds a break between trade areas, generally a zone rather than a distinctive point.

In summary and conclusion, there are apparently numerous ways in which remote sensing can be of use in the regionalization process. Some of these ways are simple and direct and others are more abstract (specific examples can be seen in Figure 11-4). To be sure, remote sensing is not a panacea for defining regions, and it should always be considered as only a data-acquisition system. However, along with field work, maps, documents, and other techniques, remote sensing data can help to unravel the problem of seeing spatial order in that which appears to be spatial chaos. We could add a phrase to Carl Ritter's famous statement, "ask the earth for its laws," which could be, "and if you don't get an answer, take a picture of the earth, interpret the return, and develop appropriate generalizations."

REFERENCES

Anderson, James, 1970, "Some Traditional Approaches to Regional Analysis with Remote Sensing," unpublished report, University of Florida, Gainesville.

Berry, B. J. L., 1964, "Approaches to Regional Analysis: A Synthesis," *Annals of the Association of American Geographers*, 54(1):2-11.

Broek, J. O. M., and J. W. Webb, 1968, *A Geography of Mankind*, McGraw-Hill Book Co., New York.

Bunge, William, 1966, *Theoretical Geography*, Land Studies in Geography, Lund.

Chorley, R. J., and P. Haggett, 1967, *Models in Geography*, Methuen and Company, Ltd., London.

Dickinson, R. E., 1970, *Regional Ecology, The Study of Man's Environment*, John Wiley & Sons, Inc., New York.

Grigg, D., 1967, "Regions, Models and Classes," in R. J. Chorley and P. Haggett, Eds., *Models in Geography*, Mathuen and Company, Ltd., London, pp. 461-509.

Haggett, Peter, 1965, "Scale Component in Geographical Problems," in R. J. Chorley and P. Haggett, Eds., *Frontiers in Geographical Teaching*, Mathuen and Company, London, pp. 164-185.

Haggett, Peter, 1972, *Geography: A Modern Synthesis*, Harper & Row, New York.

Hartshorne, Richard, 1939, *The Nature of Geography*, Association of American Geographers, Lancaster, Pa.

Hartshorne, Richard, 1958, *Perspective on the Nature of Geography*, Rand McNally and Co., Chicago.

Harvey, David, 1969, *Explanation in Geography*, St. Martin's Press, New York.

Higbee, E., 1958, *American Agriculture*, John Wiley & Sons, Inc., New York.

Holz, R. K., D. L. Huff, and R. C. Mayfield, 1969, "A Study of Urban Spatial Structure Based on Remote Sensing Imagery," *Final Report of the AAG Commission on Geographic Applications of Remote Sensing for May 1968 - May 1969*, No. 2, Association of American Geographers, Washington, D.C.

Honea, R. B., (n.d.), *The Derivation of Trade Areas and Traffic Flows from Remote Sensing Imagery*, Technical Report No. 15, Association of American Geographers, Commission on Geographic Applications of Remote Sensing, Johnson City, Tenn.

Hulfquist, N. B., G. Rushton, and R. P. Schmitt, 1971, "Identifying and Forecasting Change in a Regional System of Urban Places," *Proceedings of the Seventh International Symposium on Remote Sensing of Environment*, vol. III, University of Michigan, Ann Arbor, pp. 1553-1561.

MacPhail, D., 1971, "Photomorphic Mapping in Chile," *Photogrammetric Engineering*, 37:1139-1148.

MacPhail, D., and Y. Lee, 1972, *A Model for Photomorphic Analysis Tennessee Valley Test Site*, Technical Report 71-3, Association of American Geographers, Commission on Geographic Applications of Remote Sensing, Johnson City, Tenn.

McCarty, H. H., J. C. Hook, and D. S. Kuos, 1956, *The Measurement of Association in Industrial Geography*, University of Iowa Department of Geography Report, University of Iowa, Iowa City.

Nunnally, N. R., 1968, *Integrated Landscape Analysis with Radar Imagery*, Technical Report I, East Tennessee State University Remote Sensing Institute, Johnson City.

Nunnally, N. R., and R. E. Witmer, 1970, "Remote Sensing for Land Use Studies," *Photogrammetric Engineering*, 36:449-453.

Pattison, W. D., 1963, "The Four Traditions in Geography," paper presented at the opening session of the annual convention of the National Council for Geographic Education, Columbus, Ohio.

Peplies, R. W., and T. J. Flynn, 1972, "Spacecraft, Photomorphic Units and Regional Analysis," paper presented at 1972 Southeastern Conference of the Institute of Electrical and Electronic Engineers, University of Tennessee, April 10-12.

Peplies, R. W., and J. D. Wilson, 1970, *Analysis of a Space Photo of a Humid and Forested Region: A Case Study of the Tennessee Valley*, Technical Report 70-6, East Tennessee State University Remote Sensing Institute, Johnson City.

Robben, E. L., 1960, "Fundamentals of Photo Interpretation," in R. N. Colwell, Ed., *Manual of Photo Interpretation*, American Society of Photogrammetry, Washington, D.C., pp. 99-168.

Tudor, David, 1958, "Against Geography," *Universities Quarterly*, 12(3):261-273.

Whittlesey, Derwent, 1954, "The Regional Concept and Regional Method," in P. E. James and C. F. Jones, Eds., *American Geography--Inventory and Prospect*, Syracuse University Press, Syracuse, N.Y.

12

Remote Sensing of Environmental Quality: Problems and Potential

Homer Aschmann and Leonard W. Bowden
University of California, Riverside

Technology has advanced to a point today where the potential exists for man to indiscrimnantly disrupt environmental processes and degrade the "quality" of the environment. The realization of some of this potential already has served to stimulate and focus public attention upon environmental issues, particularly with respect to identifying and evaluating significant elements of environmental quality. Remote sensing is regarded as a potentially effective contributory data source for the latter identification and evaluation procedures. In this chapter, Aschmann and Bowden contend with the difficult task of explaining the concept of environmental quality and relating remote sensing applications to it. Discussion emphasizes subject definition, indices of environmental quality, indices that may be remotely sensed, and some implications (social and legal) of using remote sensing technology. The treatment clearly reflects the problem of elucidating the nature of environmental quality (similar to the problem faced by Peplies in dealing with the regional concept in the previous chapter), and serves an important function in stimulating thought about this critical contemporary issue.

Problems of degradative changes in the environment have long been a concern of at least a few individuals. In the United States, George P. Marsh's *Man in Nature* (published in 1864) marks perhaps the earliest attempt at a comprehensive assessment of the situation. For many decades, the theme has been important in the literature, although only recently has degradation in the quality of living come to be of concern comparable to that for the depletion of economic resources.

The environment does not exist in any defineable "pure" form--geologically or ecologically--and when we speak of pollution, it means departure from a state believed to be normal or satisfying rather than from a pure state. The key to assessment of any environmental quality is to determine change and (1) if the

---

Many of the concepts developed in this chapter were initially published in the *Professional Geographer* (Aschmann, 1971).

changes are acceptable within some broad "normal" range, (2) if the change is degradative, and (3) if there are possible alternatives. Because change is both natural and man-induced, the major concern is whether the change is directly harmful to man or has the effect of altering the natural productivity of an area.

In general, and for obvious reasons, the recognition of deteriorating environments for living occurred first among students of the urban scene. The total environment is always subject to pollution, be it volcanic dust, deer manure, or disposed bottles. Most pollutants are soon broken down or integrated into the environment through decay or burial. Over the eons, absorption, oxygenation, and consumption easily clear and dispose of modest amounts of pollutants. Interaction in the environment among land, water, air, and biomass tends to stabilize or control excessive pollution. Except in geologic time spans, little alteration occurs in the natural landscape. Even during the past several milenia when man as a farmer began upsetting cycles of erosion, deposition, and decay, there were only isolated and random occurrences that were notably destructive.

With the industrial revolution and the increase in urbanization, cultural or human pollution has expanded exponentially in the past two centuries. Streams have become sewers unable to dispose of or control the material dumped into them. Cities have often become ribbons of refuse and garbage that surround dismal housing and uncontrolled development, and are now beset by foul air. The magnitude and intensity of the problems have become so much greater in recent years that they have blossomed into major political issues. The problems have generated conflicts penetrating all segments of the economic system.

Suddenly the impact of environmental change has impressed itself on the populace at large. It is a popular national political issue; and, while there is a notable opportunity at least to maintain if not improve the quality of our environment through newly marshalled political power, there is at least equal risk of ill-informed or ill-considered popular action alleviating some problem and aggravating other more serious ones.

A simple example of the risk may be recognized in the field of the generation of electrical energy. It was easy for southern California to reduce atmospheric pollutants appreciably by requiring steam generators to shift from heavy oils to natural gas as fuels. But natural gas is a limited resource. At a foreseeable time, perhaps no more than a decade in the future, no further increases in its supply to the region can be expected, and a period of declining supply will ensue. Will society then accept higher levels of pollution or lower energy supplies? On a more general and slightly longer-term level, it is conceivable that concern about the environmental pollution caused by the generation of energy will cause the acceptance of a less expansive technological economy. The result would be a decline in capital formation so that shifts to other, as yet undeloped, forms of energy generation will not be possible when, as then must be, the country's reserves of fossil fuels and concentrated ores of uranium and thorium are exhausted.

It seems clear that no policy regarding environmental quality could be meaningful if it failed to take less than a national perspective. Perhaps only a policy based on a worldwide perspective will have long-term viability. In the relatively clearcut problem of pollution, the basic unity of the atmosphere's circulation and that of the bordering oceans means that the general load of pollutants will form a base on which local aggravations may be compounded. In the less clearly defined realm of the aesthetic appeal of culturally altered landscapes, our mobile population is already capable of spoiling one region after another. With the possible exception of Alaska, so little wilderness remains in the United States that, even if all of it were preserved, it cannot serve a population that seeks it out as a relief from its culturally blighted landscapes of normal residence.

THE NEED FOR GUIDELINES

At the present time, limited government action on environmental quality is the pattern being followed. Standards are to be set and action ordered by various local, national, or international governmental agencies. There are as yet very few guidelines for either the private citizen or private industry to follow should they wish to minimize pollution. The widely accepted concept that the only social responsibility of business is to use resources and engage in activities designed to increase profits, while staying within the societally determined rules of the game, places the burden on government to set the rules. However, damage to the environment arises from so many sources that only intense cooperation by the private and public sectors can produce the slightest positive result. In the present state of our knowledge, even the indices we use to measure the results may be misleading.

The most widely used index is the Gross National Product (GNP), which represents the goods and services produced in a given period that move through market channels. As the name implies, GNP is "gross" because it disregards the conventional kind of depreciation, the wearing out of plants and equipment, etc. However, tax deductions are allowed for depreciation, to compensate for such declines. Yet, nobody recognizes depreciation of the environment and allows for wear-out or pollution in any form. The GNP does not take account of depreciation of environmental quality. In fact, increase in GNP is often at the expense of resources. If pollution, for example, eroded rather than bolstered the GNP, government agencies and private industry might well have taken steps to clean up the environment years ago.

Unfortunately, much of our pollution is unmeasurable in monetary terms such as effect on GNP. How does one value a beer can on the landscape; the production and consumption of the beer and container added to the gross national wealth. Somehow a change in indices is necessary before individuals or agencies can take action to remove or retard pollution. A satellite may permit detection of a sugar-beet field experiencing rising salinity that will ultimately make it worthless, but to advise the farmer on action or guidelines to remove salinity requires a new political basis for action, especially if it lowers his annual income.

Indices of Environmental Quality

Because the tastes of individuals vary in genetically, culturally, and idiosyncratically influenced ways, a rigorous set of indices of environmental quality can be developed only for a single individual. For him it is likely to be valid only at a single point in his lifespan. It is, however, possible to get general agreement as to a set of parameters within which almost all members of American society would scale the quality of their environments, making for good, less good, and unattractive living conditions. Extreme values of any phenomenon are likely to be avoided if possible. For example, within the range of ambient air temperatures that occur naturally on the earth's surface, -100°F to +130°F, humans at rest will find themselves comfortable only in about 15 percent of the range, perhaps 50°F to 80°F. Within that range, individual differences hold sway and cause office feuds over the governance of the air conditioner.

Some of the parameters of environmental quality are considered at some length in the following pages.

Change. A generalization may be stated that any change from an accustomed environment will be recognized as one for the worse. A counterargument is that the absence of change is the equivalent of death. The march of the seasons and the associated atmospheric and vegetational changes assure us that some diversity will always be present on this planet.

It is recognized that throughout the earth's history and man's history the environment has evolved, placing stresses on individuals biologically and culturally. Excessively rapid change has resulted in the extinction of species, but, with the aid of culture, man has been able to adapt with far greater speed than biological evolution permits. Such adaptation has permitted migration and occupation by the human species of a wider variety of environments than by any other higher organism. However, change (in pollution levels for example) may occur so rapidly that even cultural adaptation is impossible. In a milder context, present rates of change, especially in urban areas, place severe stresses on mature individuals. A national policy of continued and accelerating economic growth with its implicit requirement for environmental change, risks placing unbearable burdens on a major fraction of the citizenry. At the least, they will regard their environment as deteriorating even as their consumption level rises.

Boundary Conditions. It is probable that with some elements of environment, or configurations of elements, there are sharp thresholds beyond which the total environment changes from perceptibly good to perceptibly bad, or vice versa, as when water changes from a liquid to a solid state. More typically, there is a transitional zone, in space or in time, the latter perhaps more relevant to a national environmental policy. Some individuals are stressed by a given level of crowding or atmospheric pollution, while others remain unaffected. At some point, all will be affected, and the community will collapse. In addition to the ambient air temperature, noted above, many environmental phenomena will be recognized by man as acceptably good only in their middle ranges, with boundary conditions at both ends of those ranges. Carbon dioxide, unpleasant or lethal at very high concentration in the atmosphere, must be present if plants are to grow. In different ranges for cities and rural areas, population densities may be so high or so low as to constitute negative environmental features. Departures from an optimum, which itself would vary according to individual and cultural preferences, would involve a considerable transitional range before discomfort was generally recognized.

Linearity. An environment may be perceived in linear or progressive fashion or synoptically with all senses and from many directions. An example or descriptive analogy might be the contrast between proceeding about one's affairs on Main Street in an American small town and attempting the same activities in the plaza of a Latin American town of comparable size. Most humans perceive in both fashions, although there are notable individual and cultural differences as to which will be dominant. Cultural environments in particular may be constructed so as to favor overpoweringly one mode of perception over the other. This one-sidedness may be a notably negative environmental feature for at least a fraction of the population, being regarded as either ordered dullness or overstimulating confusion.

Indices of Environmental Quality That May Be Remotely Sensed

Pollution Levels. Pollutants of the land, waters, and air may be identified as material by-products of human activity; they may range from unwanted to positively toxic. The quantity introduced correlates positively with level of economic activity, technological advance, and population density. They are our wastes which we ask our environment to disperse and dilute in fluids or to hold locally without extended contamination. Almost without exception, an increase in pollutants is recognized as degrading environmental quality. Since we know the situation we want to approach and the one we wish to avoid, assessing pollutant levels seems to be a simply useful task for any technology, including remote sensing, that can undertake it. Where the pollution level is especially acute, ground sensors already are monitoring it and are likely to be increasingly employed. Remote sensing may have two distinctive contributions to make: (1) providing a full distributional inventory of areas of atmospheric and water pollution to a single set of standards throughout the national territory and (2) determining the regional, national, or worldwide burden of pollutants, a burden widely believed to be increasing, that air and land are being forced to bear. Measured changes in this load may present critical signals that will remain unread from local vantage points.

Foam and the biologically induced signatures that indicate eutrophication in water bodies, and foreign materials that alter the atmosphere's transmissiveness for particular types of radiation, seem likely elements to begin sensing remotely on a systematic and inventorying plan. If the technology for this enterprise does not now exist it is well within reach (Welch et al., 1972).

Translating the generally held antipathy toward pollutants into a national or even regional environmental policy, however, brings in complications from two sources. If humans are to survive at all, they will introduce pollutants into their environment. At some level, this must be tolerated. Further, the threshold beyond which a particular pollutant becomes inescapably noxious varies with the pollutant, the individual's allergic sensitivities, and with his own experience and cultural background. There is need for research to identify these thresholds, and their limits if they prove to be zones, and to learn whether and which pollutants interact to magnify their effects or to cancel them.

Diversity. An environment with a high degree of diversity constitutes a definitely positive qualitative value. There is very little capability to increase the diversity of the natural physical environment, although unfortunately cultural practices have in many instances reduced it. Hence, it is in the cultural landscape that diversity may be thought of as varying over time and subject to influence by national policy. In scale and content, diversity means quite different things in urban and rural areas, and separate indices of diversity must be developed for each.

Two quite disparate sorts of questions arise in connection with this theme. Can rural and/or urban diversity, or some satisfactory surrogate, be sensed remotely in a meaningful manner? Field checking against extant imagery can provide an answer and can begin to build up a data base from which appropriate indices of diversity may be formed. Preceding or parallel to this inquiry, answers to much more difficult questions must be sought. How do the several sectors of the population react to varying degrees of diversity in their environments of residence and work, and in those to which they resort for recreation or restoration? What elements are meaningful to them? The extant literature on the subject consists almost exclusively of highly subjective appreciations by concerned protagonists, but not necessarily typical individuals.* At extreme levels, as with extensive public housing projects or vast stretches of nearly uniform suburban tract homes in urban areas, or with monocultural grain farming in parts of the mid-United States, general agreement could probably be obtained that the lack of diversity is a readily perceived negative environmental characteristic. In the intermediate range, where early identification of trends toward an increase or decrease of diversity might have relevant policy implications, however, we just do not know what the society wants. Fairly sophisticated field and perceptual research will be needed to establish meaningful diversity indices and to scale them in terms of environmental quality.

Privacy versus Accessibility; Security versus Interest or Opportunity. Paired sets of apparently contradictory values may be identified as apparently contributing to desirable living conditions as they are inseparably combined and balanced. It is postulated that normal individuals need both privacy and wide social contacts on a frequently alternating basis, perhaps every day, and high-quality environment will provide ready opportunities for both experiences. Again, the relative proportions of each that are sought will vary sharply over individuals and perhaps over cultural groups. Security of person and property is certainly related to privacy, but extreme privacy and isolation can involve great insecurity.

Delicately balanced relationships do play a definite part in determining an individual's well-being, but we acknowledge a lack of certainty that their physical concomitants in the cultural landscape can be clearly identified and will prove subject to remote sensing (see Estep, 1968 and Klass, 1971 for good discussions of these problems). Two situations indicate that there is at least some possibility. The contrast between the fenced yards of suburban southern California and the unfenced ones of small and middle-sized Midwestern towns is readily perceptible. It is conceivable that each system provides the desired environment for its respective residents. It is likely, however, that one system is extending and superseding the other, a fact subject to monitoring by remote sensing, and the associated reactions of residents where the changes are occurring can be investigated. Frazer Darling (1955) has perceptively noted in Northwestern Scotland that various sorts of social malaise are much more prevalent in rural districts where forest cover has been removed than in those where forest cover has been preserved.

* A large fraction of the publications of the Sierra Club fall in this category in reference to wild areas. See Jacobs (1961) in regard to the urban scene, and Aschmann (1966, 1967).

<u>Relations between Energy Consumption and the Amenities of Living</u>. Rising living standards in the developed countries of the world during the past century have been almost perfectly paralleled by an exponential increase in energy consumption. That this exponential increase must soon terminate seems clear because of both the growing scarcity of the fossil fuels from which cheap energy has largely been derived, and the incapacity of the environment to absorb the pollutants produced in the process of energy generation. A legitimate question arises: To what degree is increasing energy consumption making for better living? Some leverage in answering such a question might be gained through remote sensing of the energy flux in a wide variety of urban areas, both within and outside the United States. A number of elements of "noise" would have to be eliminated from the readings, such as natural as opposed to culturally induced radiation. The climatic stress being alleviated by energy expenditure at particular times and places, and the special concentrations of energy utilization in localities with heavy industries that serve far larger regions are possible subjects for investigation. Such an investigation, however, seems potentially possible if not within the present state of the art. The sort of information that might be gained could be an assessment of how much more unpleasant the outdoor summer climate of Manhattan is made by air conditioners.

<u>Single-Purpose Preemptive Land Use</u>. The least elastic of the resources of any nation or society is space, and the value of space is at its highest in proximity to urban population concentrations. A number of nationally and locally initiated programs are progressively preempting space, especially in and near population concentrations, for single and exclusive uses. An example is road and highway transportation and parking lots, with freeways forming the most egregious offender and making ever-increasing demands. No human value is served but that of transporting an individual to work in uncomfortable and tense privacy on a routine journey, and stowing his vehicle in a man-made desert until he retrieves it for a similar journey home. Waste-disposal areas and industrial plants make similar exclusive demands, although sometimes with more continual use and greater justification. It seems worth while to inventory in some detail the spaces in and around urban population concentrations to see what fractions of them are being preempted for a single "use" and what fractions remain for carrying on the variety of activities that constitute human life. Changes in the proportions in the direction of exclusiveness may afford a needed warning calling for modifications in land use policies.

<u>Concomitants of Blight</u>. When they are fully developed, blighted districts, both urban and rural, are easily identified visually by almost any observer. The social indices of malaise, obtained from the census, welfare records, or the police blotter, correlate almost perfectly. By the time such correlations are possible, corrective or ameliorative measures are likely to be unavailing unless they extirpate the extant population and its artifacts. We need to recognize earlier the signatures of blight; and, perhaps more significantly, we need to recognize those combinations of features in both the physical and cultural landscapes that are associated with, precede, or produce blighted neighborhoods. Many of these are readily subject to being sensed remotely.* Position in

* Abandoned cars and other machinery around farmsteads signal an impoverished rural environment, and indicators that correlate strongly with housing quality and socioeconomic conditions have been defined from aerial photographs in Chicago and Los Angeles (Wellar, 1967; Mullens, 1969; Bowden and Brooner, 1970).

relation to traffic arteries that are barriers to local communication are well recognized in American folklore by expressions such as "back of the yards" and "the wrong side of the tracks." It is truly remarkable that such wisdom never entered the consciousness of freeway engineers.

From a distant vantage point more such patterns to serve as warnings of locally deteriorating environmental quality may be apparent.

CONCLUSION

Of course, information taken from remote sensing data is useful only as a surrogate for a real, although subjectively perceived, environmental quality. An example is the case where both privacy and social contacts are sought on an alternating basis. Crowdedness, or the lack of it, of things on the land is most certainly detectable by remote sensing. What is not distinguishable is the desire for privacy or social contact. However, as one builds the totality of environment from those data bits of remote sensing, often a picture or some insight is formed. Land use, transportation facilities, energy supplies, recreation opportunities, or more simply "the role of man's activities on the land" are readily subjected to analysis with remote sensing methodology.

Occasionally, there are surprises such as finding out that vegetative condition sensed with color infrared photography is directly correlated with quality of housing and neighborhood income. On the other hand, some apparent sensors are not as useful as the engineering might lead you to believe. Thermal infrared scanners at one time seemed to be a potential tool for nighttime traffic monitoring, but as yet they have failed to make the step.

There is no question that remote sensing's greatest contribution is in the detection and inventory of land use. No other method of survey or analysis comes near to remote sensing when land use data are desired. As has been stressed earlier, once the land use is known, then the real or potential "land pollution" can be described. Just as important is that land use is a prime determinant of existing and potential air and water pollution.

Overall, the state of art of remote sensing is technically advanced to the point of being very helpful in the evaluation of environmental quality--the major outstanding questions are "what" to detect and "how will it effect policy?" In effect, before any evaluation as to cost/benefit can be made, costs that have previously been accepted as parts of the social or cultural pollution inherent in production must be recognized and introduced into the equation. Therefore, standard economic series such as GNP will acquire a rather bleak look for a long time. If pollution-control efforts should expand significantly, new guidelines will be needed to interpret what the statistical series are telling us and what the remote sensing data are telling us about economy and environment. Once the policy changes are made, the new data will not be comparable to data in use today. In the future, remote sensing of the environment will have to play a much more significant role in early detection of pollutants and serve as a method of monitoring policy and regulation enforcement.

REFERENCES

Aschmann, Homer, 1966, "People, Recreation Wildlands, and Wilderness," *Yearbook of the Association of Pacific Coast Geographers*, pp. 5-15.

Aschmann, Homer, 1967, "Purpose in the Southern California Landscape," *Journal of Geography*, 66:311-317.

Aschmann, Home, 1971, "Prolegomena to the Remote Sensing of Environmental Quality," *Professional Geographer*, 23:59-63.

Bowden, L. W., and W. G. Brooner, 1970, "Aerial Photography: A Diversified Tool," *Geoforum: Journal of Physical, Human and Regional Geo-Sciences*, 2:19-32.

Estep, S. D., 1968, "Legal and Social Policy Ramifications of Remote Sensing Techniques," *Proceedings of the Fifth Symposium on Remote Sensing of Environment*, University of Michigan, Ann Arbor, pp. 197-217.

Darling, F. Frazer, 1955, *West Highland Survey*, Oxford University Press, New York, pp. 303-305.

Jacobs, Jane, 1961, *The Death and Life of Great American Cities*, Random House, New York.

Klass, P. J., 1971, *Secret Sentries in Space*, Random House Inc., New York, 236 pp.

Mullens, R. H., 1969, "Analysis of Urban Residential Environments Using Color Infrared Aerial Photography: An Examination of Socioeconomic Variables and Physical Characteristics of Selected Areas in the Los Angeles Basin," *Interagency Report NASA-153*, U.S. Department of Interior, Washington, D.C.

Welch, R. I., A. D. Marmelstein, and P. M. Maughan, 1972, *A Feasibility Demonstration of an Aerial Surveillance Spill Prevention System*, Contract No. 68-01-0145, Office of Research and Monitoring, United States Environmental Protection Agency, 120 pp.

Wellar, B. W., 1967, "Generation of Housing Quality Data from Multiband Aerial Photography," *Research Report 32A*, Northwestern University, Department of Geography, Evanston, Ill.

Appendix 1

Glossary

A characteristic problem associated with the development of new fields of science is the definition of terminology, or technical jargon. A new field will normally borrow terms from an established field or develop its own, with a consequent requirement for assigning logical and consistent definitions. Remote sensing is still in its infancy with regard to this concern, and definitions are in a state of periodic revision. The terminology presented in this glossary represents the editors' best efforts to compile a listing of basic remote sensing vocabulary. It is not intended to be complete, and some of the definitions are legitimate foci for criticism, review, and revision. This is consistent with the philosophy of this book, which is to present state of the art information as well as subjects that stimulate further research and concerned discussion.

Aberration
A defect in an optical image. (All lens systems have some aberration.)

Absorption
A process of attenuation which an electromagnetic emanation undergoes as it passes through the atmosphere or other medium or as it strikes an object.

Absorption Spectroscope
An instrument used to determine (by means of spectral analysis) the amount of absorption that occurs when energy is directed through a specific type of surface or material.

Active System
A remote sensing system which transmits its own electromagnetic emanations at an object(s) and then records the energy reflected or refracted back to the sensor.

Angstrom (Å)
A unit of measurement equal to one ten-millionth of a millimeter.

Band
A set of adjacent wavelengths in the electromagnetic spectrum with a common characteristic, such as the visible band.

Cathode-Ray Tube
A vacuum tube generating a focused beam of electrons which can be deflected by electronic and magnetic fields. The terminus of the beam is visible as a spot or line of luminescence on a sensitized screen at one end of the tube.

Classification
(1) An administrative system wherein information, equipment, or processes are categorized according to their importance in national security.
(2) A systematic arrangement of objects (which have been imaged) into a logical structure or hierarchy.

Detector
A device or substance capable of receiving, transforming and/or recording directly energy emitted and/or reflected from objects.

Electromagnetic (EM) Spectrum
An array of all electromagnetic radiation that moves with the constant velocity of light in a harmonic wave characterized by wavelength, frequency, or amplitude.

Emission
Electromagnetic energy given off from an object created by the molecular oscillations of the body itself.

Emissivity
A ratio relating the amount of energy given off by an object to the amount given off by a "black body" at the same temperature, and normally expressed as a real positive number between 0 and 1.

Emulsion
A suspension of a light-sensitive silver halide (usually silver chloride or silver bromide) in a colloidal medium (usually gelatin) used for coating photographic films, plates, and papers.

Enhancement
Refers to various processes and techniques designed to render optical densities on imagery more susceptible to interpretation.

Gamma
A numerical measure of the degree of difference between the contrast of a subject matter on a photographic negative as compared to the actual contrast of the subject photographed. A gamma of 1.0 indicates unity of contrast; a gamma of 1.1 indicates that the negative has more contrast than the subject.

Ground Truth
Information concerning the actual state of the environment at the time of a remote sensing overflight.

Hardware
Physical equipment used for data collection and handling, including such objects as remote sensing equipment and computers.

Illumination
The "light" or energy impinging upon a given area or object. Usually this light consists of direct sunlight plus skylight.

Image-Motion-Compensation (IMC)
A process wherein film is moved backward through a camera during exposure to compensate for the forward motion of the aircraft along the flight path; this prevents image blurring.

Imagery
The visual representation of energy recorded by remote sensing instruments.

Line Scanning
The use of a facsimile device, such as an intensity-modulated cathode-ray tube, which produces an image by viewing and recording a scene a line at a time.

Low-Light-Level Television Symstems
A system where incident light is intensified by utilizing a photoemissive cathode, focusing electronic optics and a screen. Can be used to provide effective night capability in the visible and near visible spectral range.

Micrometer (u)
A unit of measurement equal to one-millionth of a meter or one-thousandth of a millimeter.

Micron (u)
See Micrometer - equivalent

Microwave
Energy transmitted at a wavelength between 10^2 and 10^{-1} cm.

Modulation Transfer Function (MTF)
An optical analogue to general systems theory whereby the total resolution of the components of an optical system can be measured in terms of brightness as a linear function.

Multiband
The use of one or more sensors to obtain imagery from different portions of the reflectance portion of the electromagnetic spectrum (most commonly used in connection with black-and-white photography).

Multispectral
The use of one or more sensors to obtain imagery from different portions of the electromagnetic spectrum.

Multispectral Scanner (MSS)
A line scanning device which employs an oscillatory mirror to continuously scan perpendicular to a platform's velocity. Optical energy is sensed simultaneously by an array of detectors in visible bands from 0.5 to 1.1 u. Platform motion provides the along-track progression of the scan lines.

Nanometer (um)
A unit of measure equal to one millimicron or one-millionth of a millimeter.

Near-Infrared (black-and-white, color)
That portion of the electromagnetic spectrum between visible light and thermal infrared with wavelengths from 0.7 to 1 u. Black-and-white infrared versus color infrared refers to the film type which is used to image in the portion of the spectrum from 0.7 to 0.9 u.

"Noise"
An unwanted disturbance recorded by a remote sensing device which makes recognition more difficult.

Optical density
The transparency of an object or the degree to which it prevents light from passing through it. It equals

$$\log_{10} \frac{\text{Intensity of incident light}}{\text{Intensity of transmitted light}}$$

Optical-Mechanical Scanner
A system utilizing a rotating mirror and a detector in conjunction with lenses and prisms to record reflected and/or emitted electromagnetic energy in a scanning mode along the flightpath.

Optical system
A system whose basic function involves the recording of a scene by the use of lenses and/or prisms.

Passive system
A remote sensing system which images energy emitted or reflected as radiation from a given scene. The system produces, transmits, and records no energy of its own.

Phonon

A quantum of sound energy analogous to the photon of electromagnetic energy. It is a function of a constant and the vibration of a sound wave.

Photographic System

A remote sensing system which produces an image directly on a film emulsion from reflected electromagnetic radiation of wavelengths in the visible and near-infrared portions of the EM spectrum.

Photon

The minimum energy unit in electromagnetic radiation; an indivisible quantity of electromagnetic energy. Intensity of radiation depends upon the number of photons for a unit area over a certain amount of time. Its magnitude is directly proportional to the frequency of the wavelengths.

Platform

The object, structure, vehicle, or base upon which a remote sensor is mounted.

Polarization

The act or process of filtering energy in such a way that the vibrations are restricted to a single plane. Unpolarized energy vibrates in all directions perpendicular to the propagating source.

Quanta

See Photon - equivalent

Radar

A sensor which directs energy from its own source at an object and then records the echo return of the transmitted beam in the radio frequency range.
Synthetic Aperture--Systems which use a physically small antenna to simulate an antenna of greater length. This is accomplished by transmitting and receiving a series of pulses which are then integrated into a single pulse for display.
Brute force--Systems using a physically fixed antenna to transmit and receive single pulses, which are then displayed directly.

Radiometer

An instrument for measuring radiant energy.

Reflectance

A measure of the ability of a body to reflect light or sound. The reflectance of a surface depends on the type of surface, the wavelength of the illumination, and the illumination and viewing angles.

Reflectance Infrared

Radiation in the spectral region from 0.7 to 3.0 u which is reflected as a result of illumination from natural sources. The portion of the infrared region which is imaged on infrared sensitive films (up to ≃ 1.5 u).

Resolution

The ability of a remote sensing system to distinguish signals that are close to each other spatially, temporally, or spectrally.

Ground Resolution--The minimum distance between two or more adjacent features or the minimum size of a feature which can be detected; usually measured in conventional distance units, e.g., feet or inches.
Image Resolution--Resolution expressed in terms of lines per millimeter for a given photographic emulsion under given situations.
Thermal Resolution--Image Resolution expressed as a function of the minimum temperature difference between two objects or phenomena.

Return
Emitted or reflected energy received by a sensor from a source.

Scattering (Rayliegh, Mie, Nonselective, Raman)
Scattering--The deflection or absorption and reemission of electromagnetic energy as it passes through a medium (usually the earth's atmosphere).
Scattering, Rayliegh--The circumference of the particles is less than about one-tenth of the wavelength of the incident radiation, thus the scattering coefficient is inversely proportional to the fourth power of the wavelength.
Scattering Mie--is produced by spherical particles where the diameter of the particles is comparable with the wavelength of the energy scattered.
Scattering, Nonselective--occurs when the size of the scattering particles become several times larger than the wavelength of the light energy causing all colors to scatter equally. This accounts for the white appearance of clouds.
Scattering, Raman--Much less common than the other types, Raman scattering takes place when a photon has a partially elastic collision with a molecule. The wavelength is altered by an amount equivalent to the amount of energy given up or received by the photon.

Sensor
An instrument used to detect and/or record electromagnetic energy associated with an environmental phenomenon(a).

Signal
A pulse or unit wave of electromagnetic energy transmitted or received by a sensor.

Signature
The unique spectral reflectance or emission response from a particular object or environmental association.

Software
Methods, techniques, and systems of interpretation of imagery; photointerpretation keys and computer programs are examples of software.

Spectrophotometer
An optical instrument used to compare the intensities of the corresponding colors of two spectra.

Specular Reflection
The reflection of electromagnetic energy without scattering or diffusion.

State of the Art
The most advanced knowledge in a field currently being used in operational systems.

Surrogate (proxy)
An indicator of the presence of some object or condition of interest which is functionally related, although not visible, to phenomena identifiable on the imagery.

Synoptic
Providing a summary of information about a whole characterized by comprehensiveness or breadth of view; i.e., the general overall view of a large portion of the earth's surface afforded by imagery obtained from high-altitude platforms such as satellites.

Target
The object or objects which are being imaged by remote sensors. It also refers to a planned array of objects being used to calibrate one or more remote sensing instruments.

Thermal Infrared
Electromagnetic energy between wavelengths of approximately 3 um and 1000 um. The intensity of emissions is dependent upon temperature and emissivity of the object being sensed.

Thermography
Word proposed to replace the phrase "Thermal Infrared Imagery." Thermography would be a record of emitted thermal energy in the same context as photography is a record of reflected energy. A thermogram would then be a quantitative thermal infrared image.

Transmission
The passage or propagation of energy through a medium.

Ultraviolet
Electromagnetic energy which is shorter than visible light but longer than x-rays, located between 10 and 400 millimicrons.

Vidicon
A camera system in which a light pattern is stored on the surface of a photoconductor, the photoconductor then being scanned by an electron beam.

Visible
That portion of the electromagnetic spectrum between wavelengths of 400 to 700 millimicrons, which corresponds to the spectral response of the human eye.

Wavelength
The distance between two successive crests or troughs of a wave at uniform frequency and oscillation, measured in the direction of the propagation of the wave. Wavelength equals velocity divided by frequency.

Window
A band of the electromagnetic spectrum which offers maximum transmission and minimal attenuation through a particular medium with the use of a specific sensor.

Appendix 2

Selected Bibliography of Remote Sensing Research

A problem frequently faced by the beginning student of remote sensing is what sources of literature to read in order to acquire a basic background in the field. A wealth of literature has been produced, but a significant proportion (contract and technical reports) is not generally available. The intent of this appendix is to provide a selected bibliography of major, easily procured works that introduce basic concepts of sensor systems and major topics of remote sensing research. These publications can then be used as a springboard from which to explore the more abundant, highly specialized literature.

In order to maximize efficient utilization, the bibliography has been alphabetized and numbered consecutively. Each publication has further been classified as a reference source for SENSORS, or SELECTED TOPICS, or both. The reader thus has two options for using the bibliography. The first option involves the following steps: (1) examination of the SENSORS and/or SELECTED TOPICS listings to find the topic of interest, (2) finding the numbered references appropriate to the topic, and (3) consulting the bibliography to acquire the full references related to the numbers. Given the name of a particular author of interest the alternative option is to (1) select a reference from the bibliography bearing his name, (2) note its number, and (3) check the number under the SENSORS and SELECTED TOPICS listings to determine the subject matter of the reference.

SENSORS

Color IR: 10, 75, 103, 109, 137, 157, 158, 159, 199, 202.

Microwave: 13, 59, 79, 90, 94, 102, 215.

Multiband: 11, 44, 108, 116, 120, 124, 132, 138, 212.

Multispectral: 48, 49, 66, 92, 105, 106, 114, 119, 125, 142, 144, 221.

Photography: 14, 15, 23, 24, 26, 29, 41, 51, 54, 55, 62, 67, 77, 83, 89, 93, 99, 104, 109, 111, 117, 118, 122, 144, 145, 156, 163, 168, 173, 184, 185, 189, 197, 208, 211, 219.

Radar: 20, 80, 84, 128, 140, 141, 151, 181, 183, 200, 217.

Thermal IR: 1, 17, 35, 45, 63, 86, 92, 95, 103, 121, 127, 131, 154, 175, 176, 181, 195, 196, 202, 213, 215, 220.

Ultraviolet: 72, 88, 147.

SELECTED TOPICS

Agriculture: 11, 32, 51, 53, 74, 77, 84, 85, 98, 115, 132, 149, 177, 178, 179, 189, 191, 207, 221.

Archaeology: 82, 126, 134, 166, 176, 187, 198, 218.

Automation: 11, 38, 60, 104, 107, 170, 190, 192, 193, 209, 217.

Environment/ Ecology: 34, 39, 42, 47, 60, 76, 79, 80, 96, 101, 108, 111, 116, 127, 129, 140, 182, 188, 195.

General Works: 4, 6, 7, 8, 12, 15, 16, 23, 25, 27, 29, 41, 43, 44, 76, 89, 99, 110, 113, 117, 118, 136, 146, 147, 148, 153, 155, 162, 174, 185, 197, 203, 205, 211.

Geology: 10, 31, 35, 69, 72, 120, 121, 127, 128, 165, 175, 181, 184, 208, 209, 220.

Image Enhancement: 24, 26, 44, 65, 171, 172, 214.

Land Use: 3, 9, 18, 19, 32, 40, 61, 78, 83, 100, 145, 146, 154, 163, 173, 181, 189, 201.

Physiography: 10, 46, 49, 69, 86, 102, 106, 109, 122, 126, 127, 128, 129, 152, 156, 157, 161, 167, 181, 184, 188, 193.

Pollution: 13, 33, 64, 66, 81, 119, 130, 160, 186, 204, 215, 216.

Quantitative/ Computer: 22, 26, 52, 57, 73, 87, 91, 100, 167, 184, 193, 194, 196.

Range Management: 36, 37, 54.

Regionalism: 1, 28, 40, 53, 85, 133, 135, 151, 163, 169, 201.

Urban: 1, 5, 21, 30, 40, 50, 56, 68, 97, 104, 123, 124, 135, 137, 138, 139, 143, 164, 168, 180, 183, 212, 213.

Vegetation/ Forestry: 2, 3, 14, 37, 45, 58, 70, 93, 103, 112, 141, 146, 150, 159, 206, 210, 216, 219, 221.

BIBLIOGRAPHY

1. Adams, W. M., L. Lepley, and S. Chang, 1970, "Coastal and Urban Surveys with IR," *Photogrammetric Engineering*, 36(2):173-180.

2. Aldrich, R. C., 1968, "Remote Sensing and Forest Survey; Present Application, Research, and a Look at the Future," *Fifth Symposium on Remote Sensing of Environment*, University of Michigan, Institute of Science and Technology, Ann Arbor, pp. 357-372.

3. Aldrich, R. C., 1971, "Space Photos for Land Use and Forestry," *Photogrammetric Engineering*, 37(4):389-401.

4. Alexander, R. H., 1967, "Man's New Views of the Earth: The Potential of Remote Sensing," in S. B. Cohen, Ed., *Problems and Trends in American Geography*, Basic Books, New York.

5. Alexander, R. H., L. W. Bowden, D. F. Marble, and E. G. Moore, 1968, "Remote Sensing of Urban Environments," *Fifth Symposium on Remote Sensing of Environment*, University of Michigan, Institute of Science and Technology, Ann Arbor, pp. 889-991.

6. American Society of Photogrammetry, 1960, *Manual of Photographic Interpretation*, Falls Church, Va.

7. American Society of Photogrammetry, 1966, *Selected Papers on Remote Sensing of Environment*, Falls Church, Va.

8. American Society of Photogrammetry, 1968, *Manual of Color Aerial Photography*, Falls Church, Va.

9. Anderson, J. R., 1971, "Land Use Classification Schemes," *Photogrammetric Engineering*, 37(4):379-387.

10. Anson, A., 1970, "Color Aerial Photos in the Reconnaissance of Soils and Rock," *Photogrammetric Engineering*, 36(4):343-354.

11. Anuta, P. E., and R. B. MacDonald, 1971, "Crop Surveys from Multiband Satellite Photography Using Digital Techniques," *Remote Sensing of Environment*, 2(1):53-67.

12. Aschmann, H., 1971, "Prolegomena to the Remote Sensing of Environmental Quality," *The Professional Geographer*, 23(1):59-63.

13. Auckland, J. C., W. H. Conway, and Dr. N. K. Sanders, 1969, "Detection of Oil Slick Pollution on Water Surfaces with Microwave Radiometer Systems," *Sixth Symposium on Remote Sensing of Environment*, University of Michigan, Institute of Science and Technology, Ann Arbor, pp. 789-796.

14. Avery, T. E., 1966, *Forester's Guide to Aerial Photo Interpretation*, Agriculture Handbook 308, U.S. Department of Agriculture, Washington, D.C., 40 pp.

15. Avery, T. E., 1968, *Interpretation of Aerial Photographs,* Burgess Publishing Company, Minneapolis, Minn.

16. Badgley, P. C., L. Childs, and W. L. Vest, "The Application of Remote Sensing Instruments in Earth Resource Surveys," *Geophysics,* 32(4):583-601.

17. Bastuschek, C. B., 1970, "Ground Temperature and Thermal Infrared," *Photogrammetric Engineering,* 36(10):1064-1072.

18. Bawden, M. G., 1967, "Applications of Aerial Photography in Land System Mapping," *Photogrammetric Record,* 5(30):461-464.

19. Belcher, D. J., E. E. Hardy, and E. S. Phillips, 1971, *Land Use Classification with Simulated Satellite Photography,* Agriculture Information Bulletin 352, Economic Research Service, U.S. Department of Agriculture, Washington, D.C., 352 pp.

20. Berkowitz, R. S., Ed., 1965, *Modern Radar, Analysis, Evaluation and System Design,* John Wiley & Sons, New York, 660 pp.

21. Berlin, G. L., 1971, *Application of Aerial Photographs and Remote Sensing Imagery to Urban Research and Studies,* Council of Planning Librarians, Monticello, Ill., 35 pp.

22. Billingsley, F. C., A. F. H. Goetz, and J. N. Lindsley, 1970, "Color Differentiation by Computer Image Processing," *Photographic Science and Engineering,* 14(1):28-35.

23. Bird, J. B., and A. Morrison, 1964, "Space Photography and Its Geographic Applications," *Geographical Review,* 54(4):463-486.

24. Birdseye, C. H., 1940, "Stereoscopic Photographic Mapping," *Annals of the Association of American Geographers,* 30(1):1-24.

25. Bock, P., and J. G. Barnby, 1969, "Survey Effectiveness of Spacecraft Remote Sensors," *Photogrammetric Engineering,* 35(8):756-763.

26. Bodechtel, J., and G. Kritikos, 1971, "Quantitative Image Enhancement of Photographic and Non-Photographic Data for Earth Resources," *Seventh Symposium on Remote Sensing of Environment,* University of Michigan, Institute of Science and Technology, Ann Arbor, pp. 469-486.

27. Borchert, J. R., 1968, "Remote Sensors and Geographical Science," *The Professional Geographer,* 20(6):371-375.

28. Bowden. L. W., 1970, "Remote Sensing of Southern California: An Attempt to Inventory a Geographic Region," in *Proceedings of the Association of American Geographers,* vol. 2, pp. 17-21.

29. Bowden, L. W., and W. G. Brooner, 1970, "Aerial Photography: A Diversified Tool," *Geoforum,* 2:19-32.

30. Branch, M. C., 1971, *City Planning and Aerial Information,* Harvard University Press, Cambridge, Mass., 283 pp.

31. Brennan, P. A., and J. Lintz, Jr., 1971, "Remote Sensing of Some Sedimentary Rocks," *Seventh Symposium on Remote Sensing of Environment*, University of Michigan, Institute of Science and Technology, Ann Arbor, pp. 253-268.

32. Brunt, M., 1961, "Air Photography in Land Reclamation," *World Crops*, 13(5): 175-178.

33. Burnett, E. S., and P. J. White, 1970, "Water Pollution, the Role of Remote Sensing," *Journal of Remote Sensing*, 1(3):9-12.

34. Cain, S. A., 1966, "Current and Future Needs for Remote Sensor Data in Ecology," *Fourth Symposium on Remote Sensing of Environment*, University of Michigan, Institute of Science and Technology, Ann Arbor, pp. 3-6.

35. Cantrell, J. L., 1964, "Infrared Geology," *Photogrammetric Engineering*, 30(6):916-922.

36. Carneggie, D. M., 1968, "Applying Remote Sensing Technology for Improving Range Resources Inventories," *Fifth Symposium on Remote Sensing of Environment*, University of Michigan, Institute of Science and Technology, Ann Arbor, pp. 373-385.

37. Carneggie, D. M., and D. T. Lauer, 1966, "Uses of Multisensor Remote Sensing in Forest and Range Inventory," *Photogrammetria*, 21(4):115-141.

38. Centner, R. M., and E. D. Hietanem, 1971, "Automatic Pattern Recognition," *Photogrammetric Engineering*, 37(1):177-186.

39. Clark, J., and B. Stone, 1965, "Marine Biology and Remote Sensing," in *Oceanography from Space*, Woods Hole Oceanographic Institute, pp. 305-312.

40. Collins, W. G., and A. H. A. El-Beck, 1971, "The Acquisition of Urban Land Use Information from Aerial Photographs of the City of Leeds (Great Britain)," *Photogrammetria*, 27(2):71-92.

41. Colwell, R. N., 1964, "Aerial Photography--A Valuable Sensor for the Scientist," *American Scientist*, 52:17-49.

42. Colwell, R. N., 1967, "Remote Sensing as a Means of Determining Ecological Condition," *Bioscience*, 17(7):443-449.

43. Colwell, R. N., 1968, "Remote Sensing of Natural Resources," *Scientific American*, 28(1):54-69.

44. Colwell, R. N., and J. D. Lent, 1969, "The Inventory of Earth Resources on Enhanced Multiband Space Photography," *Sixth Symposium on Remote Sensing of Environment*, University of Michigan, Institute of Science and Technology, Ann Arbor, pp. 133-143.

45. Colwell, R. N., and D. L. Olson, 1965, "Thermal Infrared Imagery and Its Use in Vegetation Analysis by Remote Aerial Reconnaissance," *Third Symposium on Remote Sensing of Environment*, University of Michigan, Institute of Science and Technology, Ann Arbor, pp. 606-617.

46. Condit, H. R., 1970, "The Spectral Reflectance of American Soils," *Photogrammetric Engineering*, 36(9):955-966.

47. Cooper, C. F., 1965, "Potential Applications of Remote Sensing to Ecological Research," *Third Symposium on Remote Sensing of Environment*, University of Michigan, Institute of Science and Technology, Ann Arbor, pp. 601-606.

48. Crane, R. B., 1971, "Preprocessing Techniques to Reduce Atmospheric and Sensor Variability in Multispectral Scanner Data," *Seventh Symposium on Remote Sensing of Environment*, University of Michigan, Institute of Science and Technology, Ann Arbor, pp. 1345-1355.

49. Cronin, J. F., C. E. Molineux, R. W. Dowling, and R. E. Hudson, 1967, "Multispectral Photographic Sensing of Terrestrial Features," in *Proceedings of the Symposium on Electromagnetic Sensing of the Earth from Satellite*, Polytechnic Press of the Polytechnic Institute of Brooklyn, New York.

50. Davis, Jeanne M., 1966, *Uses of Airphotos for Rural and Urban Planning*, Agriculture Handbook 315, Economic Research Service, U.S. Department of Agriculture, Washington, D.C., 36 pp.

51. Dill, H. W., 1967, *Worldwide Use of Airphotos in Agriculture*, Agriculture Handbook 344, U.S. Department of Agriculture, Washington, D.C., 23 pp.

52. Doyle, F. J., 1970, "Computational Photogrammetry," *Photogrammetric Engineering*, 36(6):567-569.

53. Draeger, W. C., and L. R. Pettinger, 1972, "A Regional Agricultural Survey Using Small Scale Aerial Photography," *Photogrammetria*, 28(1):1-15.

54. Driscoll, R. S., 1971, *Color Aerial Photography--A New View for Range Management*, USDA Forest Service Research Paper RM-67, Rocky Mountain Forest and Range Experiment Station, Fort Collins, Colo., 11 pp.

55. Duddek, M., 1970, "Lenses and Techniques for Aerial Color," *Photogrammetric Engineering*, 36(1):58-62.

56. Dueker, K. J., and F. E. Horton, 1971, "Urban Change Detection Systems: Status and Prospects," *Seventh Symposium on Remote Sensing of Environment*, University of Michigan, Institute of Science and Technology, Ann Arbor, pp. 1523-1536.

57. Duhaut, J., 1972, "Photogrammetry for Marine Studies," *The Photogrammetric Record*, 7(39):273-294.

58. Earth Satellite Wetlands Mapping Team, 1972, "Aerial Multiband Wetlands Mapping," *Photogrammetric Engineering*, 38(12):1188-1189.

59. Edgerton, A. T., 1968, "Engineering Applications of Microwave Radiometry," *Fifth Symposium on Remote Sensing of Environment*, University of Michigan, Institute of Science and Technology, Ann Arbor, pp. 711-724.

60. Egan, W. G., 1971, "Automated Delineation of Wetlands in Photographic Remote Sensing," *Seventh Symposium on Remote Sensing of Environment*, University of Michigan, Institute of Science and Technology, Ann Arbor, pp. 2231-2252.

61. Ellis, A. K., 1970, "The Utilization of Aerial Photographs to Investigate Land Use Change," *Social Education*, 34(8):882-885.

62. Erhart, R. R., and R. D. Havira, 1972, "Experimenting with Films and Filters," *Journal of Geography*, 71(5):302-306.

63. Estes, J. E., 1966, "Some Applications of Aerial Infrared Imagery," *Annals of the Association of American Geographers*, 56(4):673-682.

64. Estes, J. E., and B. Golomb, 1971, "Monitoring Environmental Pollution," *Journal of Remote Sensing*, 1(2):8-13.

65. Estes, J. E., and L. W. Senger, 1971, "An Electronic Multi-Image Processor," *Photogrammetric Engineering*, 37(6):577-586.

66. Estes, J. E., and L. W. Senger, 1972, "The Multispectral Concept as Applied to Marine Oil Spills," *Remote Sensing of Environment*, 2(3):141-163.

67. Eyre, A. L., 1971, "High Altitude Color Photos," *Photogrammetric Engineering*, 37(10):1149-1153.

68. Eyre, A. L., et al., 1970, "Census Analysis and Population Studies," *Photogrammetric Engineering*, 36(5):460-466.

69. Fezer, F., 1971, "Photo Interpretation Applied to Geomorphology--a Review," *Photogrammetria*, 27(1):7-53.

70. Finley, V. P., 1960, *Photo Interpretation of Vegetation--Literature Survey Analysis*, Technical Report 69, U.S. Army Snow, Ice and Permafrost Research Establishment, Corps of Engineers, U.S. Army.

71. Fischer, W. A., 1966, "Geologic Applications of Remote Sensors," *Fourth Symposium on Remote Sensing of Environment*, University of Michigan, Institute of Science and Technology, Ann Arbor, pp. 13-19.

72. Fischer, W. A., and D. L. Daniels, 1964, *Spectral Distribution of Ultraviolet Stimulated Luminescence*, USGS Technical Letter, NASA-3, pt.II, U.S. Geological Survey, Washington, D.C.

73. Fligor, P. D., 1970, "Computer Techniques for Remote Sensing," in *Papers from the Thirty-sixth Annual Meeting, March 1970*, American Society of Photogrammetry, pp. 171-186.

74. Frey, J. T., 1967, *Agricultural Applications of Remote Sensing: The Potential from Space Platforms*, Agricultural Information Bulletin 328, Economic Research Service, U.S. Department of Agriculture, Washington, D.C.

75. Fritz, N. J., 1967, "Optimum Methods for Using Infrared-Sensitive Color Films," *Photogrammetric Engineering*, 33(10):1128-1138.

76. Galneder, M., 1967, *Aerial Photographs: the First Hundred Years*, Bulletin 69, Special Libraries Association, Geography and Map Division, pp. 17-25.

77. Gausman, et al., 1970, "Color Photos, Cotton Leaves and Soil Salinity," *Photogrammetric Engineering*, 36(5):454-459.

78. Gimbarzevsky, P., 1966, "Land Inventory Interpretation," *Photogrammetric Engineering*, 32(6):967-976.

79. Gray, K. W., et al., 1971, "Microwave Measurement of Thermal Emission from the Sea," *Seventh Symposium on Remote Sensing of Environment*, University of Michigan, Institute of Science and Technology, Ann Arbor, pp. 1827-1845.

80. Greenwood, J. A., et al., 1969, "Oceanographic Applications of Radar Altimetry from a Spacecraft," *Remote Sensing of Environment*, 1(1):71-80.

81. Guinard, N. W., 1971, "The Remote Sensing of Oil Slicks," *Seventh Symposium on Remote Sensing of Environment*, University of Michigan, Institute of Science and Technology, Ann Arbor, pp. 1005-1026.

82. Gumerman, G. J., and T. R. Lyons, 1971, "Archeological Methodology and Remote Sensing," *Science*, 172(3979):126-132.

83. Haefner, N., 1967, "Airphoto Interpretation of Rural Land Use in Western Europe," *Photogrammetria*, 22(1):143-152.

84. Haralick, R. M., R. Caspall, and D. S. Simonett, 1970, "Using Radar Imagery for Crop Discrimination: A Statistical and Conditional Probability Study," *Remote Sensing of Environment*, 1(2):131-142.

85. Harnapp, V. R., and C. G. Knight, 1971, "Remote Sensing of Tropical Agricultural Systems," *Seventh Symposium on Remote Sensing of Environment*, University of Michigan, Institute of Science and Technology, Ann Arbor, pp. 409-433.

86. Harris, D. E., and C. L. Woodbridge, 1964, "Terrain Mapping by Use of Infrared Radiation," *Photogrammetric Engineering*, 30(1):134-139.

87. Hawkins, J. K., G. T. Eldring, K. W. Bixby, and P. A. Haworth, 1966, "Automatic Shape Detection for Programmed Terrain Classification," *Proceedings of the Society of Photo-Optical Instrumentation Engineers*, Seminar-in-depth on Filmed Data and Computers, Boston, Mass., pp. XVI-1 to XVI-9.

88. Hemphill, W. R., and S. J. Gawarecki, 1964, *Ultraviolet Video Imaging System*, Technical Letter NASA-3, pt. 1, U.S. Geological Survey, Washington, D.C.

89. Henderson, F. M., and T. J. Rickard, 1972, "Space Photographs as a Geographic Teaching Aid," *Journal of Geography*, 71(5):307-313.

90. Hodgin, D. M., 1966, "The Characteristics of Microwave Radiometry in Remote Sensing of Environment," in *Selected Papers on Remote Sensing of Environment*, American Society of Photogrammetry, Falls Church, Va., pp. 157-166.

91. Hoffer, R. M., and R. E. Goodrick, 1971, "Variables in Automatic Classification over Extended Remote Sensing Test Sites," *Seventh Symposium on Remote Sensing of Environment*, University of Michigan, Institute of Science and Technology, Ann Arbor, pp. 1967-1981.

92. Holter, M. R., 1967, "Infrared and Multispectral Sensing," *Bioscience*, 17(6):376-383.

93. Hostrop, B. W., and T. Kawaguchi, 1971, "Aerial Color in Forestry," *Photogrammetric Engineering*, 37(6):555-563.

94. Hollinger, J. P., 1971, "Remote Passive Microwave Sensing of the Ocean Surface," *Seventh Symposium on Remote Sensing of Environment*, University of Michigan, Institute of Science and Technology, Ann Arbor, pp. 1807-1817.

95. Holter, M. R., S. Nudelman, G. H. Suits, W. L. Wolfe, and G. J. Zissis, 1962, *Fundamentals of Infrared Technology*, Macmillan, New York, 442 pp.

96. Howard, J. A., 1970, *Aerial Photo-Ecology*, American Elsevier, New York, 325 pp.

97. Howard, W. A., 1969, *Remote Sensing of the Urban Environment: A Selected Bibliography*, Council of Planning Librarians, Monticello, Ill., 6 pp.

98. Huddleston, H. F., 1968, "Use of Remote Sensing for Livestock Inventories," *Fifth Symposium on Remote Sensing of Environment*, University of Michigan, Institute of Science and Technology, Ann Arbor, pp. 307-323.

99. Jensen, N., 1957, *Optical and Photographic Reconnaissance Systems*, McGraw-Hill Book Company, New York.

100. Johnson, C. W., 1971, "Computerized Land Patterns Mapping from Mono-Imagery," *Seventh Symposium on Remote Sensing of Environment*, University of Michigan, Institute of Science and Technology, Ann Arbor, pp. 1951-1965.

101. Johnson, P. L., 1969, *Remote Sensing in Ecology*, University of Georgia Press, Athens, 244 pp.

102. Kondratyev, D. Ya, Yu. M. Tomofeev, and Ye. M. Shulgina, 1971, "On the Feasibility of Determining Surface Soil Characteristics from Remotely Sensed Microwave Radiation," *Seventh Symposium on Remote Sensing of Environment*, University of Michigan, Institute of Science and Technology, Ann Arbor, pp. 1917-1920.

103. Knipling, E. B., 1970, "Physical and Physiological Basis for the Reflectance of Visible and Near-Infrared Radiation from Vegetation," *Remote Sensing of Environment*, 1(3):155-159.

104. Kracht, J. B., and W. A. Howard, 1970, *Applications of Remote Sensing, Aerial Photography, and Instrumented Imagery Interpretation to Urban Area Studies*, Council of Planning Librarians, Monticello, Ill., 34 pp.

105. Kriegler, F. J., 1971, "Implicit Determination of Multispectral Scanner Data Variation over Extended Areas," *Seventh Symposium on Remote Sensing of Environment*, University of Michigan, Institute of Science and Technology, Ann Arbor, pp. 759-777.

106. Kristof, S. J., and A. L. Zachary, 1971, "Mapping Soil Types from Multispectral Scanner Data," *Seventh Symposium on Remote Sensing of Environment*, University of Michigan, Institute of Science and Technology, Ann Arbor, pp. 2095-2108.

107. Krulikoski, S. J., and D. C. Kowalski, 1971, "Automatic Optical Profiling," *Photogrammetric Engineering*, 37(1):76-84.

108. Krumpe, P., H. R. De Selm, and C. C. Amundsen, 1971, "An Ecological Analysis of Forest Landscape Parameters by Multiband Remote Sensing," *Seventh Symposium on Remote Sensing of Environment*, University of Michigan, Institute of Science and Technology, Ann Arbor, pp. 715-730.

109. Kuhl, A. D., 1970, "Color and IR Photos for Soils," *Photogrammetric Engineering*, 36(5):475-482.

110. Lancaster, J., 1968, "Geographer and Remote Sensing," *Journal of Geography*, 67(5):301-310.

111. Langfelder, J., and D. B. Stafford, 1971, "Air Photo Survey of Coastal Erosion," *Photogrammetric Engineering*, 37(6):565-575.

112. Langley, P. G., 1969, "New Multi-stage Sampling Techniques Using Space and Aircraft Imagery for Forest Inventory," *Sixth Symposium on Remote Sensing of Environment*, University of Michigan, Institute of Science and Technology, Ann Arbor, pp. 1179-1192.

113. Latham, J. P., 1966, "Remote Sensing of the Environment," *Geographical Review*, 56(2):288-291.

114. Latham, J. P., and R. E. Witmer, 1967, "Comparative Waveform Analysis of Multisensor Imagery," *Photogrammetric Engineering*, 33(7):779-786.

115. Lauer, D. T., 1970, "Crop and Livestock Survey Techniques," *Journal of Remote Sensing*, 1(4):4-10.

116. Lent, J. D., and G. A. Thorley, 1969, "Some Observations on the Use of Multiband Spectral Reconnaissance for the Inventory of Wildland Resources," *Remote Sensing of Environment*, 1(1):31-45.

117. Leuder, D. R., 1959, *Aerial Photographic Interpretation, Principles and Applications*, McGraw-Hill Book Company, New York, 462 pp.

118. Linton, D. L., 1946, "The Use of Air Photographs in the Teaching of Geography," *Geography*, 31(154, Pt 4):129-134.

119. Lowe, D. S., and P. G. Hasell, 1969, "Multispectral Sensing of Oil Pollution," *Sixth Symposium on Remote Sensing of Environment*, University of Michigan, Institute of Science and Technology, Ann Arbor, pp. 755-765.

120. Lyon, R. J. P., 1970, "The Multiband Approach to Geological Mapping from Orbiting Satellites: Is it Redundant or Vital?" *Remote Sensing of Environment,* 1(4):237-244.

121. Lyon, R. J. P., and J. W. Paterson, 1966, "Infrared Spectral Signatures--A Field Geologic Tool," *Fourth Symposium on Remote Sensing of Environment,* University of Michigan, Institute of Science and Technology, Ann Arbor, pp. 215-230.

122. Mairs, R. L., 1970, "Oceanographic Interpretation of Apollo Photos," *Photogrammetric Engineering,* 36(10):1045-1058.

123. Marble, D., and F. Horton, 1969, "Extraction of Urban Data from High and Low Resolution Images," *Sixth Symposium on Remote Sensing of Environment,* University of Michigan, Institute of Science and Technology, Ann Arbor, pp. 807-818.

124. Marble, D. F., and E. N. Thomas, 1966, "Some Observations on the Utility of Multispectral Photography for Urban Research," *Fourth Symposium on Remote Sensing of Environment,* University of Michigan, Institute of Science and Technology, Ann Arbor, pp. 135-144.

125. Marshall, R. E., and F. J. Kriegler, 1971, "An Operational Multispectral Survey Program," *Seventh Symposium on Remote Sensing of Environment,* University of Michigan, Institute of Science and Technology, Ann Arbor, pp. 2169-2191.

126. Martin, Anne-Marie, 1971, "Archaeological Sites--Soils and Climate," *Photogrammetric Engineering,* 37(4):353-357.

127. Matalucci, R. V., and M. Abel-Hady, 1968, "Infrared Aerial Surveys in Environmental Engineering," American Society of Civil Engineers, *Journal of the Sanitary Engineering Division,* 94(SA6):1071-1084.

128. McAnerney, J. M., 1966, "Terrain Interpretation from Radar Imagery," *Fourth Symposium on Remote Sensing of Environment,* University of Michigan, Institute of Science and Technology, Ann Arbor, pp. 731-750.

129. McCurdy, P. G., 1947, *Manual of Coastal Delineation from Aerial Photographs,* Publication 592, U.S. Hydrographic Office, Washington, D.C., 143 pp.

130. McLellan, A., 1971, "Atmospheric Pollution Detection by Satellite Remote Sensing," *Seventh Symposium on Remote Sensing of Environment,* University of Michigan, Institute of Science and Technology, Ann Arbor, pp. 563-584.

131. McLerran, J. H., 1967, "Infrared Thermal Sensing," *Photogrammetric Engineering,* 33(5):505-512.

132. Meyer, M. P., and H. C. Chang, 1971, "Multiband Reconnaissance of Simulated Insect Defoliation in Corn Fields," *Seventh Symposium on Remote Sensing of Environment,* University of Michigan, Institute of Science and Technology, Ann Arbor, pp. 1231-1234.

133. Miller, O. M., 1938, "The Mapping of Northernmost Labrador," in Alexander Forbes, Ed., *Northernmost Labrador Mapped from the Air*, Special Publication 22, American Geographical Society, pp. 165-175.

134. Miller, W. C., 1957, "Uses of Aerial Photographs in Archaeological Field Work," *American Antiquity*, 23(1):46-62.

135. Mittelbach, F. G., and M. I. Schneider, 1971, "Remote Sensing: With Special Reference to Urban Regional Transportation," *The Annals of Regional Science*, 5(2):61-71.

136. Momsen, R. P., 1968, "The Orthophoto Map: Geographic Tool of the Future," *The Professional Geographer*, 20(3):177-180.

137. Moore, E. G., 1970, "Application of Remote Sensors to the Classification of Areal Data at Different Scales: A Case Study in Housing Quality," *Remote Sensing of Environment*, 1(2):109-122.

138. Moore, E. G., and B. S. Wellar, 1968, "Experimental Applications of Multiband Photography in Urban Research," *Transactions of Illinois State Academy of Science*, 61(1).

139. Moore, E. G., and B. S. Wellar, 1969, "Urban Data Collection by Airborne Sensor," *Journal of the American Institute of Planners*, 35(1):35-43.

140. Moore, R. K. and D. S. Simonett, 1967, "Radar Remote Sensing in Biology," *Bioscience*, 17(6):384-390.

141. Morain, S. A., and D. S. Simonett, 1967, "K-band Radar on Vegetation Mapping," *Photogrammetric Engineering*, 33(7):730-740.

142. Mozar, M., and R. Seige, 1971, "High Resolution Multispectral TV Camera System, *Seventh Symposium on Remote Sensing of Environment*, University of Michigan, Institute of Science and Technology, Ann Arbor, pp. 1475-1481.

143. Mumbower, L. E., and J. Donoghue, 1967, "Urban Poverty Study," *Photogrammetric Engineering*, 33(6):610-618.

144. Munday, J. C., W. G. MacIntyre, M. E. Penney, and J. D. Oberholtzer, 1971, "Studies Using Photographic and Multispectral Scanner Data," *Seventh Symposium on Remote Sensing of Environment*, University of Michigan, Institute on Science and Technology, Ann Arbor, pp. 1027-1043.

145. Munn, L. C., J. B. McClellan, and L. E. Philpotts, 1966, "Airphoto Interpretation and Rural Land Use Mapping in Canada," *Photogrammetric Engineering*, 21(3):65-76.

146. National Academy of Sciences, 1970, *Remote Sensing with Special Reference to Agriculture and Forestry*, Washington, D.C.

147. National Academy of Sciences, National Research Council, 1966, *Spacecraft in Geographic Research*, NAS/NRC Publication 1353, Houston, Tex.

148. Newcomb, R. M., 1970, "An Example of the Applicability of Remote Sensing: Historical Geography," *Geoforum*, 2:89-92.

149. Nobe, K. C., 1961, "Use of Airphoto Interpretation in Agricultural Land Economics Research," *Land Economics*, 37(4):321-326.

150. Northrop, K. G., and E. W. Johnson, 1970, "Forest Cover Type Identification," *Photogrammetric Engineering*, 36(5):483-490.

151. Nunnally,N. R., 1969, "Integrated Landscape Analysis with Radar Imagery," *Remote Sensing of Environment*, 1(1):1-6.

152. Nunnally,N. R., and R. E. Witmer, 1970, "Remote Sensing for Land Use Studies," *Photogrammetric Engineering*, 36(5):449-453.

153. Olson, C. E., Jr., 1960, "Elements of Photographic Interpretation Common to Several Sensors," *Photogrammetric Engineering*, 26(4):651-656.

154. Olson, C. E., Jr., 1967, "Accuracy of Land Use Interpretation from Infrared Imagery in the 4.5 to 5.5 Micron Band," *Annals of the Association of American Geographers*, 57(2):382-388.

155. Parker, D. C. and M. F. Wolff, 1965, "Remote Sensing," *International Science and Technology*, 43(73):20-31.

156. Parker, D. E., G. B. Lee, and C. J. Milfred, 1970, "Flood Plain Delineation with Pan and Color," *Photogrammetric Engineering*, 36(10):1059-1063.

157. Parry, J. T., and H. Turner, 1971, "Infrared Photos for Drainage Analysis," *Photogrammetric Engineering*, 37(10):1031-1038.

158. Pease, R., and L. Bowden, 1969, "Making Color Infrared a More Effective High Altitude Sensor," *Remote Sensing of Environment*, 1(1):23-30.

159. Philpotts, L. E., and V. R. Wallen, 1971, "Disease Assessment with IR-Color," *Photogrammetric Engineering*, 37(5):443-446.

160. Piech, K. R., and J. E. Walker, 1972, "Outfall Inventory Using Airphoto Interpretation," *Photogrammetric Engineering*, 38(9):907-914.

161. Quinn, A. O., 1963, "Photogrammetry to Locate Water," *Civil Engineering*, 33(8):50-53.

162. Rabchevsky, G. A., 1970, "Remote Sensing of the Earth's Surface," *Journal of Remote Sensing*, 1(5):14-17.

163. Rains, A. B., and M. A. Brunt, 1971, "An Evaluation of Air Photography for Land Resource Surveys in the Tropics," *Seventh Symposium on Remote Sensing of Environment*, University of Michigan, Institute of Science and Technology, Ann Arbor, pp. 2319-2327.

164. Rawling, F. G., 1971, "Some Considerations of the Use of Remote Sensing in the Study of Residential Dynamics," *Seventh Symposium on Remote Sensing of Environment*, University of Michigan, Institute of Science and Technology, Ann Arbor, pp. 1537-1552.

165. Ray, R. G., 1960, *Aerial Photographs in Geologic Interpretation and Mapping*, Professional Paper 373, U.S. Geologic Survey, Washington, D.C., 230 pp.

166. Reeves, D. M., 1936, "Aerial Photography and Archaeology," *American Antiquity*, 2(2):102-107.

167. Richardson, A. J., R. J. Torline, and W. A. Allen, 1971, "Computer Identification of Ground Patterns from Aerial Photographs," *Seventh Symposium on Remote Sensing of Environment*, University of Michigan, Institute of Science and Technology, Ann Arbor, pp. 1357-1376.

168. Richter, D. M., 1971, "Urban Photo Index for Eastern U.S.," *Photogrammetric Engineering*, 37(1):54-66.

169. Risley, E., 1968, "Remote Sensors for Regional Study: Some Policy Considerations," in *Geographers in Government*, Mimeographed and Offset Publication 5, *American Geographical Society*, pp. 37-45.

170. Rosenfeld, A., 1965, "Automatic Imagery Interpretation," *Photogrammetric Engineering*, 31(3):240-242.

171. Ross, D. S., 1969, "Image-Tone Enhancement," *Technical Papers*, American Society of Photogrammetry Thirty-fifth Annual Meeting, Washington, D.C., pp. 301-319.

172. Ross, D. S., 1969, "Enhanced Oceanographic Imagery," *Sixth Symposium on Remote Sensing of Environment*, University of Michigan, Institute of Science and Technology, Ann Arbor, pp. 1029-1044.

173. Rudd, R. D., 1971, "Macro Land Use Mapping with Simulated Space Photos," *Photogrammetric Engineering*, 37(4):365-372.

174. Russell, J. A., F. W. Foster, and K. C. McMurry, 1943, "Some Applications of Aerial Photographs to Geographic Inventory," *Papers of the Michigan Academy of Science, Arts and Letters*, 29:315-341.

175. Sabins, F. F., Jr., 1967, "Infrared Imagery and Geologic Aspects," *Photogrammetric Engineering*, 33(7):743-751.

176. Schaber, G. G., and G. J. Gumerman, 1969, "Infrared Scanning Images: An Archaeological Application," *Science*, 164(3880):712-713.

177. Schepis, E. L., 1968, "Time-Lapse Remote Sensing in Agriculture," *Photogrammetric Engineering*, 34(2):1166-1179.

178. Schwartz, D. E., and F. Caspall, 1968, "The Use of Radar in the Discrimination and Identification of Agricultural Land Use," *Fifth Symposium on Remote Sensing of Environment*, University of Michigan, Institute of Science and Technology, Ann Arbor, pp. 233-248.

179. Shay, J. R., 1967, "Remote Sensing for Agricultural Purposes," *Bioscience*, 17(7):450-451.

180. Shin-Yi Hsu, 1971, "Population Estimation," *Photogrammetric Engineering*, 37(5):449-454.

181. Simonett, D. S., 1968, "Land Evaluation Studies with Remote Sensors in the Infrared and Radar Regions," Interagency Report NASA-126; published in *Proceedings of the Joint CSIRO (Australia)-UNWACO, International Symposium on Land Evaluation*, Canberra, Australia.

182. Simonett, D. S., and S. A. Morain, 1968, "Remote Sensing from Spacecraft as a Tool for Investigating Arctic Environments," in H. E. Wright and W. H. Osburn, Eds., *International Association for Quaternary Research, Arctic and Alpine Environments*, Indiana University Press, Bloomington, pp. 297-306.

183. Simpson, R. B., 1966, "Radar, Geographic Tool," *Annals of the Association of American Geographers*, 56(1):80-96.

184. Smedes, H. W., H. J. Linnerud, S. J. Hawks, and L. B. Woolaver, 1971, "Digital Computer Mapping for Terrain by Clustering Techniques Using Color Film as a Three-Band Sensor," *Seventh Symposium on Remote Sensing of Environment*, University of Michigan, Institute of Science and Technology, Ann Arbor, pp. 2057-2071.

185. Smith, H. T. U., 1943, *Aerial Photographs and Their Applications*, Appleton-Century-Crofts, New York, 372 pp.

186. Smith, J. T., Jr., 1971, "Oil Slick Remote Sensing," *Photogrammetric Engineering*, 37(12):1243-1248.

187. Solecki, R. S., 1960, "Photo Interpretation in Archaeology," in *Manual of Photo Interpretation*, American Society of Photogrammetry, Washington, D.C., pp. 717-733.

188. Stafford, D. B., and J. Langfelder, 1971, "Air Photo Survey of Coastal Erosion," *Photogrammetric Engineering*, 37(6):565-575.

189. Steiner, D., 1968, "Aerial Photography for Land Use Mapping, Cattle Inventories, Yield Forecasting and Crop Disease Determination," *Transactions of the Third International Agricultural Aviation Congress*, Anaheim, 1966, International Agricultural Aviation Center, the Hague, pp. 334-365.

190. Steiner, D., 1969, "The Use of Stereo Height as a Discriminating Variable for Crop Classification on Aerial Photography," *Photogrammetria*, 24:223-241, August 1969.

191. Steiner, D., 1970, "Time Dimension for Crop Surveys from Space," *Photogrammetric Engineering*, 36(2):187-194.

192. Steiner, D., and H. Haefner, 1965, "Tone Distortion for Automated Interpretation," *Photogrammetric Engineering*, 31(2):269-280.

193. Steiner, D., and H. Mauer, 1966, "Toward a Quantitative Semi-Automatic System for the Photo-interpretation of Terrain Cover Types," Actes Symposium, *International Photo-interpretation*, 3:51-54, Paris.

194. Steiner, D., K. Baumberger, and H. Maurer, 1969, "Computer Processing and Classification of Multi-variety Information from Remote Sensing Imagery," *Sixth Symposium on Remote Sensing of Environment*, University of Michigan, Institute of Science and Technology, Ann Arbor, pp. 895-907.

195. Stingelin, R. W., 1968, "An Application of Infrared Remote Sensing to Ecological Studies: Bear Meadows Bog, Pennsylvania," *Fifth Symposium on Remote Sensing of Environment*, University of Michigan, Institute of Science and Technology, Ann Arbor, pp. 435-440.

196. Stingelin, R. W., and B. T. Traxler, 1971, "Quantitative Airborne Infrared Imaging System," *Seventh Symposium on Remote Sensing of Environment*, University of Michigan, Institute of Science and Technology, Ann Arbor, pp. 1483-1497.

197. Stone, K. H., 1964, "A Guide to the Interpretation and Analysis of Aerial Photos," *Annals of the Association of American Geographers*, 54(3):318-328.

198. Strandberg, C. H., 1967, "Photoarcheology," *Photogrammetric Engineering*, 33(10):1152-1157.

199. Tarling, L. W., 1970, "Some Observations and Recommendations for the Future of Aerial Color Photography," *The Photogrammetric Record*, 6(35):480-483.

200. Taylor, D., 1967, *Introduction to Radar and Radar Techniques*, Philosophical Library Incorporated, New York.

201. Thrower, N. J. W., and L. W. Senger, 1969, "Land Use Mapping of the Southwestern United States from Satellite Imagery," Paper AAS 69-579, presented at the American Astronautical Society National Meeting, New Mexico State University, Las Cruces, 11 pp.

202. U.S. Army Missile Command, 1965, *Basic and Advanced Infrared Technology*, U.S. Army Command, Redstone Arsenal, Huntsville, Ala.

203. U.S. Department of the Army, 1967, *Image Interpretation Handbook*, vol. 1, Technical Manual 30-245, NAVAIR 10-35-685, AFM 200-50, U.S. Government Printing Office, Washington, D.C., 358 pp.

204. Veress, S. A., 1970, "Air Pollution Research," *Photogrammetric Engineering*, 36(8):840-848.

205. Vinogradov, B. V., 1968, "Main Trends in the Application of Airphoto Methods to Geographic Research in the USSR: A Review of Publications, 1962-1964," *Photogrammetria*, 23(3):77-94.

206. Waelti, H., 1970, "Forest Road Planning," *Photogrammetric Engineering*, 36(3):246-252.

207. Waltz, F. A., 1970, "Multidiscipline Remote Sensing Research in Hydrology and Agriculture," *Journal of Remote Sensing*, 1(4):11-15.

208. Watson, R. C., 1972, "Spectral Reflectance and Photometric Properties of Selected Rocks," *Remote Sensing Environment*, 2(2):95-100.

209. Watson, R., and L. C. Rowan, 1971, "Automated Geologic Mapping Using Rock Reflectances," *Seventh Symposium on Remote Sensing of Environment*, University of Michigan, Institute of Science and Technology, Ann Arbor, pp.2043-2053.

210. Weber, F. B., and F. C. Polcyn, 1972, "Remote Sensing to Detect Stress in Forests," *Photogrammetric Engineering*, 38(2):163-175.

211. Welch, R., 1972, "Quality and Applications of Aerospace Imagery," *Photogrammetric Engineering*, 38(4):379-398.

212. Wellar, B. S., 1968, "Utilization of Multiband Aerial Photographs in Urban Studies," *Fifth Symposium on Remote Sensing of Environment*, University of Michigan, Institute of Science and Technology, Ann Arbor, pp. 913-926.

213. Wellar, B. S., 1968, *Thermal Infrared Imagery in Urban Studies*, Interagency Report NASA-135, Geographic Applications Program, Northwestern University, Evanston, Ill.

214. Wellar, R. N., 1970, "Photo Enhancement by Film Sandwiches," *Photogrammetric Engineering*, 36(5):468-474.

215. Wermund, E. G., and J. M. Kennedy, 1971, "Oil Spills IR and Microwave," *Photogrammetric Engineering*, 37(12):1235-1242.

216. Wert, S. L., 1969, "A System for Using Remote Sensing Techniques to Detect and Evaluate Air Pollution Effects on Forest Stands," *Sixth Symposium on Remote Sensing of Environment*, University of Michigan, Institute of Science and Technology, Ann Arbor, pp. 1169-1178.

217. Whiteside, A. E., and D. B. Lipski, 1971, "Computer Simulation of Automatic Stereoplotters," *Photogrammetric Engineering*, 37(3):285-291.

218. Whittlesey, J., 1966, "Photogrammetry for the Excavator," *Archaeology*, 19(4):273-276.

219. Wilson, R. C., 1967, "Space Photography for Forestry," *Photogrammetric Engineering*, 33(5):483-490.

220. Wolfe, E. W., 1971, "Thermal IR for Geology," *Photogrammetric Engineering*, 37(1):43-52.

221. Yost, E., and S. Wenderoth, 1971, "Multispectral Color for Agriculture and Forestry," *Photogrammetric Engineering*, 37(6):590-604.

Appendix 3

Institutions and Organizations Engaged in Remote Sensing Research in the United States

Preceding material has been primarily concerned with the nature of remote sensing research and the people who have been accomplishing it. One other dimension of remote sensing research is presented in this appendix to complete a perspective on the field: centers of research. Representative educational institutions and public and private organizations are listed, and a brief description of their research interests is provided.

SCHOOLS AND COLLEGES

Arizona, University of, Tucson, Arizona.	Long-focal-length tracking cameras; multiband photography.
Berkeley, University of California, Berkeley, California.	Remote sensing applications in forestry and range management; computer graphics; photographic interpretation; watershed studies.
Colorado School of Mines, Golden, Colorado.	Application of remote sensing to geologic, mineral, and water resources investigation; research on the response of rocks, soils, and vegetation to incident radiation.
Cornell University, Ithaca, New York.	Geologic and land-use photo interpretation; cost effective studies for remote sensing techniques.
Dartmouth College, Hanover, New Hampshire.	Urban land use; urban transportation; demographic studies, multispectral photography; environmental ecology.
Illinois, University of, Urbana, Illinois.	Compilation and distribution of air photo stereograms; engineering and forestry applications of remote sensing.
Kansas, University of, Lawrence, Kansas.	Radar; image-enhancement techniques for the study of agriculture and other resources.
Long Island University, Long Island, New York.	Multiband camera systems and color-enhancement techniques.
Louisiana State University, Baton Rouge, Louisiana.	Environmental inventory and land use in estuarine wetlands; study of naturally hydrodynamic features associated with deltaic shorelines using thermal imagery and photography.
Maine, University of, Orono, Maine.	Methods of estimating timber stands and individual tree volumes from medium- and large-scale aerial photography; vegetation mapping using ERTS-1 imagery.
Michigan, University of, Ann Arbor, Michigan.	Development of remote sensing equipment; multiband image analysis; compilation of spectrometric data; radar technology.
Minnesota, University of, Minneapolis, Minnesota.	Forestry applications of both black-and-white and color aerial photos; detection of tree diseases.

Ohio State University, Columbus, Ohio.	Work with NASA on Apollo, ERTS, and Skylab programs; consultation with USDA on the Corn Blight Watch Experiment; project with military agencies on Airborne Aerial Camera Calibration and Site Selection Techniques; regional ecological studies and resource management methods.
Oregon State University, Corvallis, Oregon.	Remote sensing in range management and forestry applications.
New Mexico, University of, Albuquerque, New Mexico.	Satellite Imagery Clearing House.
Northern Arizona University, Flagstaff, Arizona.	Selection and training of photo interpreters through specially designed tests; aerial photo techniques in forest inventory, with emphasis on ponderosa pines.
Northwestern University, Evanston, Illinois.	Use of statistics in ground-truth data collecting; urban information systems.
Purdue University, Lafayette, Indiana.	Automatic interpretation of agricultural crops, primarily by pattern recognition based on multiband tone signatures and spectrophotometry.
Riverside, University of California, Riverside, California.	Computer mapping; land-use studies; energy budgets; analysis of site characteristics.
Santa Barbara, University of California, Santa Barbara, California.	Oil-pollution studies; land-use studies; remote sensing in agriculture; analysis of site characteristics; vegetation studies.
South Dakota State University, Brookings, South Dakota.	Thermal and multispectral scanning; rangeland studies; remote sensing of water pollutants and water quality.
Southern Mississippi, University of, Hattiesburg, Mississippi.	Land-use change; water-quality studies.
Stanford University, Stanford, California.	Applications of multiband reconnaissance (especially in the thermal infrared region) to geologic inventories.
Stephen F. Austin State University, Nacogdoches, Texas.	Use of airborne profiler to determine timber volumes; electronic measurement of tree heights using laser beams, micro-densitometer, and aerial photography.

Virginia Institute of Marine Science, Gloucester Point, Virginia.	Applications of remote sensing in marine science; thermal infrared mapping; oil-spill studies using photography, thermal infrared, and ultraviolet; remote sensing applications in the study of suspended sediments through water color as imaged in the photographic and infrared regions.
Washington, University of, Seattle, Washington.	Applications of remote sensing in engineering, life sciences, and earth resources.
Wisconsin, University of, Madison, Wisconsin.	Multidisciplinary remote sensing; remote sensing with emphasis on water quality.

PUBLIC AND PRIVATE AGENCIES

Abrams Aerial Survey Corporation, Lansing, Michigan.	Viewing and plotting equipment; aerial photographic equipment.
Aerial Data Reduction Associates Inc., Riverside, New Jersey.	Aerial photography; photo interpretation and stereophotogrammetric mapping.
Aerojet-General Corporation, 9200 E. Flair, El Monte, California.	Microwave technology.
Agricultural Research Service, USDA, Washington, D.C.	Agricultural applications of remote sensing.
Allan Gordon Enterprises Inc., North Hollywood, California.	Photo interpretation instruments.
Barnes Engineering Company, 30 Commerce Road, Stamford, Connecticut 06902.	Thermal infrared cameras and radiometers.
Bausch and Lomb Company, Rochester, New York.	Viewing equipment; automatic photo-interpretation.
Bendix Corporation Division of Aerospace, 3300 Plymouth Road, Ann Arbor, Michigan.	Thermal infrared and multispectral scanning.
Boeing Company, Aerospace Group, Box 3999, Seattle, Washington.	Digital manipulation and information services; image interpreter training; performance measurement and image-quality evaluation.
Boeing Scientific Research Seattle, Washington.	Terrestrial and extraterrestrial applications of remote sensing.
Brookhaven National Laboratory, Associated Universities Inc., Upton, Long Island, New York.	Applications of remote sensing to measuring particle concentrations in plumes (industrial) to better understand the diffusion processes in the atmosphere.
Bureau of Land Management, 3853 Research Park Drive, Ann Arbor, Michigan.	Applications of remote sensing in range management and wildland resource inventory.
Calma Company, Reston, Virginia.	Computer graphics; digital manipulations and information services.

Cambridge Research Laboratory, USAF Terrestrial Science Ltd., L.G. Hanson Field, Bedford, Massachusetts 01730.	Determination of surface composition using spectroscopy at optical wavelengths; measuring of spectra of minerals, rocks, and soils in the visible and near-infrared to determine spectral signatures.
Center for Research in Engineering Science (CRES), Lawrence, Kansas.	Image analysis systems.
Conduction Corporation, Ann Arbor, Michigan.	Radar technology.
Daedalus Enterprises Inc., P.O. Box 1869 Ann Arbor, Michigan.	Airborne infrared sensors, multispectral sensors, quantitative systems and special signal processing equipment; data reduction; image analysis; services such as consulting, installation, and training.
Earth Sciences Division, National Research Council, Washington, D.C. 20418.	Applications of remote sensing in the earth sciences and life sciences.
Earth Satellite Corporation 1747 Pennsylvania Avenue Washington, D.C. 22206	Integrated operational resource inventories; basic research and development of remote sensing techniques.
Eastman Kodak Company, 381 Kodak Park, Rochester, New York 14650.	Photographic films and cameras; image-quality research.
Economic Research Service, USDA, Washington, D.C.	Cost effective studies for various applications of remote sensing in agriculture.
Electronic Vision Corporation, 11526 Sorrento Valley Road, San Diego, California 92121.	Developments in photoelectronic imaging devices.
Environmental Sciences Services Administration, Hillcrest Heights, Maryland.	Applications of remote sensing in meteorology and other environmental sciences.
Environmental Systems Corporation, Suite 203 Parkway Building, 1212 Pierce-Parkway NW, Knoxville, Tennessee.	Thermal mapping; airborne infrared line scanning; multispectral aerial photography studies in noise and acoustics; cooling-tower monitoring and environmental-impact studies.
Ewen Knight Corporation, East Natick, Massachusetts.	Microwave technology.
Fairchild Camera and Instrument Corporation, Mountain View, California 94040.	Aerial photographic equipment; viewing equipment.

Fish and Wildlife Service, USDI, Washington, D.C.	Applications of remote sensing in the inventory of big game animals, waterfowl and fish.
Forest Service, USDA, Northern Forest Fire Laboratory, Missoula, Montana.	Inventory of timber, forage, and other wildland resources by remote sensing; thermal infrared remote sensing for fire detection.
General Aniline and Film Corporation, New York, New York.	Aerial photographic films.
General Electric Corporation, Division of Space Systems, P.O. Box 8555 Philadelphia, Pennsylvania.	Recoverable capsule systems for space reconnaissance.
Geographic Applications Program, United States Geological Survey Washington, D.C.	Land-use and population estimation with computer graphics.
Goodyear Aerospace, Litchfield Park, Arizona.	Radar technology.
Grumman Aerospace, Operations Research, Plant 5, Department 661, Bethpage, New York 11714.	Radar technology; digital photometric mapping; multispectral photography; thermal infrared scanner applications.
Honeywell, 2 Forbes Road, Lexington, Massachusetts.	Development of radiometers and oculometers; multispectral scanner; applications of remote sensing to medicine and air pollution measurement and control.
HRB Singer Inc., State College, Pennsylvania.	Infrared technology.
Hughes Aircraft Company, Space Division, Box 90919, El Segundo, California 90009.	Multispectral photography especially in mineral exploration; side-looking airborne radar processing and interpretation; infrared line scanning.
Hunting Surveys and Consultants Inc. 10 Rockfeller Plaza, New York, New York 10020.	Multispectral photography especially in mineral exploration; side-looking airborne radar processing and interpretation; infrared line scanning.
Hycon Company, 700 Royal Oaks Drive, Monrovia, California 90009.	Manufacturee of cameras and camera equipment.
International Imagery Systems, Mountain View, California.	Data processing; density slicing; multispectral photography.

Interpretation Systems Inc., Box 1004, Lawrence, Kansas 66044.	Data processing and image enhancing devices.
Itek Corporation, Arlington, Virginia.	Multispectral photography.
Jet Propulsion, Image Processing Laboratory, 4800 Oak Grove Drive, Pasadena, California 91103.	Digital processing of images especially from Ranger, Surveyor, and Mariner space flights.
Keuffel and Esser Company, Morristown, New Jersey.	Aerial photographic equipment.
Litton Aero Service, Philadelphia, Pennsylvania.	Remote sensing in mineral exploration and resource evaluations; radar technology.
Lockheed Corporation, El Camino Real, Houston, Texas 77058.	Reconnaissance vehicles and remote sensing systems with electric readout.
McDonnell-Douglas Astronautics Corporation, Information Systems Subdivision, 5301 Bolsa, Huntington Beach, California.	Radar technology; ultraviolet and lasers.
North American Rockwell Corporation, 12214 Lakewook Boulevard, Downey, California 90241.	Geothermal remote sensing; sensing of coastal bathymetry; thermal discharge surveys; water-quality control; aerial surveillance methods; coastal studies; geologic studies; mineral surveys and digital/analog analysis.
Perkin-Elimer Corporation, Main Avenue, Norwalk, Connecticut 06852.	Photoemissive surface research; ion implanted detector material formulation; nonlinear materials development for infrared-to-visible up-conversion experiments.
Philco-Ford Corporation, Space and Re-entry Systems Division, Palo Alto, California.	Data processing; density slicing.
Raytheon Company/Autometric, Boston Post Road, Wayland, Maryland 01778.	Developing applications of existing sensor technology; automated extraction of relevant data banks in the photogrammetric mapping process; extraction of topographic products from SLAR imagery; improvement of orthophoto map production and application of satellite technology to the tracking of free-roving wildlife; microwave technology.

Resources Technology Corporation, 1275 Space Park Drive, Suite 111, Houston, Texas 77058.	Automatic photo interpretation; side-looking radar analysis and other sensor data systems; remote sensing in detecting pollutants, especially oil; concrete analysis using radiometers.
Science Applications Inc., P.O. Box 2351, La Jolla, California 92037.	Development of CO remote sensor; designing multipollutant sensor suitable for satellite usage.
Space Sciences and Applications, NASA, Houston, Texas.	Remote sensing of earth resources and meteorological phenomena.
Spatial Data Systems, Goleta, California.	Data processing; density slicing.
Statistical Reporting Service, USDA, Washington, D.C.	Inventory of crops and livestock by means of remote sensing.
Superior Oil Company, Geophysical Division, Box 1521, Houston, Texas 77001.	Remote sensing in exploration of natural resources, especially techniques to isolate specific mineral occurances to provide geologic and structural information.
Technology Inc., Division of Remote Sensing, 3821 Col. Glenn Highway, Dayton, Ohio.	Reconnaissance studies and analysis; electrooptical analysis; IR countermeasure analysis.
Teledyne Geotronics, 725 East Third Street, Long Beach, California.	Thermal infrared and scanning instrumentation; multiband photographic cameras; terrain-probing radar.
Texas Instruments, Box 5621, Dallas, Texas.	Infrared technology; multiband remote sensing equipment; military and geoscience applications of remote sensing.
United States Geological Survey, USDI, Washington, D.C.	Remote Sensing in geology, hydrology, and geography; photogrammetry; oil mapping.
Westinghouse Electric Corporation, Box 746, Baltimore, Maryland 21203.	Radar technology.

INDEX

absorption, 21-22
active system, 17
aerial photography, 2-6, 150, 204, 207
agriculture, 6, 89, 167, 170, 172, 189-223
agricultural data requirements, 190-192, 196
agricultural surveys, 189-190, 196-201, 212
albedo, 84, 96
archaeology, 6
automation, 6, 8, 68-74, 84, 89, 111, 168, 175-176, 195, 207
black-and-white infrared photography, 105-106, 111, 142, 159-160
cameras, 29-35, 105, 112-113, 226, 255, 262
census data, 226-227, 234, 247, 261
Census Cities Project, 226-227, 257
central places, 287
classification systems, 168-169, 175-176, 283-284
colorimetry, 111
color infrared photography, 19, 28, 97-98, 105, 111-112, 146, 149-151, 158, 170, 206-208, 211-212, 225-227
computer, 51-81, 84-85, 89, 175, 227, 287
contrast, 19, 64, 169
contrast ratio, 20
crop surveys, 69, 205-206
densitometry, 54, 67, 111
discriminant analysis, 69, 176, 255
ecological vegetation maps, 157-160
edge enhancement, 62-63, 176
electromagnetic spectrum, 15-16, 105-106, 112, 116, 120, 226
energy budget, 17, 91, 95, 133
environmental quality, 83, 233, 293-301
field work, 9, 45-46, 128, 149, 234, 236, 252
fire detection, 97-99
floristic vegetation maps, 145-150
forestry, 4, 67, 97-99, 234
formal regions, 287
Fourier analysis, 70, 96, 176, 286
geology, 4, 85-86, 234
geology, qualitative, 105-108, 111-113, 115, 117, 120, 294
geology, quantitative, 105-106, 109-111, 115, 119
ground truth, 45
haze, 226, 235
housing data, 233, 235-236, 262-265
housing quality, 235-236, 252-257
hydrology, 89-90, 92, 94-97, 107-108, 110, 112-115, 118, 120, 233
illumination, 19-20
image, 28
image enhancement, 53, 60-62, 176, 206
image interpretation, 44-47, 51-52, 64-66
image processing, 42-44, 46-47
interpretation equipment, 5
interpretation keys, 4, 6, 67, 109, 171-172, 284
interpreter training, 5, 8, 171
landforms, 106, 109-111, 113-114, 117-120
land use, 6, 8, 167-187, 190, 204-205, 209, 285, 299-300
land use change, 174-175, 226, 244, 262
land use classification, 258, 260, 285
land use data, 226-227, 233, 236-237, 245-246, 254, 257-259, 261, 263
land use maps, 226-228, 257
land use surveys, 226
laser, 17, 86
line-trace data, 57-58
livestock surveys, 190, 211-212
maximum likelihood ratio, 68-69
meteorology, 84, 89-95, 233
microdensitometry, 73, 233
microwave, 37-42, 96-97, 199-201
Mie scattering, 22
military, 4
multiband, 33, 133-134, 151, 160, 193, 235
multicategory vegetation maps, 146
multidate, 99, 170-171, 176, 201, 212, 226
multispectral, 17, 89, 91, 97, 226
multispectral scanner, 7, 68, 89, 128-129, 151, 160, 170, 199-200
natural resources, 83-103, 130
nodal regions, 287
oceanography, 95-97

optical density, 89
optical mechanical scanner, 37, 57
parallax, 119
passive microwave, 37-39
passive system, 17
pattern recognition, 52-56
photogeology, 105-109
photogeomorphology, 106-107
photography, 2, 20, 28, 56-57, 89, 96-97, 105-106, 109-115, 170, 172-173, 201, 205, 211, 225, 231-232
photointerpretation, 107, 113-114, 120, 226, 231
photomorphic concept, 285-287
photomorphic regions, 286
physiognomic vegetation maps, 150-157
physiography, 85-87, 106-109, 112-113, 115, 117-120, 234, 294
photomosaics, 109, 113
polarization, 89, 175-176
pollution, 95-96, 226, 233-234, 293-301
population estimation techniques, 235
preprocessing, 58-60
quanta, 16
quantitative methods, 51-81, 173, 226, 231, 255
radar, 39-42, 57, 85-87, 96-97, 99, 105-106, 109, 115-120, 134-136, 151-157, 160, 170-171, 199-200, 206, 211, 225, 236-237, 244, 286
range management, 99, 150, 210-211
range surveys, 189, 210-211
Rayleigh scattering, 21
regional analysis, 6, 277-291
regional classes, 281-282
regional concept, 277-281
remote sensing, 7, 9, 15, 105-106, 281, 297-300
remote sensing history, 1-13
resolution, 26, 39, 42, 66, 93, 135, 169, 197
return beam vidicon, 7, 57
ronchi grating, 109
sampling, 249
satellites, 6, 7, 85-99, 113-114, 168-169, 174-175, 206, 210, 212, 226-231, 286
scanning densitometers, 206
scanning systems, 27, 35-36, 57, 207
scattering, 21-22
soils, 69-70, 86-89, 107, 109, 112-113, 115, 201-204, 211
spectroradiometers, 25, 89, 205
stereoscopy, 109-110
structural vegetation maps, 150-157
sun angle, 20
thermal infrared, 6, 21, 36-37, 86, 90-93, 96-99, 105-106, 115, 131-133, 144, 158, 160, 170-171, 206-207, 211-212, 225, 234, 237, 282, 300
tone, 16, 89, 197
topographic mapping, 3
transportation, 190, 226, 231, 237, 245, 254, 258
ultraviolet, 26-28, 91, 96, 233
urban, 6, 8, 167, 170, 172-173, 175, 225-241, 243-275, 287-289, 294, 296, 298-299
urban change, 244-245, 247, 250, 252
urban information systems, 245, 247, 249-250
vegetation, 4, 6, 89, 97, 107, 109, 127-165, 170, 204, 227, 300
vegetation boundary delineation, 142-145
vidicon systems, 57, 90
visible spectrum, 19, 28, 233
water quality, 233-234
wavelength, 15-16, 226